THE DISHWASHER MANUAL

Graham Dixon

DIY Plumbing □ Maintenance □ Repair

First edition published 1990
Revised second edition published 1993
Reprinted 1994
Revised third edition published 1999
Reprinted 2000 (with minor amendments)
Reprinted 2003
Reprinted 2005
Revised fourth edition published 2009

Published by: Haynes Publishing,
Sparkford, Yeovil, Somerset BA22 7JJ, UK

A catalogue record for this book is available
from the British Library

ISBN 978 1 84425 555 9

Printed in the USA

Contents

Contents

Contents

Introduction

The repair and servicing of today's modern domestic appliances may possibly seem a daunting task to perform oneself. The myth consists of several elements:

a) The mystique created by the manufacturers that their machines are more complicated than they actually are.

b) The inbuilt fear of electrical wiring that most laymen seem to have (this is not a bad thing as electricity is to be respected at any voltage, and at all times when working on a machine **it must be isolated from the main supply**).

c) The lack of detailed manuals to suit the person that can overcome a and b.

d) The fact that if you get past a, b and c, the parts are – in most instances – difficult to obtain.

One may be forgiven for thinking that this is a good reason for leaving the repair of your machine to someone who possesses the skills, manuals and parts. This unfortunately generally proves expensive in call-out and labour charges, often only to find that it was a five minute job, with the cost of parts £10.00, and the call-out and labour £80.00. In the customer's mind, £90.00 is little expense for such complicated and unsafe items. Yet their DIY husband (or wife) will gladly strip down the engine or brakes on their family car, and will take the family out for a drive that afternoon. It is acceptable for car repairs to be carried out by the DIY enthusiast as the information and parts are readily available. This obviously means that the DIY car owner saves a labour charge of only £45 to £50 per hour. Until now, the DIY enthusiast has been unable to repair any major faults to his dishwasher due to the manufacturers and repair companies not wishing to disclose the information. This state of affairs can be remedied by studying the following chapters, coupled with the application of a little common sense and adherence to safety precautions. There is now a comprehensive range of 'blister packed' spares appearing in most good DIY chain stores, public market stalls and by mail order. Many are packaged for the general public and are usually clearly marked with the type of machine and application. We hope that this manual will be of great assistance in not only reducing your repair costs, but giving the satisfaction which is obtained when a repair is successfully completed. It has been thoughtfully designed to help you understand the function and operation of the internal components of your dishwasher.

Flowcharts, diagrams and step-by-step photographic sequences have been used to attain a logical pattern to fault finding. This enables the reader to follow a sequence of events in theory (using the flowcharts), in practice (using the photographic sequences) and in detail (using the diagrams).

This manual will assist you in finding the fault and in giving you the knowledge to repair it. Another important aspect is the regular checking and maintenance of your machine, which is covered in the individual sections, and also a checklist section in Chapter 9.

We hope you will use this manual to assist in the Do It Yourself repair of your machine. With most repairs you will find it speedier than calling a repair company, and at the same time save the added burden of call-out and labour charges that repair companies must charge to cover overheads and operating costs.

With this in mind, we hope that your faults are few and far between, but remember . . . prevention is better than cure, and regular checks and servicing of your machine can prevent any bigger problems arising in the future.

Acknowledgements

The author would like to extend his thanks and gratitude to the following people and organisations for their help in the compilation of certain sections.

Oracstar for their help and information that was used in the plumbing section.
UK Whitegoods.
Thanks also to Andrew Morland for much of the photographic work and Jack Whitehead for additional graphics.

Chapter 1
The dishwasher

Today, modern kitchens contain many labour saving appliances, many of which we have come to look upon as essential and not merely a luxury. The automatic washing machine fits into this category along with such items as electric toasters, irons, etc. However, one major appliance, the dishwasher falls somewhere between, being a most welcome but luxury item. After its initial purchase and use however, it is regarded as being essential.

It has been calculated that for the average family of four, over 546 hours or three full weeks each year will be spent washing dishes! On these figures alone, any machine that would ease this burden on the household could hardly be classed as a luxury.

Not only is a dishwasher a labour saving appliance, it is, if kept well maintained, a very hygienic way of washing soiled dishes and eating utensils. Three main reasons for this claim are:

1 The wash temperatures are higher than can be used if washing by hand and the machine will also wash for a longer period of time at the higher temperature.

2 The load is then well rinsed in clear, fresh water – something rarely done when washing by hand.

3 Drying is done by heat within the machine and not by a tea towel. Tests have proved that, although many people wash their dishes clean, they then proceed to dry them with a tea towel which may transfer contamination back onto the dishes prior to them being put back into cupboards. People are now realising that the true benefits of dishwashers are not only labour saving, but also the most hygienic way of washing dishes, etc.

As with all such labour saving devices, they can be taken for granted, and regular maintenance and inspection procedures ignored, and it is only when the machine develops a fault which puts it out of action, that the owner/user realises how useful the machine really is!

How they work

To aid in the correct usage of a dishwasher and to help with maintenance and repair, it will be necessary to fully understand the way in which they operate and carry out their functions.

Understanding the wash procedures will be of great help when diagnosing faults that may arise. The workings of a dishwasher are in principle quite simple, yet many repair engineers themselves do not fully understand them and tend to treat them as being rather complex and troublesome to repair. Their lack of confidence is often transferred to the customer and DIY repairer when obtaining spare parts. The aim in writing this manual is to give you not only the knowledge for repairing your machine, but also the confidence to do it. Dishwashers are basically much less complicated than automatic clothes washing machines although they are similar in many respects, ie:

a) The thorough and efficient cleansing of soiled items.
b) Thorough rinsing to remove all traces of detergents.
c) To dry items following the wash and rinse programmes.

The main differences are:
a) It is the wash water under pressure that is moved OVER the pots (unlike the clothes washer where clothes are agitated through the wash water by drum rotation).
b) Less water is needed for both the wash and rinse cycles.
c) Drying obviously cannot be done by spinning, but by heating the load inside the cabinet to evaporate excess water.

As you see, the requirements are basically the same for both machines, but the results are achieved by different processes and actions of the machine. We will deal later with the similarity of functional parts between these two different types of machine. What follows is a general description of a typical wash cycle which is not based on any particular model. It is just a simple guide to help you to understand the procedures involved.

With the machine loaded and checked to make sure the spray arms will not be obstructed by utensils or pan handles, etc., protruding either above or below their working position (a gentle tap to spin them will confirm this and they should spin freely), the detergent dispenser filled with the recommended type and quantity of detergent and the door firmly closed, select the programme suitable for the degree of soiling on the dishes, etc. The machine is now ready to be switched on, which depending on the style of machine may involve a separate switch, simply pulling out the timer selection knob or pressing a 'start' button on electronically controlled machines.

The machine will then begin to fill with water via the inlet valve until it reaches a preset level and then the heating of the water and washing takes place. **Note:** *On average, the machine will take in only around 9 litres of water per fill (see Water level control). Generally, the water used will have been softened by the machine's own water softening device. This is covered in more detail in the chapter on internal water softening and regeneration.*

Washing of the dishes is by means of spray arms mounted either above or below the load baskets. Water is pumped to the spray arms under pressure by a large single phase asynchronous induction motor called the wash pump or circulation pump. Most wash pumps have a pump rate of 150 litres per minute. The bottom spray arm is usually mounted directly in line with its outlet and takes approximately two-thirds (100 litres per minute) of this flow rate and the top spray arm is fed the remaining third (50 litres per minute). This arrangement allows the more delicate items to be cleaned in the top basket, while pots and pans with heavier soiling can be cleaned in the lower basket. Some makes and models will have variations on this basic theme.

Water is fed to both spray arms simultaneously. Each spray arm has a series of angled slots cut or formed in the flat surface of each arm and a hole at each end of the arm on opposing sides. The dynamic force of the water propelled from the slots and holes cause the arms to rotate in a given direction. This rotation then delivers water under pressure with the cleaning agent in suspension to all areas of the inner cabinet and blasts clean the contents of the machine. A more detailed description of spray arm is found later in the book. Although the means of supplying water to the top spray arms differs between manufacturers, the basic principle remains the same.

The lower section of the load compartment is shaped so as to cause a sump effect and a reservoir for the wash pump, thus causing a sealed system of continuous wash water movement.

Heating of the water is via a partly submerged element in the load compartment or a remote through-flow heater located out of sight beneath the load compartment. With both variations heating takes place simultaneously with the wash action. At a pre-set time or temperature, the detergent container is energised to release its contents to the water. Washing will now continue for the duration of the type of programme selected, i.e. Long – heavy soiling, Short – light soiling etc. At the end of this temperature/timed sequence, the machine will empty out the now dirty water containing the soiling in suspension, after first filtering out any large pieces of debris by means of a cleanable filter situated in the sump recess.

After the time allowed for emptying has elapsed, the timer will move on and initiate a rinse sequence. The machine will fill to correct level, again engaging the wash pump when this level is reached, but this time, without the heater in circuit as only cold rinsing is required. After a timed sequence, the machine will empty out the first rinse water in readiness for the second rinse which unlike the first rinse, is heated. Following a preset time, an additive from the rinse aid compartment is added to the water (see: *Detergent and rinse aid dispensers*). On completion of the last hot rinse, the water is pumped away and the latent heat of the dishes etc., will effect quick and uniform drying of the load by evaporating off the excess moisture. The moisture from the drying process is retained within the appliance by condensing it in the air vent system by allowing it to come into contact with a chamber of cold water held there. The condensed water runs down into the sump to be pumped away at the start of the next wash cycle.

Times and temperatures and the number of rinses will vary depending on make and model of your machine, but again the basic principles remain constant.

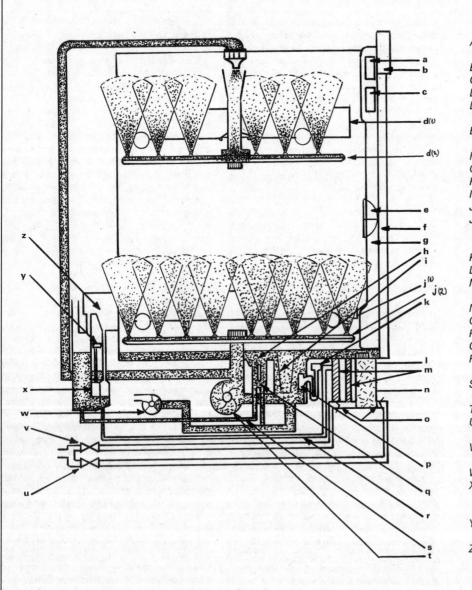

A   Programme or timer unit (in this instance, mounted in the door).
B   Door facia and handle.
C   Rinse aid unit.
D (1) Upper load basket.
D (2) Upper spray arm (could also be supplied by lower water jet).
E   Door mounted detergent dispenser.
F   Door outer.
G   Door inner.
H   Venturi float system.
I   Large base mounted filter.
J (1) Bottom load basket.
J (2) Bottom spray arm (could also supply jet from centre to supply upper arm).
K   Overfill pressure switch.
L   Water softener unit.
M   Sealed resin compartments of softener unit.
N   Refillable salt reservoir.
O   Softener feed non-return valve.
P   Overfill pressure vessel.
Q   Venturi float valve system.
R   Softened water supply to load compartment or venturi.
S   Venturi hose system (if used on your machine).
T   Main circulation pump chamber.
U   Inlet valve with reduced outlet or regeneration cycle.
V   Main inlet valve for machine (via softener unit in this instance).
W   Outlet pump chamber.
X   Pressure vessel for level system (may also be float on some machines).
Y   Pressure system level switch and hose.
Z   Steam vent and air break unit.

Shown is a theoretical layout of the internal parts of a dishwasher. This layout includes float system, pressure system and venturi level systems. It is not meant to represent your particular machine, but to give some help in identifying parts and the general operation of dishwashers

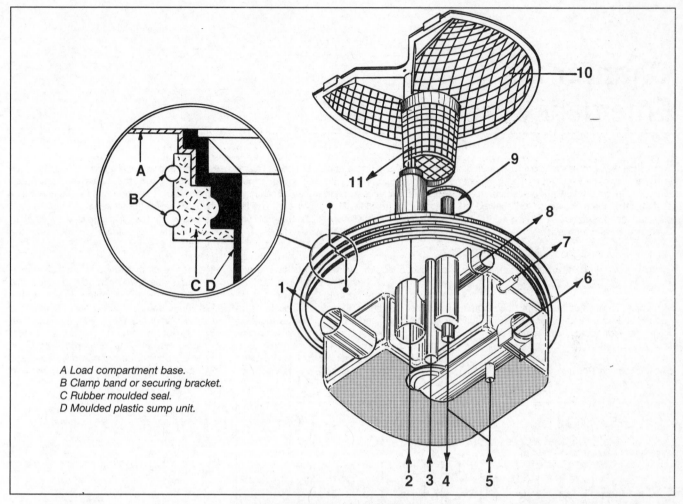

A Load compartment base.
B Clamp band or securing bracket.
C Rubber moulded seal.
D Moulded plastic sump unit.

One version of sump moulding fixing

Shown is a typical sump moulding unit. It is not representative of any particular machine but shows the basic requirements of the sump. Some units may incorporate the circulation pump chamber and outlet pump chambers within the unit. Not all have connections for venturi level systems. This unit highlights most, if not all variations and connections.

1 Connection to main circulation pump feed.
2 Supply from the main circulation pump for both upper and lower spray arms.
3 Inlet for venturi level valve.
4 Outlet for venturi level valve.
5 Drain tube connection from venturi level chamber.
6 Connection for outlet pump.
7 Overfill pressure tube connection (extra internal pressure chamber).
8 Supply to upper spray arm (2 and 8 interconnect).
9 Venturi float unit.
10 Main sump water filter with both large and fine filter mesh.
11 Lower spray arm supply and mounting point.

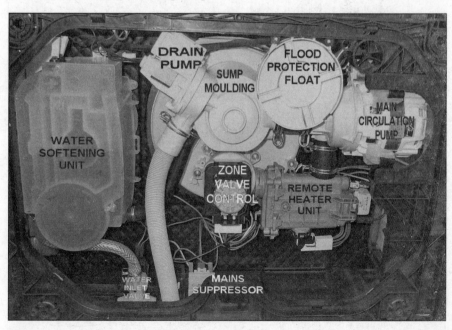

Typical electro-mechanical components housed beneath the load compartment in most makes and models

Chapter 2
Emergency procedures

With such symptoms as leaking, flooding, unusual noises, blowing fuses, etc., it is best to carry out the following procedure. It is essential that the machine is NOT allowed to continue its programme until the fault has been located and rectified.

Firstly – do not panic

a) Isolate the machine from the mains supply. That is, turn the machine off, switch off at the wall socket, and remove the plug from the socket.

b) Turn off the Hot and Cold taps to which the fill hoses of the machine connect. This is done because, even with the power turned off, if a fill valve is at fault, it may be jammed in the open position. The machine will still fill, as turning the power or the machine off will make no difference to this type of fault.

c) At this point, the power and water should be disconnected. Even now, if there is still water in the machine, it could still be leaking. Any water remaining in the machine can be extracted by lifting the outlet hose from its usual position, and lowering it below the level of water in the machine. This will allow the water to drain (unless of course, there is a blockage in the outlet hose!). The easiest method is if the outlet hose will reach to an outside door, where all that is needed is a little movement, and the water should drain. Alternatively, the water can be drained into a low bowl using the same technique. To stop the water, lift the pipe above the height of the machine. Repeat this process until the machine is empty.

d) Do not open the door until all of the previous steps have been carried out, and a few minutes have elapsed to allow the machine to cool. In cases where the machine was on a very hot wash, wait about half an hour. **Note:** *Avoid contact with water that contains dishwasher detergent, as it is extremely powerful when mixed with water. If skin contact occurs wash thoroughly with clean water.*

When all of these steps have been carried out, and the load has been removed from the cabinet, it is then possible to calmly sit down and start to work out what the problem may be, and form the plan of action in a logical and concise manner.

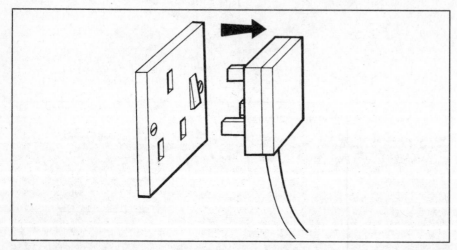

a) Isolate electrical supply

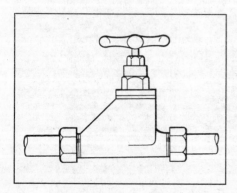

b) Turn off taps on machine

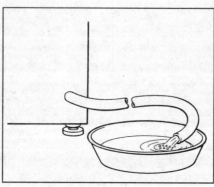

c) Drain machine

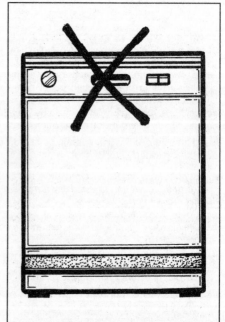

d) Do not open the door until all the previous steps have been carried out and the machine has been allowed to cool

Chapter 3
A general safety guide

Electricity at all voltages is to be respected. Those who do not observe the basic rules of electricity are not only a danger to themselves but to those around them. Electrical accidents should be regarded as avoidable. Most are due to plain carelessness and the failure to follow basic rules of electricity even when they are already known.

There are in the region of sixteen million homes in Britain supplied with electricity, each home having on average twenty-five electrical appliances. With such a volume of items, it may be a surprise to find that fatalities due to electrical accidents are less than eighty per year. Although this is a small percentage figure in terms of population and only represents 1 per cent of the eight thousand deaths resulting from accidents in the home, the figure is still too high.

The three most common causes of shock or fires from electrical appliances are:

1 Faulty wiring of the appliances, ie frayed or damaged flex or cable, incorrect fuse, poor socket, poor/damaged plug, incorrectly wired plug, etc.

2 Misuse of the appliance; for example, a hairdryer or similar electrical appliance being used in the bathroom, or an electrical power tool being used outside in the rain or in the wet. The rules relating to electrical items in bathrooms are strict for good reason. The combination of water and electricity greatly increases the possibility of injury.

3 Continuing to use an electrical appliance knowing it to be unsafe, for example with a cracked casing, faulty plug, damaged cable, faulty on/off switch, etc.

By being aware of the need for safety, several of the above faults can be avoided. Others can be eliminated by regular inspection and immediate correction of faults, failure or wear. As for misuse, this may be due to a purely foolhardy approach or genuine ignorance of danger. This can be overcome by understanding and, above all, acting upon the guidelines in this book. If at anytime you feel you lack the ability to do a particular job yourself, then it is best not to try. You can still carry out the diagnosis of the problem thus ensuring that any work carried out by a repair company is correct. This alone can sometimes save a great deal of time and expense.

Do's

● Thoroughly read all the information in this book prior to putting it into practice.
● Isolate any appliance before repair or inspection commences.
● Correctly fit the mains plug (see: *Plugs and Sockets*), ensuring the connections are in the correct position, tight and the cord clamp is fitted on the outer insulation of the cable.
● Check that the socket used is in good condition and has a sound earth path (see: *Basics – electrical*).
● Take time to consider the problem at hand and allow enough time to complete the job without rushing.
● Follow a methodical approach to the stripdown of the item and make notes. This helps greatly with reassembly.
● Double-check everything.
● Ask or seek help if in doubt.
● Ensure that a Residual Current Device (RCD) is in circuit when using electrical equipment outdoors.

Dont's

● Do not work on any machine that is still plugged in even if the socket switch is OFF. Always isolate fully – PLUG OUT.
● Do not allow portable mains appliances to be used in bathrooms or shower rooms from a socket outside the room. It may seem harmless to run an extension lead from a convenient socket on the landing so that a portable fan heater or hairdryer can be used in the bathroom, but it is extremely dangerous and MUST NOT be done under any circumstances.
● Do not use mains-powered equipment outdoors in rain or damp conditions.

● Do not in ANY circumstances repair damaged flex or cables with insulation tape.
● Do not sacrifice safety by affecting a temporary repair.

General

Consider your own safety and that of other people.
Act in a way that prevents incidents from becoming accidents.
Use your common sense and think before acting.
Tidy workplaces make safer workplaces.
Identify hazards.
Observe the rule of Safety First.
Never underestimate the dangers.

Switch off! Always withdraw plug and disconnect from mains.
Appliances vary – make sure you have a suitable replacement part.
For screws use a screwdriver, for nuts a spanner, for knurled nuts use pliers.
Examine and clean all connections before fitting new parts.
Tighten all screws and nuts firmly.
Your safety depends on these simple rules.

Fuses: Up to 250W 1 amp; 750W 3 amp; 750 to 3000W 13 amp.
Insulation is for your protection. Don't interfere.
Renew worn or damaged appliance flex.
Secure flex clamps and all protective covers correctly.
Test physically and electrically on completion.

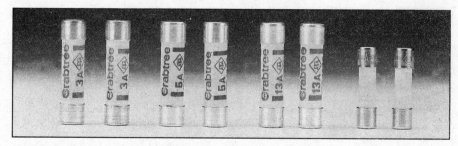

Ensure that only the correct rated fuse is used. It is dangerous to exceed the required rating. Even if the appliance appears to work normally little or no protection will be afforded should a fault occur

Plug wiring

Plug wiring must be connected according to the following code to ensure safety. The colours are as follows:

Live – Brown (or Red), symbol L

Neutral – Blue (or Black), symbol N

Earth – Green/Yellow (or Green), symbol E

The colours in brackets are those used until the current international standards were introduced. They may still be found on some equipment. Plug terminals are identified either by colour (old or new) or by the letter symbols shown.

Physical safety

Great care must be exercised when removing or handling the panels of any dishwasher. The edges of formed metal parts are rarely cleanly finished after pressing or moulding during manufacture. Generally only the edges that the user would normally come into contact with are deburred and finished. Edges exposed during a repair can be extremely sharp especially on formed stainless steel panels and seam welded joints on the outer of the load compartment. Take care not to slip when servicing or removing components within these areas and avoid running fingers along or near exposed panel edges.

Chapter 4
Basics – electrical

Special note: *Variations may be present in supply systems used in countries other than the UK.*

As detailed in the text in this chapter, various types of earthing systems may be encountered – one of the most popular being the PME system whereby neutral and earth are BONDED (linked) at the supply point to the property. The choice of which supply system (and ultimately which earth system your property has) is a matter for your supply authority. The requirement of a sound earth path however is common to all domestic systems.

For the sake of safety around the home or office, a basic understanding of electricity is essential. Even if you don't intend to carry out any repairs or servicing of your appliances yourself, a sound understanding of household electrical supply will prove invaluable in the long run. Ignorance is no protection against either your or a third party's errors, whether it be on repairs, servicing or the installation of appliances. It is with this in mind that this chapter has been written. It is not an in-depth study of the subject – there are many books that contain more detailed information for those who want to know more about electricity.

In this instance, the aim is to impart a safe knowledge without too much technical data. Some may argue that a little knowledge is a dangerous thing, but I believe that total ignorance is a much greater danger. To be informed is to be enlightened – to be aware of danger helps one to avoid it and to understand how and why certain safety criteria should be adopted.

The top illustration shows a simplified, but typical household supply. The substation has power supplied to it at very high voltage (400,000 volts) in three-phase form. This supply is converted at the substation, via a transformer, down to 230 volt single-phase and is then distributed to our homes. In normal circumstances, current flows from the live supply of the substation's transformer, through the electrical items being used in the house and back via the neutral conductor (cable) to the substation transformer's neutral pole (a closed loop). The neutral terminal of the transformer is in turn connected to the ground (earth – meaning in this case, the general mass of the earth), as shown in the centre illustration. It is usual to use the armoured sheath of the electricity supply authority's cable in order to provide a low impedance continuous link back to the supply transformer's start point. Various types of

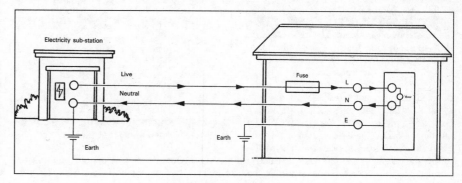

Typical household supply

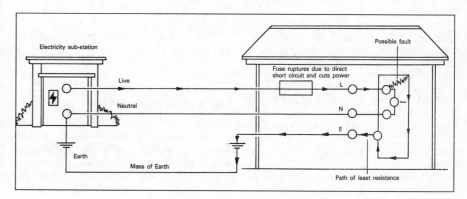

Earth path if fault occurs

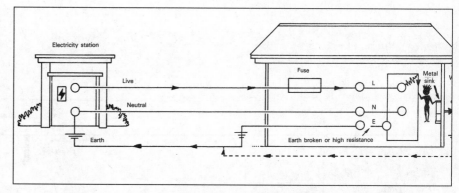

Result of high resistance or break in normal earth path. Fault will find path of least resistance

earthing can be encountered: connection to the armoured sheath of the authority's supply cable; own earth rod; transformer earth rod via general mass of the earth; or the increasingly popular neutral conductor of the authority's supply cable (often called PME – protective multiple earthing or TN-C-S system).

The earth loop path is designed to encourage current to flow, in the event of an earth fault, to enable the protective devices within the consumer unit (fuse, MCB or RCD) to operate in order to isolate the supply to the circuit. Failure to cause the protective device to operate will result in the appliance remaining live with the consequence that any person

Plug-in earth loop tester, details of which can be found in the *Plugs and sockets* chapter

A versatile test meter incorporating 500 V DC insulation test facility

a Miniature Circuit Breaker (MCB) in place of fuses. Each circuit leading from the consumer unit has its own rating of fuse or MCB and only that fuse rating and no other must be used.

NOTE: *Even when the consumer unit is switched off there is still a live supply to it. Do not remove the covers of the consumer unit or tackle any inspection or repair to this item without seeking further information. Faults other than fuse renewal are best left to skilled electrical engineers. Although assistance may be available from other publications, extreme care should be exercised. As mentioned earlier, it is not the aim of this book to encourage the repair or maintenance of items that are not fully isolated.*

touching the appliance will receive a nasty, possibly fatal, electric shock. Remember, electricity always takes the route of least resistance, therefore a person standing on the ground touching a live appliance can provide a low resistance alternative earth path resulting in a severe shock or worse. For this reason, the resistance of the earth loop path must be low enough to allow sufficient fault current to flow to operate the protective fuse or circuit breaker.

The term used for testing the earthing resistance of the supply outlet is earth loop impedance, which means checking to see if the current flow is impeded and if it is, by how much. This test requires a specialised meter giving resistance figures in ohms, the maximum reading recommended by the IEE (Institution of Electrical Engineers) being 1.1 ohms for a domestic earth path, unless a Type 1 MCB is in circuit in which case a 2 ohm maximum is acceptable.

Note: *A professional earth loop test meter or plug-in earth loop tester (details of which can be found in the* Plugs & Sockets *chapter) provide a clear indication of earth quality by means of a resistance reading or indication.*

What is an earth fault?

An earth fault is defined as the condition where electricity flows to earth when in

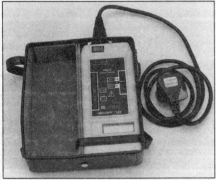

A professional earth loop test meter gives the only true indication of the earth path quality

normal circumstances, it should not do so. There are two recognised ways in which this may happen: direct and indirect.

Direct – when contact is made directly with the current-carrying conductor which is designed to carry that current.

Indirect – touching a part of an appliance, that would not normally carry current but is doing so due to a fault.

What is a consumer unit?

The consumer unit is where the supply into the house is split into separate circuits, i.e. those for lights, sockets, etc. It houses a main isolation switch or combined RCD which is used to isolate (remove power from) all the circuits in the house. Also housed within the unit are various fuse-carriers for cartridge or rewirable fuses or

All about fuses

Two versions of fuse are to be found: the cartridge type and the rewirable type. The rewirable type is difficult and fiddly to rewire and the cartridge type, although easier to renew, is often difficult to obtain. Both these systems have drawbacks in being awkward and not very 'user friendly'.

An ordinary fuse is simply a weak link designed to break at a preset rating. If a circuit is overloaded or a short circuit occurs, the resulting overload will cause the fuse to melt and sever the supply. Unless a direct short circuit occurs, however, the overload on the fuse may not be enough to cause the fuse to blow because it has a fair degree of leeway over its rating value. It therefore offers only basic safety and will not afford any personal safety as the time taken to break is usually too long.

To the old familiar imperial ratings for fuses and circuit breakers have now been added

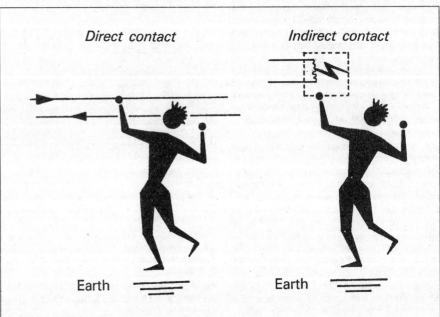

Direct contact   Indirect contact

Earth   Earth

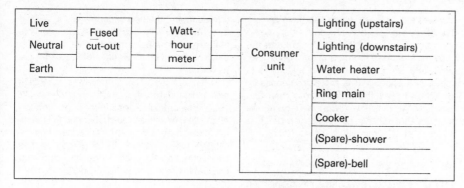

A typical house insulation

the international Renard ratings. A complete changeover will eventually be effected for European standardisation.

Fuse manufacturers are still using the imperial sizes whilst circuit breaker manufacturers have mostly changed to the new ratings. An equivalence chart is shown below:

Current Rating Imp	Renard	Typical Circuit
5	6	Lighting
10	10	
15	16	1mm. htr
20	20	
30	32	Ring main
45	40	Cooker/shower

Typical older-style consumer unit with isolation switch and wired fuses only

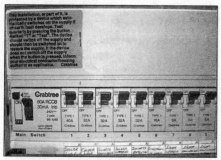

Modern consumer unit with RCD main switch and MCBs on all circuits

Miniature circuit breakers

The miniature circuit breaker (MCB) is now widely used and overcomes all the problems associated with ordinary fuses. The MCB is a small sophisticated unit that affords a much higher degree of protection than an ordinary fuse. It is tamper-proof and the unit involved is easily identified when one has tripped (switch moves to 'OFF' position). Most importantly, MCBs cannot be reset if the fault still exists which

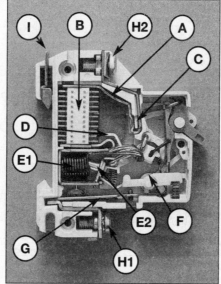

Mechanism of miniature circuit breaker

A   Arc runner
B   Arc chamber
C   Fixed contact
D   Moving contact
E1 Solenoid coil
E2 Moving core
F   Trip bar
G   Thermo-metal
H1 Wiring terminal
H2 Wiring terminal
I   Fixing

eliminates the practice of putting in the wrong fuse wire or cartridge to get things working – a foolish and most dangerous practice. MCBs are available in similar ratings to ordinary fuses and operate in two ways. Referring to the accompanying photograph, current flows into the unit at H1 and along G through coil E1 and on to the moving contact D (shown here open circuit). Contact D in the ON position would be resting on fixed contact C and so current would flow to H2.

Two fault conditions may arise; firstly – short circuit. This type of fault would quickly increase the current flow through the unit. Section E1, being a coil would increase its magnetic field and as a result attract E2 into the coil centre. This action trips the mechanism arm F and causes C–D to open circuit. Conductor A and arc chamber B act to suppress the arc formed on the contact point. This is done by the arc runners drawing the arc across the arc chamber where it is chopped into small arcs which are quickly extinguished. The action of the MCB is much quicker than an ordinary fuse wire. The second type of fault could simply be an overload on the circuit and, although exceeding the safe working load of the circuit, it would not cause the solenoid to trip. In this type of situation, the current flowing through G causes the conductor to heat up. The conductor is made of a tri-metal plate that bends when heated. The bending action of the conductor trips arm F, causing C and D to open circuit as before. This operation again is much better than fuse wire and calibration to higher tolerances is possible.

Note: *These units are factory-calibrated to extremely accurate tolerances and must not be tampered with nor attempts made to readjust them. The internal workings are only shown to help understand their operation. In the event of faults or failures, a new replacement unit must be fitted. No repair or adjustment is possible.*

Unfortunately, neither fuses nor miniature circuit breakers alone can give protection to anyone involved in a DIRECT EARTH situation. Indeed, the same can apply in the case of an INDIRECT EARTH contact. This may sound confusing, but it should be realised that in a 'direct contact' situation a person is literally shorting out Live and Earth, whereas in an 'indirect' contact situation, the Live to Earth path is already there because the equipment itself is connected to earth. The reason the fuse hasn't blown or the circuit breaker tripped is because the fault is not great enough to operate the safety mechanism, yet is great enough to be fatal. For instance, a 10A fuse would never blow with an 8A earth fault on the circuit, yet 8A constitutes a very dangerous level of earth fault current.

Residual current devices

To afford a higher degree of protection, another device has been developed, and is available in various forms.

1 Mounted within the consumer unit to protect all or selected circuits.

2 As individual socket protection.

3 An adapter to be used as portable protection and used where required.

The name given to this device in all its forms is the Residual Current Device (RCD). It may also be called a Residual Current Circuit Breaker (RCCB). In the early days of its introduction, it was known as an Earth Leakage Circuit Breaker (ELCB).

The primary protection is the integrity of the earthing, RCDs, in addition to the earthing, provide a much higher degree of protection depending upon the degree of sensitivity. For personal protection it is recommended that a sensitivity of 30mA is used.

It is generally considered that an earth fault of 1A or more is a fire risk, 50mA or more provides a shock risk which can have varying effects upon the human body depending upon the value of earth fault current and the body resistance of the person and, of course, their state of health. The heartbeat cycle is about 0.75 second. It is therefore necessary to cut off the fault current in less than one cardiac cycle. The Wiring Regulations stipulate that for Indirect Contact protection isolation must occur within 0.4 second.

How does an RCD work?

An RCD protects by constantly monitoring the current flowing in the live and neutral wires supplying a circuit or an individual item of equipment. In normal circumstances the current flowing in the two wires is equal but, when an earth leakage occurs due to a fault or an accident, an imbalance occurs and this is detected by the RCD which automatically cuts off the power in a split second.

To be effective, the RCD must operate very quickly and at a low earth leakage current. Those most frequently recommended are designed to detect earth leakage faults in excess of 30mA (30/1000ths of an amp) and to disconnect the power supply within 200ms (the rated sensitivity); these limits are well inside the safety margin within which electrocution or fire would not be expected to occur.

It should now be apparent that RCDs are designed to sever mains current should your electrical appliance malfunction electrically, or should you cut through the mains cable of your lawnmower for instance. They are simply a fail-safe device and should be used as such. In my opinion, used correctly they are an invaluable asset to your household.

Note: *The use of an RCD must be in addition to normal overload protection, i.e. fuses or MCBs, and not instead of it. All residual current devices have a test button facility. It is essential that this is tested regularly to verify that the device operates. For use with adapters or sockets, or for outside use, test before each operation. If failure occurs (does not trip, or trip appears sluggish or hard to obtain) have the unit tested immediately. This will require an RCD test meter and is best left to a qualified electrician.*

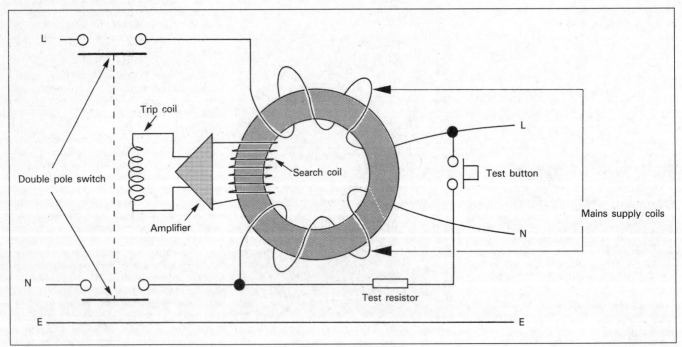

A simplified RCD circuit

Chapter 5
Plugs and sockets

Problems with electrical appliances may not always be the result of a failure of the item itself but with the electrical supply to it via the socket. A three-pin socket must have a Live supply, a Neutral return and a sound Earth path. When a plug from an appliance is inserted in the socket, a firm contact must be made at all three points. If the live or neutral pins of the plug or connection point within the socket fail to make adequate contact or are free to move, localised heating will occur within the socket. Appliances used from spur outlets must be connected correctly and securely. The spur outlet must also have a double pole isolation switch and great care must be exercised to ensure the outlet is switched OFF prior to disconnecting or working on the appliance. It is good policy and strongly recommended to isolate the spur outlet by both its switch and by removing the relevant fuse (or switching OFF the MCB) supplying that circuit at the consumer unit. Furthermore, confirm the spur has no power by using a non-contact voltage-sensing device like the one shown. DO NOT simply rely on the fact that the appliance connected to the spur outlet does not work, power could still be present. Ensure you check before proceeding.

Problem spotting

Tell-tale signs of this type of fault often show themselves as:
1 Burn marks around one or both entry points on the socket.
2 Plug hot to the touch after use of appliance in that socket.
3 Pungent smell from socket when appliance is in use.
4 Pitting and burn marks on and around the pins of the plug.
5 Radio interference to nearby equipment caused by internal arcing within the socket creating spurious radio emissions. These may pass along the ring main to hi-fi units, etc.
6 Intermittent or slow operation of the appliance being used.
7 Failure of the fuse in the plug. In this instance, this is not caused by a fault within the appliance but by heat being transferred through the live pin and into the fuse which fails by over-heating.

All these conditions are more likely with appliances such as washing machines, heaters and kettles, etc. which draw a high current when in use.

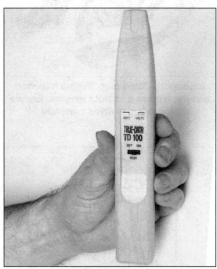

Non-contact voltage testers are used to check if a spur or outlet is isolated. This particular type of tester has a self-test facility to maximise safety and emits both audible and visual indication if voltage is detected. The use of neon test screwdrivers should be avoided at all costs

Why does it happen?

The reasons for such problems are various and may be caused by one or a combination of any of those listed below:
1 Repeated use of the socket, opening up the contact points within the socket. In other words general wear and tear.
2 Poor quality socket or plug.
3 Loose pins on plug.
4 The use of a double adapter. This can cause a poor connection purely by the weight of cables and plugs pulling the adapter partially out of the wall socket. Worse still is allowing a number of high-current-draw appliances to be run through one socket thus causing overloading. Examples might be a fan heater and kettle or washing machine and tumble dryer. Whenever possible, avoid the use of adapters by provision of an adequate number of sockets and do not exceed 3 kW load on any single socket.
5 Use of a multi-point extension lead when the total load on the trailing socket can easily exceed the 3 kW load of the single socket supply.
Note: *It is unwise to use a washing machine or similar items via an extension lead. Make provision for a convenient 13A supply socket to accommodate the original length of the appliance cable.*

Socket highlighting overheating. Both plug and socket will require replacing

This adapter was overloaded by connecting a washing machine and a tumble dryer to it and often using them at the same time. This effectively draws 26 amps through the single 13-amp connection. The weight on the adapter also created a poor connection within the socket. The result was severe overheating and the potential for a fire. DO NOT use adapters for major appliances and check all electrical fittings (plugs and sockets) regularly. When damage of this nature is found ensure that both the plug and socket are renewed

Note: *The corrosion on the earth pin of this plug also indicates that it was exposed to moisture. In this instance it was plugged into the double socket behind the kitchen work top with the right-hand socket used to power the kettle. Unfortunately, the kettle spout was often left pointing towards the protruding adapter resulting in condensation forming on and within it – quite simply a disaster waiting to happen. It was spotted during an unrelated repair visit from a knowledgeable service engineer.*

Rectification

First, DO NOT use the socket until the problem has been rectified. If the socket is found to be showing any of the previously described faults, it must be renewed

Internal view of severe burn out caused by poor connection to terminal. A new plug is required and the cable cut back to sound wire or renewed

Incorrectly fitted plug. Wiring bunched and not trimmed to right lengths. Ensure all plugs are fitted correctly

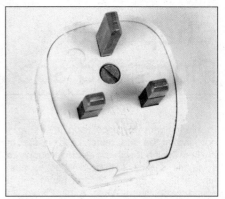

Typical resilient plugs which can stand up to rugged use without cracking

High quality three-pin plug ideal for home appliances

Always look for the ASTA/BS sign when purchasing electrical fittings

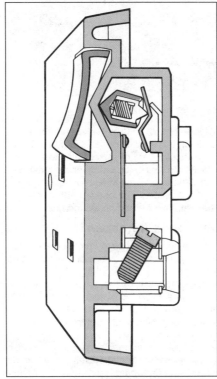

Internal view of 13A socket

The earth

All of the faults mentioned previously relate to the 'live' supply and neutral return on the socket, the plug or both. There is, of course, a third pin. Although it takes no active part in the operation of the appliance, it is, however, the most important connection of all. The function of the earth system is explained in *'Basics – electrical'*. Products that have three core cable must have the yellow and green earth wire securely connected to the earth pin of the plug or pin marked E.

The earth path of an appliance can be checked easily using a simple test meter *(see Electrical circuit testing)*. Remember, a path of low resistance is required from all items within the product that are linked into the earth path via the yellow and green cable.

Note: *The earth path of an appliance from its exposed metal parts to the earth pin of the plug should be a maximum of 1 ohm (BS3456).*

Checking the socket will require the use of an earth loop test meter which needs to be operated correctly. As these meters are expensive and problems could be encountered with distribution boards fitted with an RCD, it is advisable to have these tests done by a qualified electrical contractor. A simple plug-in tester like the one shown can be found in most good electrical shops and DIY outlets. This is most useful for checking the socket for reverse polarity. In other words, it will show if a socket has been incorrectly wired. An incorrectly wired socket can still work and outwardly give no sign of any problem. This type of fault is dangerous and not uncommon. The plug-in tester also indicates if an earth path is present. However, the quality of the earth in the socket is not shown. That is to say, it may have a very high resistance but would still allow the neon of the tester to light. If the earth resistance is high, remember this may result in a failure to

completely. If it is a single socket it may be wise to have a double socket fitted as a replacement. Numerous DIY books describe the renewal of sockets, so I won't duplicate the instructions here. Suffice to say that caution should be exercised when tackling socket renewal. When buying a replacement socket, make sure it is a good quality one as there are many of dubious quality to be found. Price is a good indicator of quality in this field.

It is advisable to renew all plugs that have been used in the faulty socket because damage may have been caused. It is possible, of course, that a faulty plug damaged the socket. To continue using the old plugs could result in premature failure of your new unit.

As with sockets, plugs can be found in many styles and qualities. While some of the poorer quality plugs may prove to be reliable on low current consumption items like lamps, TV and radios, they may not be so good for washing machines and heaters, etc. Although British Standards do apply to these items, quality does vary considerably. When buying plugs and sockets, go to outlets that can give advice and that carry a good selection. This will allow you to compare quality and build of the products. Look for the ASTA mark which proves that the design and manufacture has been approved by the Association of Short Circuit Testing Authorities. Replacement fuses should also carry this mark.

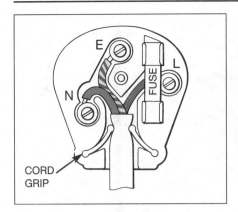

CORD
GRIP

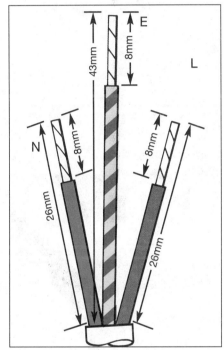

Simple plug in socket tester

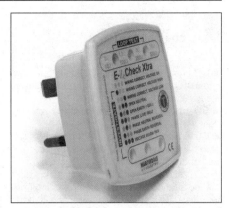

Plug in earth loop tester

However, when the plug-in tester applies say another 15mA during its test, then the circuit has a cumulative total of 35mA (original 20 + 15 for the test) and this will result in tripping the RCD protective device. Even the most expensive of 'non-tripping' earth loop test equipment can be affected by cumulative effect. It can also result in what appears to be nuisance tripping of a protective RCD when two appliances are used at the same time (i.e. washing machine and dishwasher etc.) but each will function without tripping if used individually.

Plug fitting

The fitting of a plug is often believed to be a straightforward task that needs little or no explanation. On the contrary, this is an area where many problems are to be found and dangers encountered if the fitting is not done correctly. Do not neglect this most important item.

The following text and photo sequences deal specifically with modern 13A flat-pin plugs. If your property has round-pin plugs and sockets, the indication is that the house wiring may be old and it would be wise to have it checked thoroughly by an expert.

When wiring a plug, it is good practice to leave the earth wire (yellow/green) longer than is necessary merely for connection to the earth terminal to be accomplished. The extra length is taken up in a slight loop shape within the plug. Doing this means that, should the appliance flex be pulled hard accidentally and the plug's cable grip fail to hold, the live and

neutral wires will detach from the terminal first, leaving the earth loop intact to provide continued safety cover. The photo of the pillar type plug shows how the extra little bit of earth wire is contained inside the plug.

Moulded plugs

Some appliances may be supplied with one-piece moulded 13A plugs fitted to the mains cable. If for any reason this type of plug has to be removed (e.g. to allow the cable to be slotted through a hole in a work surface, or due to damage), because of its moulded construction, it is not possible to take it off in the normal way. The plug has to be cut off with suitable wire cutters and a new plug fitted correctly as shown.

Warning: *Any moulded plug removed in this way must be disposed of immediately. It is wise to remove the fuse and to bend the pins of the plug as soon as it is removed to make sure that it cannot be inadvertently plugged into a socket. Do not leave it lying about or dispose of it where children can find it and plug it in.*

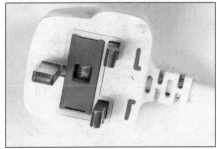

Typical moulded plug

blow the fuse which may cause overheating at the high resistance point or allow a flow of electricity through anything or anyone else that can give a better route to earth.

There is however, a plug-in tester that in effect combines the abilities of the expensive contractor's earth loop test equipment with the simplicity of use of the basic plug-in tester. This type of unit retails at around £50 and when used automatically provides a whole range of checks as well as an earth loop test. Although they are often quoted as being able to test RCD-protected circuits without tripping you must always ensure that you have access to reset the RCD prior to testing should tripping occur. To prevent an RCD tripping the device uses a very low test current which is below 30mA. However, if the circuit/property being tested or an appliance connected to it already has a slight earth fault (below the RCD's 30mA limit) when the test unit is used it is possible for the RCD to trip due to something called cumulative effect. This simply means that an existing earth fault of say 20mA would not cause a 30mA RCD to trip.

Make sure a moulded plug removed from an appliance cannot be inadvertently plugged in. Remove the fuse and bend the pins

Do's and don'ts

● DO ensure the cable insulation is removed carefully. Use of correct wire strippers is recommended.
● DO make sure that connections are the right way around.
● DO ensure that wires are trimmed to suit plug fixing point and no bunching is present. See poorly fitted plugs illustrations.
● DO make sure that all connections are tight and no strands of wire are left protruding from terminals. To prevent this, twist the strands together as shown, prior to fitting.
● DO make sure that the cord grip is fitted correctly around the outer insulation only.
● DO ensure correct rating of fuse is used to suit appliance.
● DO ensure the plug top/cover fits tightly and securely with no cracks or damage present.

● DO NOT damage the inner core of wires when removing the outer or inner insulation. If you do, cut back and start again.
● DO NOT fit tinned ends of cables into plugs. Some manufacturers tin (dip in solder) the end of the exposed inner conductors. The tinned/soldered end, if fitted to the plug, will work loose and cause problems associated with loose connections. Although tight when fitted, constant pressure over a long period will compress the soft solder resulting in a loose joint. A second problem associated with tinned conductors is the excessive length of exposed inner wire which the manufacturer usually provides. This can protrude below the cord clamp bunch within the plug to allow the cord clamp to grip the outer insulation only. Both of these practices are dangerous and must be avoided. Always cut cable lengths to suit the plug. If this poor method of fitting is found on an appliance it must be corrected immediately.

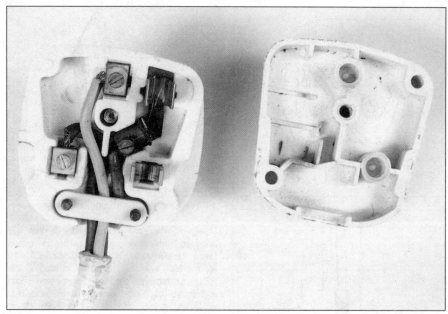
Wiring not cut to correct length. As a result the cord grip is fixed across inner wires, not outer sheath

● DO NOT allow strands of wire to protrude from any fixing points.
● DO NOT fit incorrect fuse ratings. Always match fuses to appliances and observe the manufacturer's instructions.
● DO NOT reuse overheated or damaged plugs.
● DO NOT bypass the internal fuse.

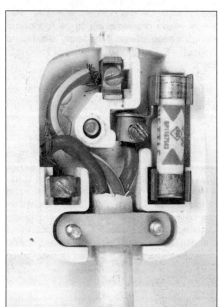
Conductor wire protruding from plug pins

Note: *All of the above photographs are used to illustrate the lack of attention to safety to this small but vital component. Always fit plugs correctly and safely. To give further assistance, a step-by-step photo guide for the two types is given.*

Wiring a plug – pillar type

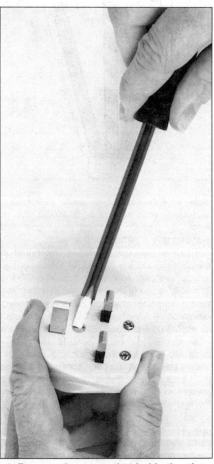
1 Remove the screw that holds the plug top-cover in position, taking care not to lose it

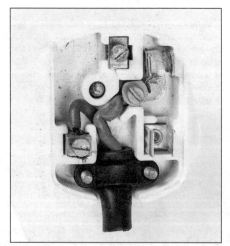
Wiring incorrectly bunched into plug to allow cord grip to hold outer sheath

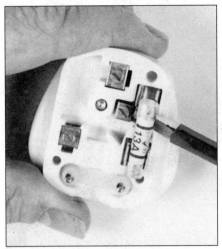

2 Ease the fuse from position (if using a screwdriver, take care not to damage the fuse)

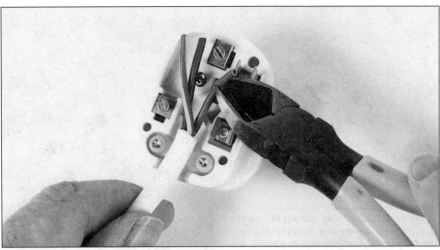

5 Offer the wiring to the plug base with the outer sheath in its correct position resting in the cord clamp area. Next, cut the inner cables as per the manufacturer's instructions, if these are not available allowing 13mm (½in) past the fixing point. Don't forget to allow a little extra on the earth cable to form a slight loop

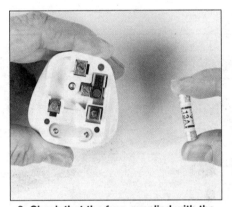

3 Check that the fuse supplied with the plug is of the correct rating for the appliance. Many plugs are supplied with 13A fuse already fitted, but do not be tempted to use it unless it is right. In this instance a 13A fuse was required

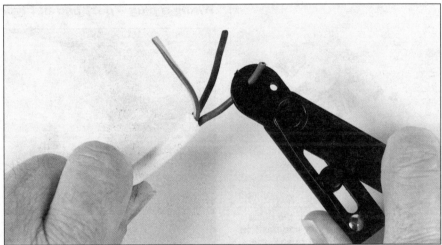

6 Carefully remove 6mm (¼in) of insulation from the end of each wire. This must be done with care to avoid damaging or cutting any strands of the conductor

4 Carefully remove the outer cable sheath to expose the inner wires. If damage should occur to the inner wires in the process, cut back and start again

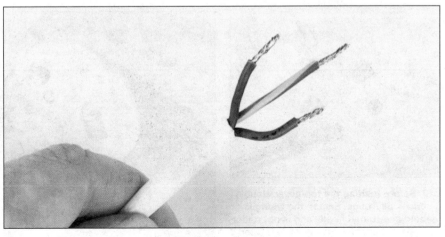

7 Twist the strands of each wire securely together. Make sure there are no loose strands

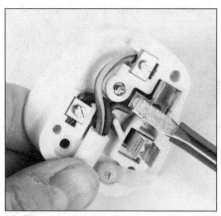

8 Fit each wire into its correct pillar and tighten each screw ensuring that it grips the conductor firmly (with thin wires it will help if they are folded over on themselves first). Make sure the wire fits up to the insulation shoulder and no wires or strands protrude from the pillar

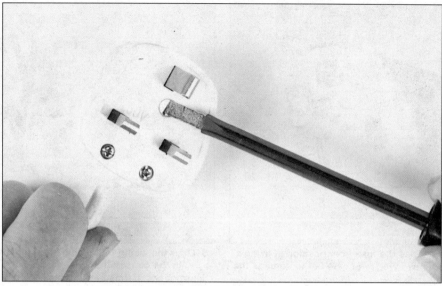

11 With top/cover refitted tighten the securing screw

Wiring a plug – post and nut type

9 Fit the cord clamp over the outer sheath and screw it firmly into position while being careful not to strip the threads of the plastic grip

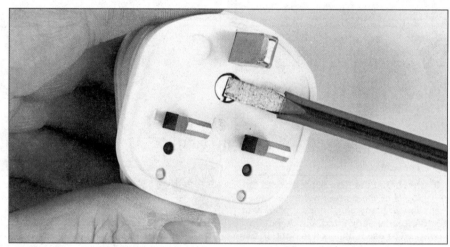

1 Remove the screw that holds plug top/cover in position

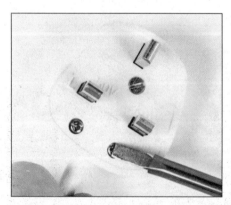

10 Before refitting the top/cover, double check all fixings. Ensure the wiring is seated and routed neatly and is not under stress or bunched. Fit the correct rated fuse, making sure that it is firmly and securely positioned

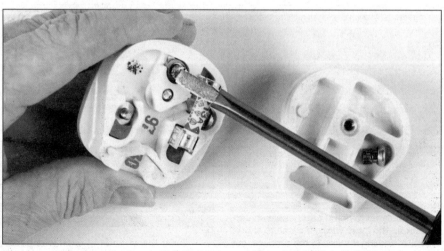

2 Remove the knurled/slotted nuts and place them safely in the top

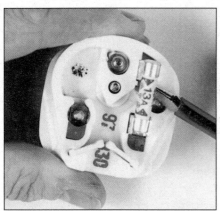

3 With the plug top/cover removed, the fuse can be eased from its position. If using a screwdriver, take care not to damage the fuse

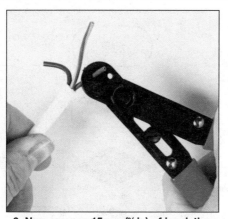

6 Now remove 15mm (⅝in) of insulation from the end of each wire. This must be done with care to avoid damaging or cutting any strands of the conductor

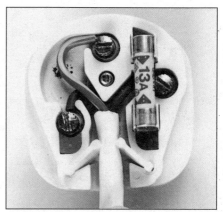

9 Fit each conductor (wire) to its correct terminal. Make sure each is fitted in a clockwise direction, otherwise it will be pushed out as the nut is tightened. Ensure only the conductor is gripped and not the outer insulation

10 Securely tighten all three nuts. Ensure that the wire fits up to the insulation shoulder and no wires or strands protrude from the terminal. Before refitting the top/cover, double-check all fixings. Ensure the wiring is seated and routed neatly and is not under stress or bunched. Fit the correct rated fuse, making sure that it is firmly and securely positioned

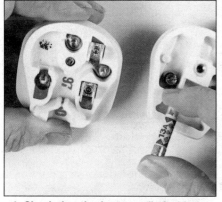

4 Check that the fuse supplied with the plug is of the correct rating for the appliance. Many plugs are supplied with 13A fuse already fitted but do not be tempted to use it unless it is right. In this instance a 13A fuse was required

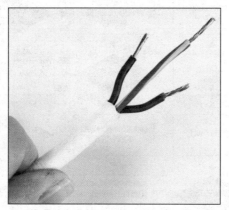

7 Twist the strands of each wire securely together. Make sure there are no loose strands

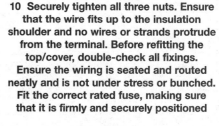

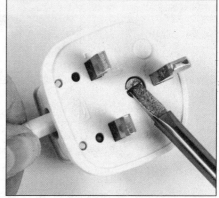

11 With top/cover refitted tighten the securing screw. This type has a captive screw with a shockproof washer to prevent it working loose during use

5 Carefully remove 43mm (1¾in) of the cable sheath to expose the inner wires. If damage should occur to the inner wires in the process, cut back and start again. Next, cut the inner cables as per the manufacturer's instructions, in this instance trim the live and neutral wires to 34mm (1⅜in)

8 The prepared cable can now be inserted into the cord grip ensuring only the outer sheath of the cable is gripped

Plugs and sockets

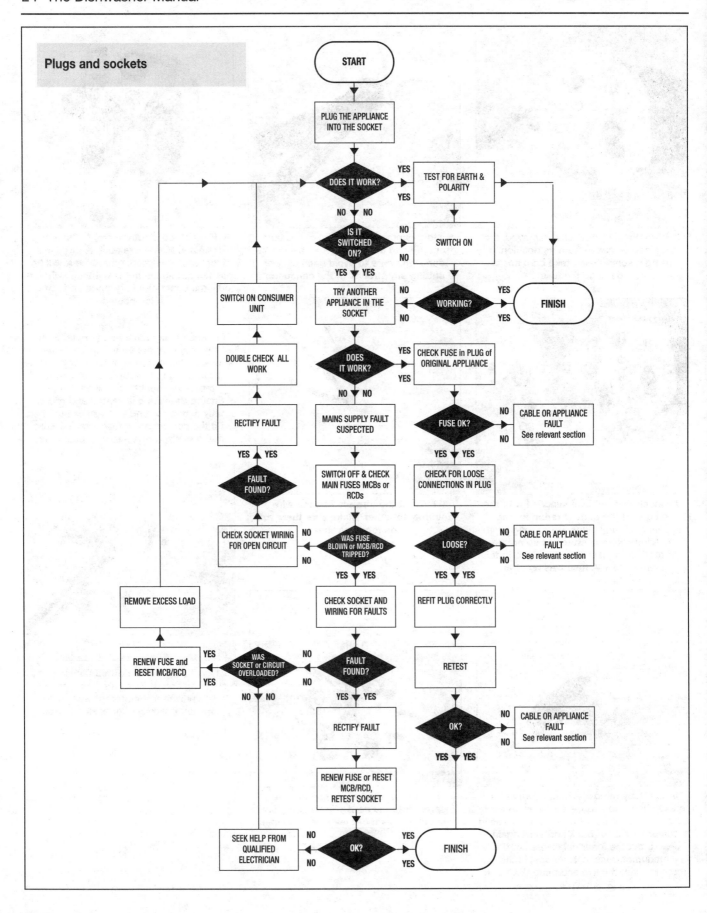

START

PLUG THE APPLIANCE INTO THE SOCKET

DOES IT WORK? — YES → TEST FOR EARTH & POLARITY

NO ↓

IS IT SWITCHED ON? — NO → SWITCH ON

YES ↓

TRY ANOTHER APPLIANCE IN THE SOCKET — NO ← WORKING? — YES → FINISH

DOES IT WORK? — YES → CHECK FUSE in PLUG of ORIGINAL APPLIANCE

NO ↓

MAINS SUPPLY FAULT SUSPECTED

FUSE OK? — NO → CABLE OR APPLIANCE FAULT See relevant section

SWITCH OFF & CHECK MAIN FUSES MCBs or RCDs

CHECK FOR LOOSE CONNECTIONS IN PLUG

WAS FUSE BLOWN or MCB/RCD TRIPPED? — NO → CHECK SOCKET WIRING FOR OPEN CIRCUIT

LOOSE? — NO → CABLE OR APPLIANCE FAULT See relevant section

CHECK SOCKET AND WIRING FOR FAULTS

REFIT PLUG CORRECTLY

WAS SOCKET or CIRCUIT OVERLOADED? — NO ← FAULT FOUND?

RETEST

RENEW FUSE and RESET MCB/RCD — YES

OK? — NO → CABLE OR APPLIANCE FAULT See relevant section

REMOVE EXCESS LOAD

RECTIFY FAULT

RENEW FUSE or RESET MCB/RCD, RETEST SOCKET

SEEK HELP FROM QUALIFIED ELECTRICIAN — NO ← OK? — YES → FINISH

SWITCH ON CONSUMER UNIT

DOUBLE CHECK ALL WORK

RECTIFY FAULT

FAULT FOUND?

Chapter 6
Tools and equipment

Modern automatic dishwashers do not require very specialised tools. Many of the routine repairs such as blocked pumps, faulty inlet valves and hoses can normally be completed with a selection of the following tools: crossblade, flatblade and Torx screwdrivers, combination pliers, simple multimeter, and pliers. Most people who are DIY orientated will own one or more of these items already. A useful addition to this selection would be a self-locking wrench, a socket and/or box spanner set, soft-face hammer, and circlip pliers. These would help with the larger jobs, such as motor removal and bearing removal, etc. Bearing removal/renewal and the like may also require certain things such as bearing pullers. As these can be expensive to buy, it is advisable to hire them from a tool hire specialist for the short period that you require them. Local garages may also be willing to let you hire them for a small deposit.

In addition to the standard fixings some makes and models may have security/anti-tamper screws/bolts which prevent removal

by standard tools. There are many different types and sizes in use and to remove them you will require a tool with the correct end style and size. Adapter sets like the one shown which has 5 different styles in a wide range of sizes are now quite readily available from many appliance parts suppliers and good tool shops.

It will not prove difficult to build up a selection of tools capable of tackling the faults that you are likely to encounter on your machine. Most of the large DIY stores will stock the tools that you require, often at a good saving. An excellent safety related addition to the household tool set would be a plug-in loop earth tester similar to that described and shown in Chapters 4 and 5.

When buying tools check the quality; a cheap spanner or socket set is a waste of money if it bends or snaps after only a short period of use. Having said that there are many tools on the market that are of a reasonable quality and are inexpensive. Try to buy the best that your budget will allow. Remember, the tools that you buy are a long-term

investment and should give years of useful service.

As with any investment, it is wise to look after it and tools should be treated the same. Having spent time and money on tools, they should be kept in a clean and serviceable condition. Ensure that they are clean and dry before storage.

 Tri-wing

 Allan and Hex Key – with centre pip

 Off-set cross-head

 Slotless

 Torx – with centre pip

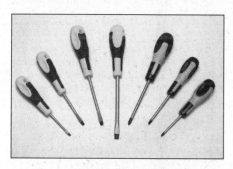

Screwdriver set

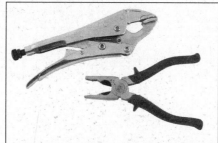

Grips/pliers

Security/Anti-tamper bit set

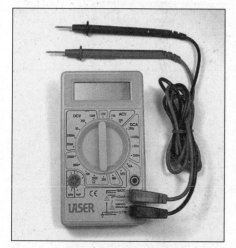

Simple digital multimeter

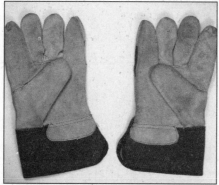

It is recommended that a sturdy pair of leather gloves are worn when removing and refitting cover panels on dishwasher. The exposed edges of the stainless steel inner cabinet can be extremely sharp

A lighter alternative to leather gloves are those made from 'Kevlar'. Although lighter and easier to use these type of gloves offer excellent protection against cuts. Remember the exposed edges of the stainless steel inner cabinet can be extremely sharp always wear protection when removing exterior panels and working near such edges

Chapter 7
Basics – plumbing

Although the machine may have been working correctly in its present position for some time, the incorrect installation of a machine may cause faults several months later. Because of this time span, the faults are not associated with bad plumbing and can cause the DIY engineer to look for other faults, which is very time consuming and annoying. Having said this, it is therefore worth a few minutes examining the existing pipework, and checking the manufacturer's installation details. These details will be found in the manufacturer's booklet that came with the machine. Even if the installation of your machine was left to an Expert, it is still advisable to read this section, as the chances are that they will not have read the installation details either!

For those of you who cannot find the manufacturer's booklet – what follows is a brief description of plumbing requirements that apply to nearly all automatic dishwashers and washing machines, and the reasons that they should be adhered to.

Inlet hose

If the machine is to be plumbed in Hot and Cold, then isolation taps must be fitted. (If your dishwasher has only one inlet hose connection, it is advisable to plumb the machine to the cold supply only.) This enables the water supply to be cut off between the normal house supply and that of the washer.

Note: *The rubber hoses connected to these taps should be positioned so that they don't get trapped when the machine is pushed back or rub against any rough surfaces during the machine's operation. Both these conditions can cause the hose to wear, due to the slight movement of the hose when the valves open and close. Ensure also that no loops have been formed in the hot supply hose (if fitted). In the beginning this will not cause any trouble, but as the hose gets older and the hot water takes effect, the hose will soften and a kink will form. This will then cause a restriction or complete stoppage of water to the machine. This can also happen to the cold hose, although it is very rare, due to the increased pressure in the cold system.*

The next thing to do is check that there is adequate water pressure to operate. First select a normal wash cycle and switch on. The machine should fill to working level within FOUR minutes. The same should apply when a rinse cycle has been selected. This gives a rough indication that the water pressure is adequate to open and close the valves. This is because the valves are pressure operated and a 4psi minimum is required for their correct operation. The cold pressure is usually governed by the outside mains pressure, but the hot water pressure is governed by the height of the hot water tank or its header tank.

Problems can arise when the tanks are less than eight feet higher than the water valve they are supplying. This is often found in bungalows and some flats. If a slow fill is

suspected, check the small filter that can be found inside all valves when the inlet hose is unscrewed. These can be removed and cleaned by simply pulling them out gently with pliers. Care must be taken not to damage the filter or allow any small particles to get past when you remove it. Clean water is normally supplied to the valves, but in many cases old pipework or the limescale deposits from boilers, etc. can collect at these points.

Many modern dishwashers now incorporate anti-flood systems, some of which use larger and more specialised inlet hoses – for details of these types of systems, refer to the chapter: *Flood protection systems.*

Outlet hose

The outlet hose MUST fit into a pipe larger than itself, thus giving an 'Air Brake' to eliminate syphoning. The height of the outlet hose is also important if syphoning is to be avoided. Syphoning can occur when the end of the outlet hose is below the level of water in the machine. This would give rise to the fault of the machine emptying at the same time as filling, and if the machine were to be turned off, would continue to empty the water from the machine, down to its syphon level.

Kinks and loops can also affect the outlet pipe, and cause several problems to the wash, rinse and dry programmes.

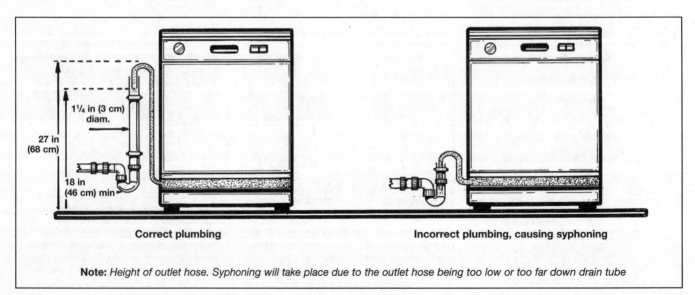

Correct plumbing   **Incorrect plumbing, causing syphoning**

Note: *Height of outlet hose. Syphoning will take place due to the outlet hose being too low or too far down drain tube*

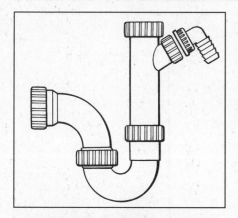

Discharge into a combined sink and dishwashing machine trap. This trap allows water from the sink to drain away as normal but has an extra branch for attaching the dishwashing machine hose (outlet). There are many variations of this type of system and incorrect installation/poor fitting can lead to apparent problems with the machine, such as failure to empty (due to blockage/restriction), back syphoning (the machine fills with water when not in use, due to water from the sink waste flowing down into the appliance), poor wash results, etc.

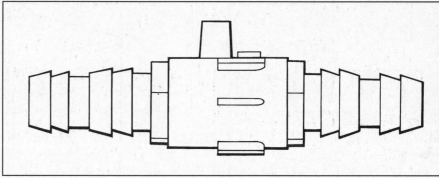

Siroflex anti-syphon unit
This unit provides an in-line air break to prevent syphonage occurring via your appliance drain hose. Full fitting instructions are supplied with every unit

Self plumbing inlet

When a machine is to be fitted in close proximity to an existing sink unit, you can take advantage of the new style SELFBORE taps and outlet systems now available. These simple and effective DIY fittings will save both time and money.

In most cases, the fitting of these taps can be done with only a screwdriver and no soldering is required. You do not even need to drain or turn off the main water system at all.

At this stage, I feel it is better to give you some visual help rather than pages of text. The following pages show you how easy the fitting of such units can be!

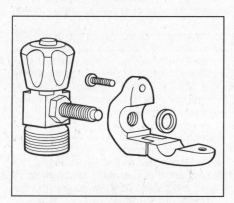

1 First, unscrew tap and open clamp

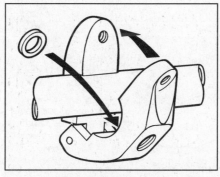

2 Fit clamp around copper pipe in required position. Make sure washer is in position

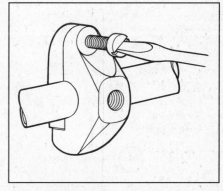

3 Engage screw and tighten until clamp is secure. Do not overtighten

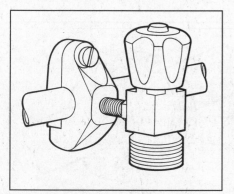

4 Insert tap assembly into clamp. Ensure tap is in 'off' position

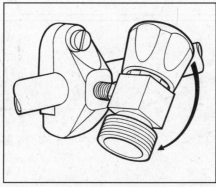

5 Turn clockwise until pipe is penetrated. Set tap to position required

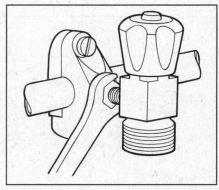

6 Tighten hexagonal nut towards the pipe. This secures tap in position

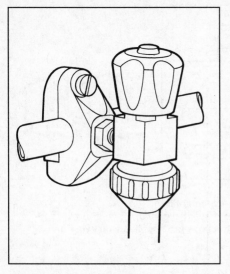

7 The tap is now ready for use. Connect hose to ¾ BSP thread on tap and turn on

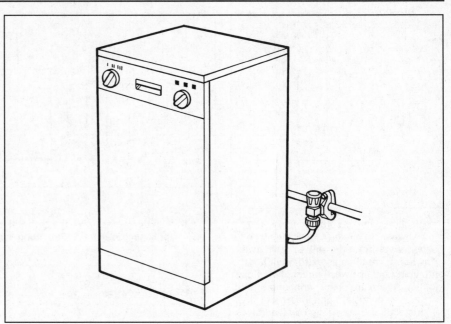

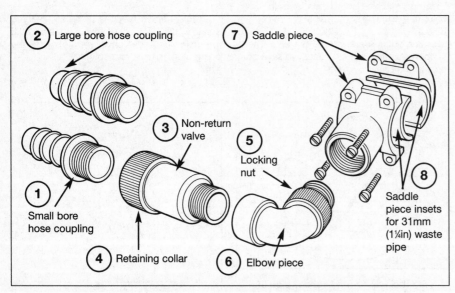

2 Large bore hose coupling

7 Saddle piece

3 Non-return valve

5 Locking nut

1 Small bore hose coupling

4 Retaining collar

6 Elbow piece

8 Saddle piece insets for 31mm (1¼in) waste pipe

Diagram shows the disconnected components of a typical self-plumb drain kit. All components with this type of kit can be unscrewed by turning anti-clockwise

Self plumbing outlet

1 Select the most convenient place in the waste pipe 31mm (1¼in) or 38mm (1½in) dia.

2 Disconnect components (as shown in illustration left). Place saddle halves around waste pipe, removing saddle inserts if pipe is 38mm (1½in) dia. Ensure that the O-ring is seated in recess. Tighten screws by stages to give an even and maximum pressure on waste pipe.

3 Insert cutting tool and screw home (clockwise) until hole is cut in waste pipe. Repeat to ensure a clean entry.

4 Remove cutter and screw in elbow. Use locking nut 5 to determine final position of elbow and tighten, or screw non-return valve 3 directly into saddle piece.

5 To complete installation, choose correct size hose coupling to suit drain hose and

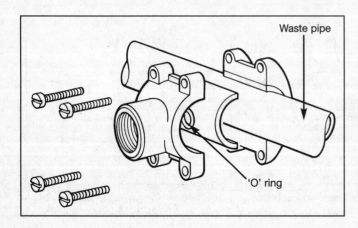

Waste pipe

'O' ring

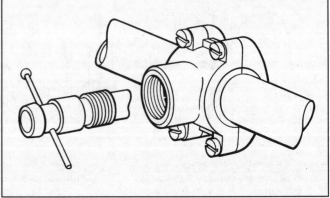

secure hose with hose clip (not included in kit).

*It is important to regularly remove and clean deposits from non-return valve. Simply unscrew retaining collar 4.

This information has been kindly supplied by Oracstar, a leader in the field of Self Plumbing kits, whose wide range of DIY fittings and accessories can be found in most leading DIY stores.

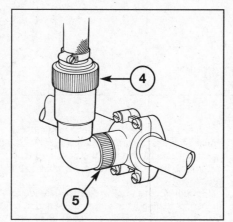

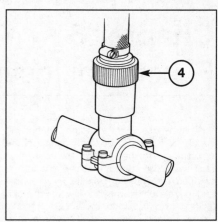

Under sink drain connections

It is now common practice for dishwasher drain hoses to be connected to a combined sink and drain connection or self bore plumbing out kit as shown in this chapter.

Both these types of drainage systems have the drain hose of the appliance fitted onto a small drain connection rather than into a larger free standing pipe as recommended by most appliance manufacturers. Although this does not break any rules or water by-laws the smaller diameter outlet point can block more easily if badly installed or poor fittings are used.

The self plumbing out kit has an internal non return valve to prevent waste water from the sink entering the appliance drain hose when the sink is emptied. Although this prevents water from entering the drain hose waste from the sink and/or the dishwasher debris can collect at this point resulting in poor draining or a complete blockage.

The combined sink and appliance waste system does not have a non-return valve thus allowing the back feeding of waste water from the sink into the dishwasher. This occurs when the drain hose of the appliance leads directly to the combined drain connection.

This can lead to a wide range of problems such as:
• Foul odour from machine when left un-used for a short period of time.
• Poor wash results due to the machine using the dirty sink water for part of the wash fill cycle.
• If the appliance is not used for several days but the sink is, it is possible for the back feed water to become visible in the load compartment and in certain circumstances to reach the door level and flood out when the door is opened to load the appliance.
Note: *This fault must not be confused with*

that of a weeping water inlet valve (see Chapter 19) as in this instance the water would be dirty water from the sink as opposed to clean water simply dripping in via a faulty inlet valve.

It is unlikely that to cure the problem of back feeding you would opt for changing the plumbing system so the following alternative is the often the best option.

To prevent waste water from running down the drain hose and back filling the appliance ensure that a portion of the drain hose is looped as high as possible up the side of the sink.

This simple yet effective action will prevent water from running all the way down to the appliance. It will not of course prevent sediment building up between the connection point and the outlet hose so regular checking and cleaning is advisable.

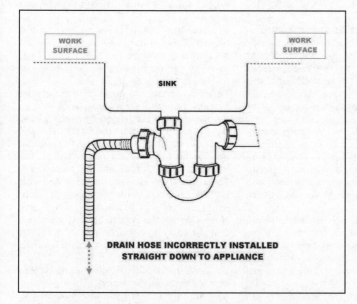

Poor under sink system. When the drain hose of a dishwasher is connected to an under sink waste like this the water can flow both ways allowing waste from the sink to back fill the appliance

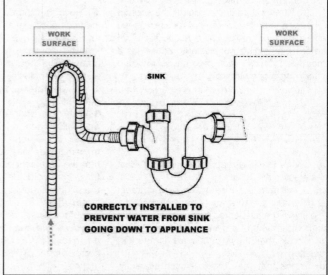

Re-routed under sink system. To prevent back flow from the sink, ensure that the drain hose is positioned as high as possible in relation to its connection point. This will only allow water to pass out of the appliance and prevent back filling when the sink empties

Chapter 8
Functional testing

Whenever possible the symptoms of the fault should be confirmed by the operation of the machine up to the point of the suspected fault, whereupon the machine should be stopped, disconnected from the mains supply and the relevant flowchart followed. For major leaks, blown fuses, etc. this is NOT practical (more damage may result by repeated operation of the machine). In these cases, the fault is known and further confirmation would be of little benefit. This may in fact, result in further damage to the machine or its surroundings.

Being able to assess and locate a fault may at first seem a difficult thing to do, but if a few simple procedures are carried out prior to starting the work, they will help cut down on the time spent on the machine. Hopping in a random fashion from one part of the machine to another, hoping that you will come across the fault and subsequently repair it, is hardly the best approach to repair work. This is not the way to tackle any job. Without doubt, the best method of fault finding is to be gained from your own experience of the machine, the fault with it and its location and rectification based on all the available information. Always remember a methodical approach to the work in hand, saves time and effort by eliminating unnecessary replacements based on guesswork. However there are a few things that can be done before such testing. These will confirm if it is the machine itself that is at fault or if an external/user fault is the source. Indeed, a large percentage of repair calls are not a fault of the machine at all; therefore before jumping to conclusions, pause for a moment. You will not only save time and effort, but money as well.

A few simple checks

a) Check that the machine is turned ON at the electricity socket.
b) Check that the fuse in the plug is intact and working. This can be checked by replacing the suspected fuse with one of the same rating out of a working item.
c) Check that the tap/taps are in the ON position.
d) Check that the door is closed correctly, and that a wash cycle is selected and the knob or switch has been pulled/pushed to the ON position.
e) Check that the machine is not on a 'rinse and (pre-rinse) hold' position. This on most machines will cause the machine to stand idle until instructed to do otherwise.

If the fault still remains, the next step is to determine its true nature, and subsequent repair.

Throughout this book, reference is made to functional testing to ensure that the action of the machine is correct and that the installation is suitable. Use the following sequence as a guide after installation, repair or servicing has been carried out to confirm that the machine and installation are working correctly. By following the sequence, you will be able to test where practical, all the functions of the machine and its plumbing installation in a safe and efficient manner. Although slight modifications may be necessary to suit model variations, the test will suit most if not all makes of machines that use mechanical timers/programmers.

Note: *Prior to functional testing, make sure that the machine is as near to level as possible, ideally this should be within 2° of horizontal. All machines have adjustable feet for this purpose.*

A typical installation and functional test routine

1 Check that the door fits smoothly into the load compartment aperture and latches easily and securely. (On uneven floors, further levelling adjustment may be necessary to compromise between a level position and ease of door closing).
2 Turn on water and electrical supplies to the machine.
3 With the door of the machine down, manually open and close the detergent dispenser several times to verify free movement of the latch mechanism. Ensure that the detergent compartment is clean and free from old detergent residue. Clean thoroughly if required.
Note: *Types of dispenser differ between manufacturers and also the quantity of powder/liquid detergent that they hold. It is not necessary to use detergent or fill load compartment with crockery for functional testing.*
4 Check that the rinse aid dispenser is not empty and make sure that the dosage setting is correct – see chapters on *Detergent and Rinse aid dispensers* and *Common causes of poor washing results.*

5 Check that the salt container level indicator is showing there is sufficient salt in the reservoir (if fitted). See chapter on *Internal water softeners.* Ensure that adjustment is set to correct hardness of water supply.
6 Close the door securely and select the rinse and hold sequence and switch to the 'on' position. Reference to your particular machine's handbook may be required to obtain the correct setting.
6a Fill time should be within 4 minutes.
6b When the wash action starts, i.e. main circulation pump, check for visible leaks from door seal, base, etc. If there is any leakage, end the test sequence and isolate the machine before tracing the problem. See Chapter 11, *Determining the fault.*
6c During the cycle (averaging between 8 and 12 minutes), listen for water circulating through the spray arms.
6d Before the cycle has finished, switch off and wait a few seconds to allow the spray arms to come to rest. Open the door and check the level of water within the machine and the position of the spray arms. Close the door securely and switch on for 10 to 15 seconds. Turn off, pause then open the door and check that the arms have come to rest in a different position, thus indicating free rotation. **Note:** *Opening the door too quickly will result in water spraying out since the arms will not come to rest the instant the machine is turned off.*
6e Close the door again, switch the machine on and allow the remainder of the rinse and hold cycle to continue.
7 Allow the machine to impulse normally to the empty/drain position.
7a Visually check the outlet hose stand pipe to verify that the drain is capable of taking all the water being discharged by the machine, i.e.: not overflowing from the top of the stand pipe. Blockages in stand pipe drains are not uncommon but they are not a fault of the machine, see Chapter 7 *Basics – plumbing.*
7b At this point, unlatch the door and only partially lower it in order to check the door safety switch – all functions should cease.
Note: *Opening the door too quickly will result in water spraying out since the arms will not come to rest the instant the machine is turned off.*
7c Close the door and allow the machine to impulse to the stop position.
8 Turn the machine off, open the door and confirm that the emptying cycle did in fact drain the machine correctly. If the machine fails to empty correctly, refer to Chapter 11 – *Determining the fault.*

Chapter 9
General care and attention

For many repairs it is best if the machine is laid on its back or side. Because of the need for as large a load compartment as possible, most of the functional parts of a dishwasher are mounted below the load compartment floor and are easily accessible.

Always ensure that the outer shell of the machine is protected with a suitable cover when laying the machine down. The machine should be lowered slowly, and when doing this it is a good idea to place a strip of wood under the edge of the machine, to provide room for the fingers for lifting the machine back into its correct position after the repair.

When laying the machine over, care should be taken to protect oneself from injury. Firstly, ensure that the machine is completely disconnected from the main supply, and that the inlet and outlet hoses are removed.

Secondly, before attempting to lay the machine over, decide if you need any help. These machines are heavy and a little help may prevent a back injury. Thirdly, before attempting to move the machine, ENSURE THAT THE FLOOR IS DRY. A wet floor has no grip, especially if any of the water on it is soapy.

The correct rating of fuse must be used as per the manufacturer's instructions. The author would like to point out that any references to manufacturer's names or model numbers, etc. that are used throughout this manual are for the readers' information and reference purposes only. Whilst every precaution has been taken to ensure that all information is accurate in every detail, the author cannot accept any responsibility for any errors or omissions appertaining to this

manual, and shall not be responsible for any damage or injury caused whilst using this manual.

Regular inspection points

A regular internal inspection of your dishwasher may enable you to identify a part that may not be running properly, or find a perished hose before a leak occurs. It is recommended that the following points be checked regularly. **Note:** *As many of the hoses within a dishwasher carry water under pressure, it is essential that all such hoses and clips are in 'A1' condition. If in doubt, renew any suspect hose or clip to avoid future major leaks.*

Inspect	When	Special notes
Main filter	Weekly – as per manufacturer's manual. Often dependent on usage	Remove and clean thoroughly both small and large particle filters. Rinse thoroughly.
Spray arms	Weekly – as per manufacturer's manual. Often dependent on usage	Remove blockages from slots on the spray arms and check for free rotation.
Rinse aid dispenser	Weekly – as per manufacturer's manual. Often dependent on usage	Check level/content of rinse aid tank. Top up as required.
Salt container	Weekly – as per manufacturer's manual. Often dependent on usage	Check level/content of container. Top up as required.
Valve filters (hot and cold)	6 months	If dirty, pull out with pliers and wash out.
Door seals	6 months	If seal is tacky to the touch, it may be in need of renewal. Clean and remove all food and fat deposits, etc.
All hoses	6 months	As above. Ensure that all corrugations in all hoses are checked thoroughly.
Pump and sump hoses	6 months	Check for any items that may have collected in or at these points. Remove as necessary.
Level machine	Yearly, if machine is moved	Check that the machine is standing firmly on the floor and does not rock. Adjust by unscrewing the adjustable feet or packing under the wheels.
Check plug and connectors	Yearly, prior to every repair	After repair, look for poor connections in the plug socket. Also look for any cracks or other damage. Renew as necessary.
Taps and washers	Yearly, prior to and after every repair	Check taps for free movement, corrosion and/or leaks.

The importance of levelling

For dishwashers to function correctly it is essential that they are as near to level as possible and adjustable feet are provided for this purpose. However, this requirement is often overlooked in the haste to install and use a new appliance or simply forgotten when the appliance is removed from its position for decorating or repair etc.

Unfortunately it is not uncommon for flooring to be uneven and if no attempt is made to adjust the feet to suit the conditions is made, problems will arise.

Sloping forwards can lead to weeping at the bottom of the door seal due to too much water pressing on the point where the outer and bottom door seals meet when the door is closed. This leads to leaks at one side of the front of the appliance or the other depending on the sideways slope of the appliance.

Adjustment is not as straightforward as it may seem especially on very uneven flooring. The construction of a dishwasher is designed to produce as large a load compartment as possible and this results in a large square opening into which the door fits when closed. The construction of other appliances such as fridges and washing machines results in a more rigid construction which means they are a little less affected by uneven flooring. However, the large open front of the load compartment is susceptible to twisting out of shape if not adjusted correctly.

This means that instead of a square opening for the rigid square shaped door to fit into the square opening is distorted into a parallelogram shape. The result of this is that the door will have difficulty in locating into the opening resulting in difficulty in closing the door as easily as it should and, with severe misalignment, may not close at all.

The appliance needs to be correctly levelled to its working position. This involves assessing the appliance in its working position and making adjustments to the relevant feet. With severely uneven flooring you may need to work out a compromise of level and distortion of the door opening. What you need to remember is that adjustment is not simply carried out using the accessible front feet you will also need to ensure that the rear feet are also adjusted correctly. This may mean that you have to pull the appliance out to make adjustments, refit the appliance and check if that cured the problem. You may need to repeat this process to obtain the best result.

How an uneven floor effects a particular make or model of dishwasher depends on the way the load compartment has been constructed. Some makes have more rigid construction whilst others flex very easily when the door is open. How resistant a particular model is to distortion of the load compartment opening can be tested by fully opening the door and with one hand pressing on the top of the appliance exerting a little sideways

At the centre of the front plinth of this dishwasher is a plastic nut with an 'Allen' key centre (arrowed) which connects internally to a plastic rod

Close up of the rear height adjustment unit. On models with this feature door alignment will need to be carried out using the two adjustable front feet

force in each direction. How much the opening of the load compartment distorts (or not) gives an indication to the resistance (or not) of the appliance to uneven flooring. Dishwashers with removable side panels screwed to a frame surrounding the load compartment are often less rigid than those with a solid (welded) shell construction into which the load compartment is secured.

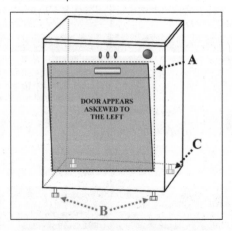

This diagram shows a door that appears to be skewed to the left in relation to the load compartment opening A. To alleviate this problem foot C will need to be screwed further out and feet B should not need to be touched

With the base plate removed the plastic connecting rod and central adjusting foot on the rear of the appliance are clearly visible. This system allows rear height adjustment to be made from the front of the appliance while the appliance is in its working position

For peak performance ensure that all filters are cleaned on a regular basis

The following diagrams are provided to help with the important aspect of door alignment which is generally carried out using the rear adjustable feet. The diagrams are an exaggerated view used to illustrate the problem. When viewed on, an appliance the door will be square and it will be the load compartment opening that will be out of shape.

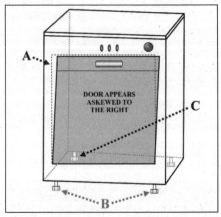

This diagram shows a door that appears to be skewed to the right in relation to the load compartment opening A. To alleviate this problem foot C will need to be screwed further out and feet B should not need to be touched

Chapter 10
Using a flowchart

Flowcharts are used throughout the book, and are designed to help you quickly locate the area or areas of trouble, and to show that a step-by-step approach to even the most difficult of faults is by far the best way to ensure they are found and rectified easily.

The use of flowcharts to those with some experience of home computers will need little explanation. To those of you who will be seeing them for the first time, here is how they work.

How flowcharts work

To the uninitiated, the use of flowcharts may seem a difficult way of fault finding. This is not the case, and will be quite simple if a few small, but important points are remembered. As you will see in the examples, there are only three main types of symbols used. A rectangular box, a diamond and an ellipse. With a little practice, you will become aware how invaluable this method can be in all areas of DIY work. The construction of one's own flowchart before attempting the job in hand will be of help when the time comes to reverse the stripdown procedure, i.e. notes can be made next to the relevant boxes on the flowchart, of what was encountered at that point, i.e. number of screws, positions of wires, etc. Small points – but so vital, and so often forgotten with an unplanned approach.

The rectangular box

This is a process, i.e. in the box is an instruction. Carry it out and rejoin the flowchart where you left it, travelling in the direction indicated by the arrows.

The diamond

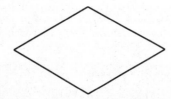

This asks a question, i.e. if the answer to the question in the diamond is yes, then follow the yes line from the diamond. If the answer is no, follow the no line.

The ellipse

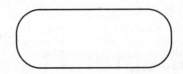

This is a terminator. When this box is encountered, you either start a new chart or finish one. The text in the box will indicate the action.

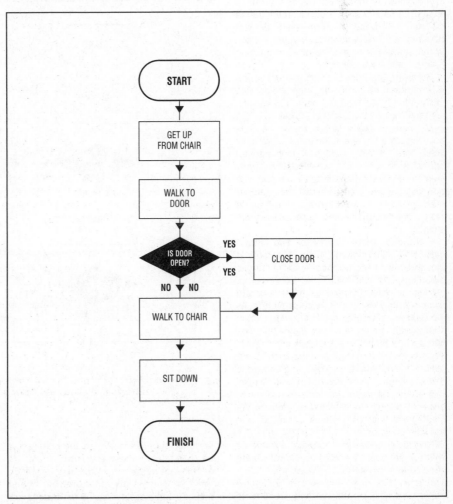

This example flowchart illustrates the steps involved in carrying out the simple task of making sure a door is closed. The arrows indicate the direction to the next step, so as to guide you through the logical sequence

Chapter 11
Determining the fault

Throughout the manual, flowcharts are used to aid the fault-finding process. The location of faults will become much easier as you become more conversant with your machine ie through regular servicing of your machine before faults have arisen.

Selecting the correct flowchart for the job will be made easier if it is remembered that faults fall into three main categories: mechanical, electrical and chemical.

Mechanical faults will normally become apparent by a change in the usual operational noise level of the machine. A high pitched squealing noise on a washing cycle may indicate a bearing fault on the wash pump. A banging noise from inside the cabinet may indicate a worn spray arm bearing which would allow the arm to wobble excessively.

Electrical faults fall into two major categories; Component faults – a fault is classed as a component fault when a complete unit has failed. i.e. if the pump, heater, motor, etc. should fail, the fault is said to be a component fault. Impulse path faults – a fault is classed as an impulse fault when an internal, pre-determined instruction has failed, i.e. if the thermostat does not close or open at the required temperature, or the timer fails to move on after a given time sequence this constitutes an impulse path fault. Simply, this is the failure of the machine to move correctly through its selected programme. An instance of this type of fault is explained in the flow chart.

Chemical faults are normally associated with the detergent being used and will create such problems as: poor washing, scaling problems, blocking, etc. A comprehensive guide to washing problems and useful hints will be found at the rear of this manual, in the Chapter *Common causes of poor washing results.*

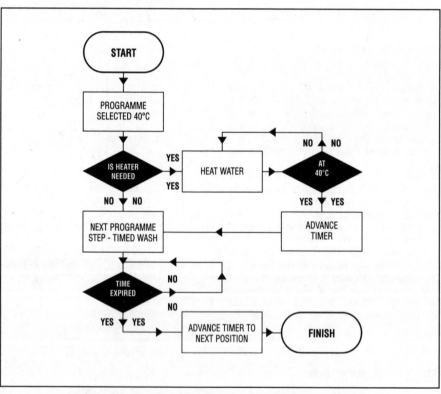

Shown is a simplified flowchart of the operation described

The timer supplies power to the heater, but due to a fault in the thermostat circuit, the timer is not supplied with the information that the correct temperature has been reached. Because of this, the timer does not move on, but remains on the heat position and exceeds the selected temperature. It should be noted that there is no fault in the timer, just in one of its impulse paths. A similar fault would arise if the thermostat circuit was OK, the thermostat closed at the correct temperature, but the timer failed to move on after the correct time had elapsed. This would be a fault of the timer's internal impulse path via its timing mechanism.

Fault-finding guide	Chapter title
Machine will not work at all	Basics – electrical Functional testing Door safety switches Flood protection systems Timers (programmers)
Machine leaks	Emergency procedures Leaks fault-finding flowchart Water level control Pumps Door seals Inlet valves
Machine will not empty	Emergency procedures Pumps Basics – plumbing Wiring harness faults
Machine empties all the time	Flood protection systems
Machine will not fill/take powder	Functional testing Inlet valves Flood protection systems Detergent and rinse aid dispensers
Machine does not wash clean	Spray arms Common causes of poor washing results Basics – plumbing Pumps
Machine is noisy	Check loading Pumps Spray arms
Machine won't move through programme	Thermostats and thermistors Heater Inlet valves Flood protection systems Timers (programmers) Wiring harness faults
Machine sticks through programme	Basics – plumbing Pumps Inlet valves Heater Door safety switches Timers (programmers) Wiring harness faults
Machine blows fuses	Emergency procedures Basics – electrical Low insulation Wiring harness faults

The lists following the main fault headings indicate the sequence with which they should be examined

Chapter 12
Dishwasher noise when new

It is now common place to see appliance advertising and sales literature displaying the working noise level of a product in decibels (dB). However, few people fully understand the meaning of such figures and more often than not when faced with a choice choose the lower decibel figure. This will result in selecting the appliance with the lowest noise level during operation when compared to a particular range of appliances but not provide an indication of exactly how noisy it really is.

How noisy any piece of equipment is when in use under normal working conditions and free from faults depends on a wide range of factors such as the type of function being carried out and the way in which the appliance is constructed and dishwashers are no exception to this rule.

Dishwashers are designed to provide as large a load compartment as possible which

in effect results in a large thin walled hollow load compartment (usually of thin stainless steel). Water sprayed at high pressure during the wash cycle to clean the wash load also bombards the inner surface of the load compartment and both of these actions produce noise.

To reduce the external noise level produced by the spray action manufacturers employ a range of sound retaining and absorbing methods. However, the addition of sound reducing materials has a cost penalty which means that low end models may have little in the way of sound reduction whereas high end models in the same range do. Although a range of appliances from one manufacturer may have almost identical functional components (circulation motor, drain pump etc.) the additional sound reduction materials fitted to the higher end

models will result in distinctly lower noise levels when in use.

Basic sound reduction usually equates to a black bitumen-like panels being glued to the outer of the load compartment. This goes some way to reducing the noise from load compartment surface but the gap between it and the outer shell of the appliance will still act as a sounding chamber.

In addition to the basic sound reduction method above mid-range models will have additional sound absorbing material such as thick non-woven material (similar to carpet underlay) placed at strategic points within the space between the outer of the load compartment and the outer case (shell) of the appliance.

Top of the range models will have most if not all spaces between the outer of the load compartment and shell of the appliance, door inner void, lid and front base gaps filled with die cut sound absorbing material and the addition of baffles (plastic or metal inserts) isolating the various other voids or joints.

The following lists provide simple to understand guide to what the decibel (dB) scale relates to:

Decibels (dB)	Average human perception
0	Weakest a human can hear
30	Very quiet such as a library
60 to 70	Typical conversation level
80	Telephone dial tone
85	In-car city traffic noise
90	Street level lorry traffic
95	Underground train
90 to 95	Sustained noise at this level can result in hearing loss
107	Petrol powered mower
115	Rock concert (loud)
125	At this level pain is felt
140	Even short-term exposure at this level results in permanent damage
140	Typical jet engine
180	Destruction of hearing tissue
195	Loudest possible sounds

What may be a better indication is a human's ability to perceive changes in decibel levels. For instance a 1dB change is essentially imperceptible with a 3dB change being just perceptible, whereas a 5dB change will be definitely noticed. A 10dB change will be perceived as being twice as loud and a 20dB change four times as loud.

The above relate to the normal functions of machines and appliances and it must be remembered that when mechanical problems occur they inevitably result in changes in noise level.

With its door panels removed it can be seen that this dishwasher has minimal noise reduction with only the top half of the inner lining having a sound reducing panel stuck on to it

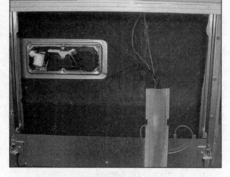

With its door panels removed it can be seen that this dishwasher has a sound reducing panel covering the whole of the inner stainless steel lining providing good sound reduction

In addition to bitumen-like pads the internal spaces of this dishwasher also has shaped sound absorbing material between all inner and outer panels providing a high level of sound reduction

A covered or solid plastic base also helps reduce the overall noise level

Chapter 13
Noise faults

Unusual or excesive noise can be one of the first signs that something is going wrong with your dishwasher. It is quite common for noise faults to be ignored initially, but then over a period of time, they become accepted as the norm. Obviously, it is advisable to investigate any noise as soon as it is heard, hopefully avoiding larger problems in the future.

As with other faults, noise faults become easier to identify and locate the more conversant you are with your machine.

Noise faults and their most common causes

A rhythmical bumping/banging noise during a wash cycle could simply be poor loading of the dishes, which can be easily remedied by turning the machine off, waiting a few seconds for the spray arms to stop and then repositioning the offending items. **Note:** *It is important to pause before opening the door as the spray arms are still rotating and could possibly spray very hot water out of the machine.* Alternatively, this noise could be caused by loose or worn spray arm mounts which would allow the spray arm to wobble excessively and catch the load baskets (see *Spray arms*).

A high pitched squealing would indicate bearing wear of the wash pump or outlet pump, possibly caused by water penetration due to worn shaft seals, etc. A similar noise can he made by worn spray arm bearings. This can often be confirmed by excessive movement on its shaft. If you experience any difficulty in determining whether the noise is emanating from the circulation pump bearing or the spray arms, simply secure the spray arms to the top and bottom baskets to prevent them rotating, (this can be done simply with tape). If the noise is still present during the wash cycle, this will then confirm a seal or bearing fault on the main circulation motor or impeller. Conversely, if the noise has stopped, then a fault on the spray arm is indicated. Noise on the outlet cycle would indicate a fault with the bearings or seal on the outlet pump. More details can be found in the relevant *Pumps* sections.

A whistling type noise could signify a more unusual fault with the water inlet either

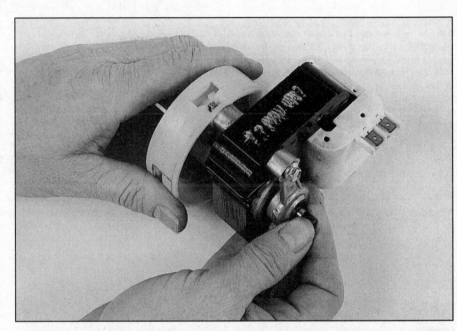

Check worn drain pump bearings for lateral movement (side to side) – none should be found. However, a degree of end float (movement in and out) will be found on shaded pole pumps

This main circulation motor has an obvious shaft seal problem. It is possible for a high pitched noise to accompany such a fault (apart from a leak) due to water/detergent mix affecting the ceramic seals, motor bearing or both

at the valve or the air break system. Simple cleaning or a reduction in pressure at the isolation tap could rectify this. (See *Inlet valves, Air break systems* and *Steam vent*).

If large items are allowed to get past the main filters (this may happen if care is not taken when they are removed for cleaning), they may foul the wash pump impeller. Prolonged usage with an item lodged in this area will seriously damage the impeller, and if it jams completely the whole motor could be affected. To avoid this happening, take great care when removing filters and make sure they are refitted securely. Small spoons or cocktail sticks are the most popular items to find their way into the filters. In the event of broken dishes in the machine, ensure that all the pieces are removed, especially if it is glass, as glass in water is extremely difficult to detect. Take care. **Note:** *Such accidents should not happen if a little care is taken in loading the machine. All modern machines are extremely gentle on all articles of glass, china, etc. but having said that, it is advisable to check the suitability of any item before putting it in the dishwasher.*

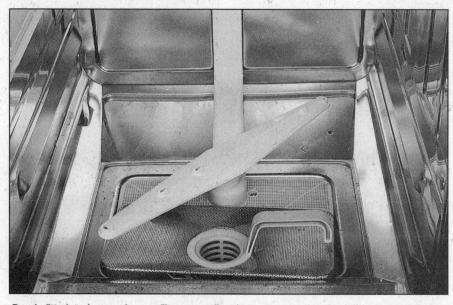

Poorly fitted or damaged sump filters can allow items to enter the circulation pump chamber causing noise and damage to the pump impeller, main motor or both. Renew damaged filters immediately and investigate and correct noises as soon as they become apparent

Chapter 14
Door hinges and counterbalance systems

The construction of dishwasher doors makes them heavy. They are therefore counterbalanced by springs to assist the normal opening and closing of the door. However, this counterbalance arrangement can at times make it awkward to carry out certain repair tasks. Great care must be taken whenever dismantling the door as removing panels will lighten the load on the return springs and cause the door to close without warning. This can be avoided by placing an alternative weight on the inner surface of the open door prior to removing the outer panel. See photo below left. Alternatively the hinges on some makes and models can be locked in the down position by catches or the insertion of rods placed through aligning holes in the hinge. See photo below right.

Note: *When the door is in the down position the counterbalance springs are under tension and no attempt to adjust, disturb or dismantle them must be made. Any adjustment and replacement must be made with the door closed and with the least tension on the return springs. Mark the position of the springs prior to removal and make a note of the way in which the mechanism operates prior to removal. DO NOT over adjust the tension. Ideally the mechanism should simply cancel out the weight of the door, thus allowing minimum effort to open or close the door. The door should not drop open nor should it require constant holding to keep it in the open position.*

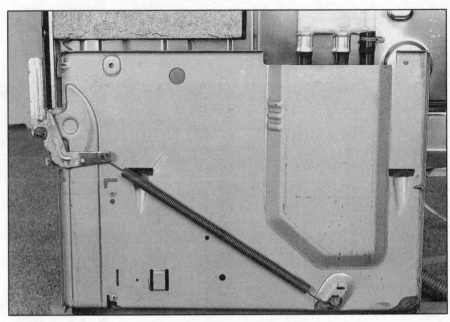

Large spring counterbalance system

Built-in or integrated machines often have the facility to have matching kitchen door panels fixed to the outer of the door. These types of dishwasher will normally have the provision to adjust the counterbalance to take into consideration the additional weight of the large wooden door panel. Adjustment is normally by means of a discreet adjusting screw or bolt head. Refer to the installation booklet for your particular model to ensure correct adjustment. **Note:** *If each side can be adjusted separately ensure they are adjusted equally.*

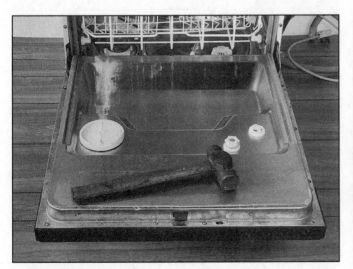

Counterweight the door prior to removing the front panel. This prevents the door closing when the panel is removed

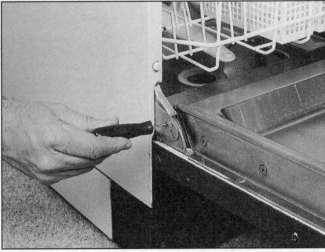

This hinge unit can be locked in the down position by inserting a metal rod in both hinges. Check closely for this facility

This Whirlpool series dishwasher uses a flat spring steel brake band as the flexible link between the tension spring and door hinge mechanism. It is not uncommon for this part to need replacing. Note: *Do not lubricate the band or contact surface of the plastic guide. Restrict lubrication to parts that show signs of being lubricated during manufacture*

The tension of this door spring can be adjusted by moving the top securing pin (arrowed) into various locating holes in the support member

The tension of the above door counterbalance can be adjusted by repositioning the spring into the rectangular holes (arrowed) in the metal link rod. Note: *The rod is slightly crimped to help retain the spring in the correct position. If the spring is repositioned ensure the rod is re-crimped*

The connection between the door hinge arm and the counter-balance tension spring may be high tensile cord looped around a series of pulleys as in this instance

Chapter 15
Door safety switches

All dishwashers have at least one door safety switch. These are generally very simple ON/OFF switches, and although their size and shape differs with different makes and models, their function remains the same. They are normally open switches and will only make contact when the door of the dishwasher is correctly closed or latched. If the door is inadvertently opened during the normal cycle, the switch will return to its normally open position. The door safety micro switch is normally on the live feed to the timer and will therefore effectively cut off the power to all parts of the machine. **Note:** *Opening the door mid-cycle whilst the machine is running can be dangerous. Although the power is cut off, the spray arms continue to rotate for a few seconds. If the door is opened quickly the hot water in the machine may spray out. Pause before opening the door for any reason and keep your face away from the opening when you do so.*

For extra safety, an elongated arm often operates the switch. The position of the switch can vary – some are mounted in the door whilst others may be mounted in the main body at the latch position. Some are actuated by a protruding peg mounted either on the door or body of the machine. When the door is closed, the peg enters into a recess and actuates the switch at a given position.

On other machines, the switch is an integral part of the handle and latch system, and is actuated only when the latch is in its

 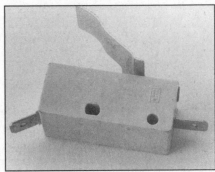

Typical door safety switches. Note the operating arms. As the switch carries all the power it is liable to overheating problems due to poor connections or contacts

Peg operated door switch

Latch operated switch. Note also the overheated connection of this machine

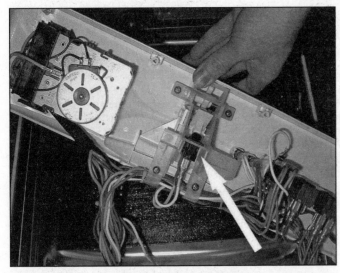

This latch mechanism uses a simple on/off 'rocker' switch which can be replaced as a separate item

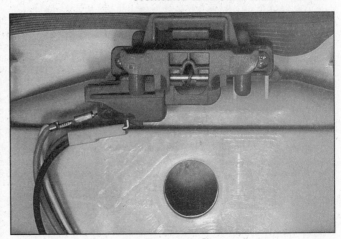

The door latch and safety switch on most makes and models can be accessed by removing the front facia/door panel allowing action and operation of both the switch and latch mechanism to be easily checked. The version shown is common to many models in the Indesit and Hotpoint range of dishwashers

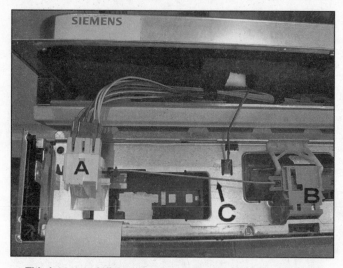

This integrated dishwasher has the main ON/OFF switch (A) mechanically linked to a purely mechanical door latch mechanism (B) by a metal rod (C)

Internal view of door showing position of door safety switch

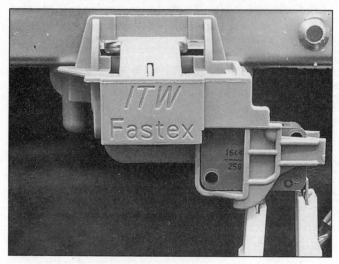

The door latch and safety switch on this particular model consists of a small latch mechanism and a micro-switch. The micro-switch is held in place by plastic lugs and the latch unit by two screws so both item are easy to change once the front facia is removed

Close-up of recessed switch position

correct position. Adjustment is possible on both variants. Under no circumstances should safety switches be bypassed. The switches themselves often fail due to the amount of operations during normal use and especially if the user has a habit of opening the door when the machine is running.

If the machine is dead, a simple check on some models is to listen for the audible click of the micro switch when you open and close the door WITH THE MACHINE ISOLATED. Failure to hear the switch would give only an indication of a possible switch problem and a thorough check would be needed to verify the

fault. **Note:** *It may not be possible to hear the action of the door switch on machines with combined latch and switch mechanisms due to the noise created when the latch mechanism snaps shut.*

Chapter 16
Door seals

Because of the action and the force of water within the dishwasher, it is important to have a watertight seal around all edges of the load compartment door. This sealing effect is achieved by a moulded rubber strip around the outer edge of the load compartment opening, and a second strip fixed along the lower edge of the door inner liner. When the door is closed and latched correctly, enough force is exerted to form a secure watertight seal.

There are as many variations of the extruded rubber seals as there are makes of dishwashers, but all are there for the same purpose.

Normal wear and tear can give rise to leaking, especially evident at the corners. Always ensure that the seal and its corresponding contact area are clean and free from food particles as the seal depends on a good contact area. Regular cleaning of the seal and contact area will greatly extend the life of the seal. Before renewing the door seal, always check the level of the machine (normally recommended to be within 2 degrees of horizontal), water level, correct quality and dosage of detergent, seal and contact area and check that the door is closing securely and tightly on the seal.

Adjustment or cleaning maybe all that is required to cure the problem. If these methods fail, change both seals, making sure that you obtain the correct seal for your particular make and model of machine as shape, size and thickness vary greatly. A point to watch out for is that the load baskets do not foul the seal when they are pushed in and out. On some models, this can cause problems and may require adjustment to the basket height or position.

The fixings of the outer seal can be one of two types:

a) A moulded rubber strip with a solid flat edge that is held in place by a separate metal/plastic outer fixing secured in place by screws. To fit a new seal, first loosen the fixing screws and pull the old seal free. Refitting is a simple reversal of the removal procedure but make sure the seal is not stretched or forms loops or bumps by being slack.

b) Simply a push fit into a preformed recess (some maybe lightly glued into the recess. To remove, simply pull from one end to free it from the recess). When refitting, start at one end leaving about 20mm protruding out of the bottom. Push the seal firmly into its position. Do this carefully in stages and avoid stretching or leaving it to go slack. If care is not taken at this stage, the new seal will not function properly. When in position all the way round, press again firmly with your fingers to ensure a snug fit. If the seal appears loose, check for stretching and adjust as necessary. Should the new seal simply be a loose fit in a metal recess, tap the recess edge slightly to narrow the recess width.

The bottom seal can be either fixed by screws or riveted into position. The removal is by slackening the fixing screws or drilling of the holding rivets. When refitting, it is best to start at the middle and work outward, at the same time making sure the seal is positioned correctly. The use of a self-locking wrench as a third hand can be most useful for this job. Some machines simply secure the lower seal by allowing it to fit over the lower lip of the load compartment – these are the easiest of all seals to renew. Refer to the chapter *Door hinges and counterbalance systems*.

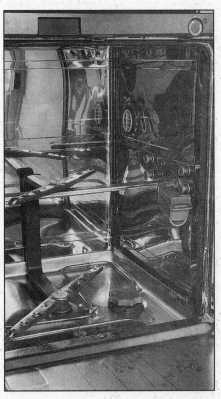

Outer door seal

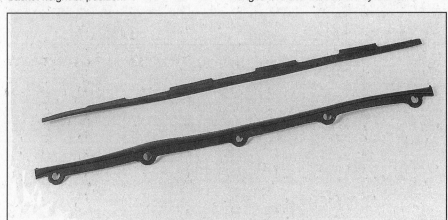

Two types of lower door seal

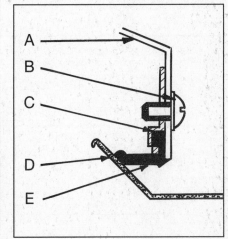

Lower door seal fitting
A Door inner
B Fixing bolt or rivet
C Inner clamp plate
D Bottom panel of load compartment
E Formed rubber seal in correct position

Chapter 17
Spray arms

What are they?

The spray arms are the units that direct and distribute the wash and rinse water to all parts of the load compartment. Most machines have two spray arms and some have more. The top and bottom spray arms may look the same but take care not to mix them up and refit them incorrectly.

How do they work?

Supported on a central pivot point, both top and bottom spray arms are free to rotate. Water, under pressure from the main circulation pump, is directed or fed directly to them both. Along the upper face of each spray arm there are slots that are slightly angled. Each end of the spray arms have corresponding but opposing holes in them. The angle and position of these holes are so aligned that the water supplied at pressure to the arm is forced out and gives a driving momentum. This in turn causes the arms to rotate as the water is sprayed from them. This movement, combined with detergent and heating is how the dishwasher cleans the wash load.

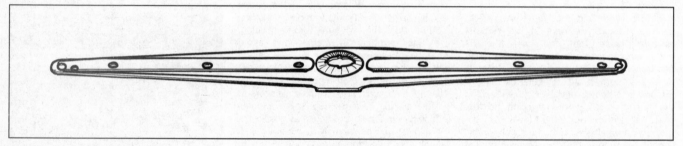

A typical spray arm

View of spray arm system. In this instance the top spray arm is fed by a central column. Many variations of supplying the top spray arm can be found. Check for wear on spray arm bearings and ensure washers or spacers are in good condition

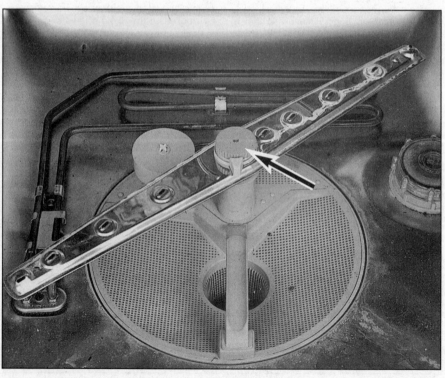

Simple hand-controlled flow control

What are they made of?

The material used for spray arms is either plastic or stainless steel. The means of supplying water to the top spray arm differs as some are fed directly (see diagram) and others are indirectly fed a jet of water from above or below. A bottom jet fed system would simply invert the funnel shaped catch point and the supply jet would emanate from the centre of lower spray arm pivot.

For the machine to work efficiently and effectively the spray arms must be:

a) Free to rotate on both its pivot points and not be jammed by items protruding above or below its position.
b) All the slots within the arm must be clear of debris to allow the jets to operate correctly.
c) Must be sound – look for splits or cracks along the seams or joints. These may be hard to spot but when under pressure they will open up and reduce the power to the arm.

Although the unit may look simple in itself, if it is not maintained and cleaned regularly or its rotation has been impeded in any way, problems such as poor wash, poor rinses, leaving food on items and noise could result.

Some machines have the facility to vary the pressure to the top spray arm for use on delicate items. There are three basic ways in which this adjustment can be made.
1 By hand – This is a relatively simple operation carried out by the user and normally involves turning a selector (control valve) on the upper jet or catchment funnel. This simply reduces/increases the flow of water supplied to the upper spray arm, thus altering the cleaning action. With this system the user must remember to reset to normal following the special wash procedure.
2 Automatically – With this type of system flow control to the upper spray arm is

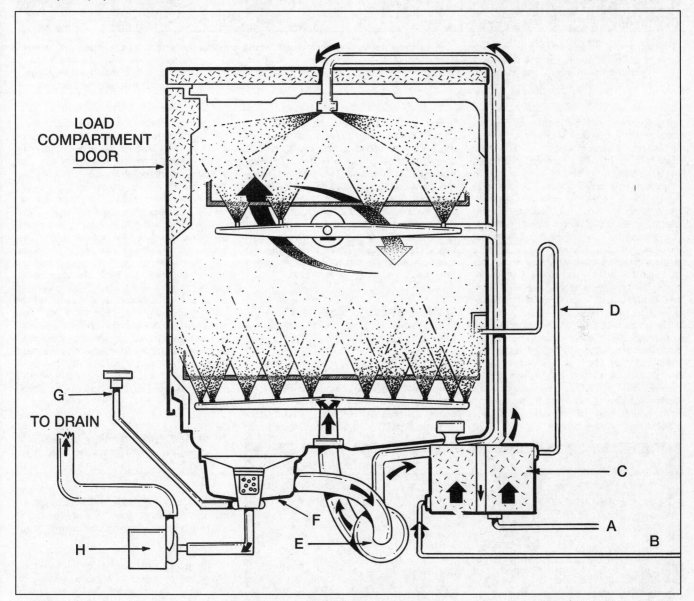

Typical water flow in a dishwasher
Water inlet is via points (A) for normal inlet and (B) for regeneration sequence. (C) is the water softener unit with outlet (D) to load compartment. (E) is the main circulation pump supplying both top and bottom spray arms and jet in this instance (means of supply may vary, i.e. jet of water or direct supply as shown). Supply of water is drawn from sump unit (F). Pressure system and switch (G) control water level (could also be float system). Outlet of water to drain is by outlet pump (H) via supply from sump

This top spray is secured by a ribbed locking ring (arrowed) and can be quite difficult to remove when wet. If tight use a cloth to assist grip but do not use metal tools such as grips

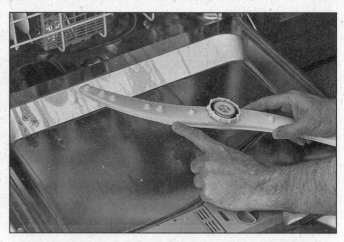

Check plastic spray arms for splitting. If an appliance with plastic spray arms gives poor wash results even when the appliance appears to be working and used correctly check the spray arms closely for splitting along their moulded joints and seams

adjusted automatically dependent on which programme and level of soiling was selected by the user. The way in which restriction takes place is by means of a mechanically operated valve situated in the supply route of the top spray arm. The method of restriction can be by means of a simple solenoid operated device with in effect two settings i.e. de-energised full flow or energised restricted flow. Alternatively a small motor similar to that used on mechanical timers may be used to rotate a disc within the water flow which acts as a variable valve arrangement. The use of this system can allow varying degrees of flow control and therefore more programme/wash options for the user.

3 Zone valve – This electromechanical valve is positioned in the hose supplying the top spray arm and works in a similar way to that described in (2). The main difference between the two variations is that a zone valve cuts off the flow of water to the top spray arm not merely restricts it. This allows the machine to have a half load facility with items only stacked on the lower basket.

Both automatic systems only operate when selected by the programme. However, as with any mechanical device problems can and do occur. The main problems being: blocking of the device, open circuit of the solenoid, motor drive or wiring to them and leaking (especially on those with motor drive systems). Fault symptoms will depend in which position the device has failed. The most noticeable will be if either type has failed in the fully restricted position or is blocked. This will be evident when items placed in the top basket, particularly if heavily soiled receive a gentle wash.

Jammed/blocked spray arm detection

The ability to detect and react to blocked or jammed spray arms may be incorporated in some microprocessor-controlled machines. The system works in a similar way to flow control detailed in the *Water level control* chapter later in this book. In this particular

instance a permanent magnet is attached to the lower spray arm shaft and rotates in unison with it. A reed relay is located in close proximity on the outside of the sump unit and reacts to the passing magnet by closing its contacts each time the magnet passes. In this way the rotation of the lower spray arm is interpreted by the microprocessor as a series of on/off reed switch pulses. If the spray arm is jammed or blocked no rotation will occur and no pulses will be detected. In this situation the processor may terminate the current programme to prevent damage to the main circulation pump or indicate to the user (audible bleep/light on panel) that a problem exists. **Note:** *Lack of water flow through the sump filters may also result in failure of the spray arm to rotate. This is normally a result of insufficient/irregular cleaning of the filters. In order to maintain peak performance it is essential that ALL the filters are cleaned on a regular basis, especially the micro-filters used in many of today's modern dishwashers.*

Half load, zone washing, power clean and self-cleaning filter action

Many dishwashers now have a range of selectable features such as half load, zone washing and self-cleaning filter action.

Half load

As it states, this feature, when selected, allows the appliance to wash a reduced or half load. Selecting the half load option results in reducing the amount of water taken in for both washing and rinsing and restricting the flow from the main circulation (wash) pump to the upper spray arm. However, there are models which also allow the user to select between upper or lower spray arms. In all

This LCD display shows all the selectable programme options including the ½ load icon bottom left of the display

instances whenever a half load feature is selected it is essential that the correct basket is loaded. Preventing the flow of water to the relevant spray arm is carried out by means of an electrically operated 'gate' valve situated between the main circulation pump outlet and the relevant spray arm.

The valve can be electromagnetically opened or closed by the action of a coil and plunger or by a small motor which when energised turns a disc with holes to block or allow the water to flow. In addition to simply being used for half load selection some makes and models use the motorised valve system to change the water flow during normal programme operation (no half load selected). Rotating the valve disc on these models to a specific point on the disc changes the flow of water being supplied to the spray arms. Holes in the disc combined with motor activation could produce varied wash actions such as – position '0' both upper and lower spray arm receive water – position '1' one minute upper and two minutes lower, position 2 – three minutes lower and one minute upper.

In addition to these mechanical actions some makes and models may also reduce the flow of water to the spray arm by reducing the main circulation motor's speed.

An important point to note is that economically (water, electricity and detergent wise) it is always best to operate a dishwasher fully loaded and programmed accordingly. In most households you do not have to wait too long before a dishwasher ends up fully loaded.

Zone washing

Zone washing is essentially another term used to describe the ability to select which spray arm will be used during the wash and rinse programme. As with the half load option described earlier, zone wash selection utilises electromagnetically operated valves or a small motor which when energised turns a disc with holes to block or allow the water to flow.

In addition to simply being used for half load selection some makes and models use the motorised valve system to change the water flow during normal programme operation (no half load selected). Rotating the valve disc on these models to a specific point on the disc changes the flow of water being supplied to the spray arms. Holes in the disc combined with motor activation could produce varied wash actions such as – position '0' both upper and lower spray arm receive water – position '1' one minute upper and two minutes lower, position 2 – three minutes lower and one minute upper.

Dependent on the make and model, the water flow to the spray arm may be varied by reducing the main circulation motor's speed.

Power cleaning

Power cleaning is a selectable feature used on some makes and models that in addition

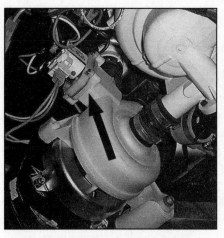

The main circulation pump chamber outlet on this dishwasher has an electro-mechanical ½ load option zone valve (arrowed)

to the usual spray arms found on all dishwashers have a set of fixed jets pointing towards the rear of the lower load basket. When programmed to do so and as part of a normal wash programme the high pressure water from the main circulation pump can be directed through the fixed jets effectively blasting any item placed in the lower basket pointing toward them such as grill pans, heavily soiled oven trays etc. This feature is extremely useful for robust items with burnt on food etc and eliminates the need for pre-rinsing in most instances.

Self-cleaning filter action

Sometimes referred to as auto clean this feature is not selected by the user but takes place automatically if certain parameters are not met during filling and washing. The benefit of a dishwasher to self-clean its own filters is to maintain a satisfactory flow through the filter system and therefore maintain optimum flow rate to the spray arms. However, it does not totally eliminate the need for the user to clean the filters. However, it is capable of informing the user via the control panel that it has been unable to clean the filter sufficiently itself and that manual cleaning is required. Automatic filter cleaning may only take place on certain wash programmes and when it does so it usually extends the length of the normal programme by a considerable length of time i.e. 40 or more minutes in most instances.

The self-cleaning process will normally be engaged automatically if either of two events are detected:

1 A specific pressure switch fails to detect an initial intake of water (usually around 2 litres) which is monitored by a flow sensing system (refer to chapter *Water level control*). This will occur if the filter is preventing or slowing down the water entering the pressure switches pressure vessel.

2 A high pressure, pressure switch connected to the main circulation pump

The operation of this type of motorised valve is determined by the requirements of the selected wash programme. It has an integral motor that rotates a disc which when rotated diverts the water from the outlet of the main circulation pump. In this particular make and model three positions are available – position '0' upper and lower spray arms receive simultaneous water flow – position '1' water from the circulation pump alternates between the two spray arms as follows – one minute on the upper spray arm and two minutes on the lower spray arm – position '2' water from the circulation pump alternates – one minute on the upper spray arm and three minutes on the lower spray arm. To prevent incorrect wash action the position of the motorised valve is reset prior to starting the next programme

chamber detects a drop in pressure within the chamber. This will occur if the filters are not allowing enough water into the pump chamber inlet i.e. it is pumping out more than it is getting back and therefore pressure within it drops. This pressure switch is also often used to protect a through flow heater (refer to chapter *Heaters*) i.e. no pressure detected effectively means no water flow through the system and this would damage the heater so the switch within the unit reverts to the 'open' position.

If either of the above events is detected by the programme processor the appliance will take in more water than normal and begin a sequence of pulsing the main circulation pump motor and heater on and off. This should result in the food debris on the filters being broken up allowing it to be pumped away. During the hot rinse phase of the programme the filter cleaning process is once again carried out. If after this the system still detects a problem then the hot rinse will be repeated. However, if this second attempt at self-cleaning fails then the programme will be terminated and an alarm and error message will be displayed. The remedy of which is the manual cleaning of the filters.

48

Chapter 18
Leaks fault-finding flowchart

Box 1

It is essential that dishwashers are within 2 degrees of level. Before commencing with any leak checking, ensure that the machine is as near level as possible. Refer to the instruction booklet that came with your machine on how this is done for your particular machine.

Box 2

Inspect and clean the door seals at this point, at the same time look for flat spots on the seal, splits or perishing.

Box 3

Check that the bottom and outer seals are securely held in place. Refitting the seal correctly maybe all that is required. Other faults normally result in both seals being replaced.

Box 4

Inspect the air break unit. Blockages in this system can result in leaking only when the machine fills. Both main wash and rinses can be affected. Although the spillage maybe small on each fill, after the main wash fill and possibly four rinses, the pool of water can become quite large.

Removal of a side panel is usually required to gain access to this unit. Small scale blockages in the inlet jets can cause the water to be deflected from its normal course. Check and clean thoroughly.

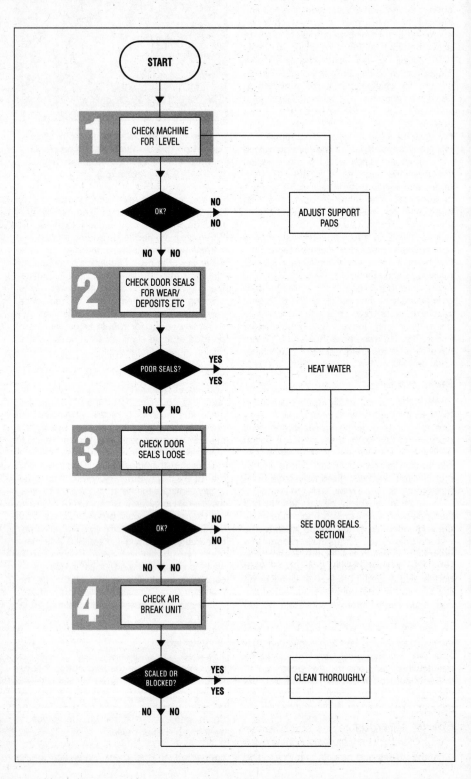

Box 5

The outlet pump may conceal a shaft seal leak. Close inspection of this unit is required. If the machine has had a leak for sometime which has gone unnoticed, a shaft seal leak can be easily identified. Corrosion or scaling is often evident on the mounting bracket or rear of the pump housing. See Chapter on *Pumps*.

Box 6

As with Box 5, closely inspect the main circulation pump looking for discharges or weeping in the same areas. Noise often accompanies these larger shaft seal leaks.

Box 7

Sump hose fittings to the sump vary – some are clip fitted and others are grommet fitted. Check clip and grommet and seal if in doubt. Hose to spray arms will require very close inspection as these hoses are under high pressure from the circulation pump, and small holes or ill-fitting clips on them can result in very large leaks. Such high-pressure leaks are unsafe as they can spray water over the machines electrics when in use. As with all leaks, trace and rectify before further problems arise and do not compromise safety.

Box 8

Check this hose for loose fitting, perishing and kinks and especially look for rubbing against other hoses or panels. Check the whole length of hose and renew if in doubt.

Box 9

Look for ill-fitting grommets or discharges from them. Perished grommets should be renewed.

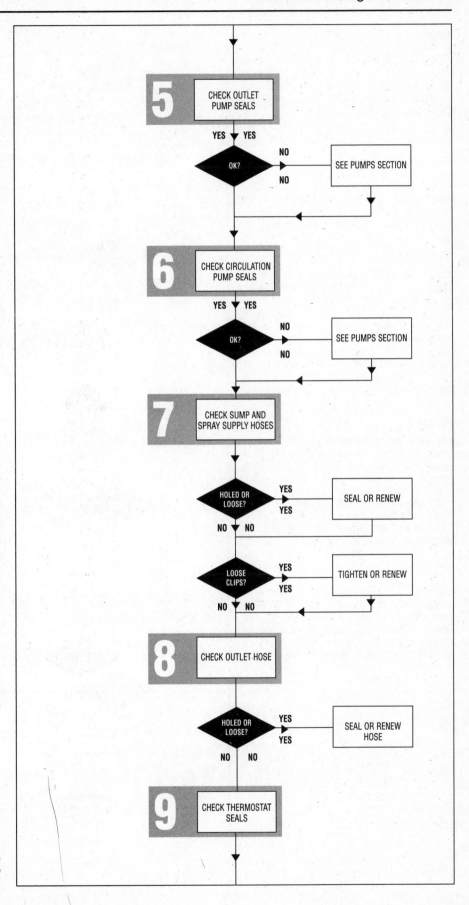

Box 10

Pressure system faults can give rise to leaks that range from small to major. Always check thoroughly and clean all pressure hoses and vessels. This also applies to float systems. See *Water level control* chapter.

Box 11

The hoses and clips on the inlet valves should now be checked in conjunction with *Inlet valves* chapter: On earlier valves there is a slight chance that the top of the valve can split. This is often shown by a small brown rust patch on the top of the valve.

Box 12

The rails supporting both upper and lower basket runners may be fixed to the cabinet sides with bolts or self-tapping screws. These fixings are sealed but over long periods of use, may become loose. When in use the pressure within the cabinet will force water past and result in a tricky leak to locate. The outer panel of the affected side may have to be removed to gain access to the nuts of any fixing bolts.

Box 13

The inner load compartment is made up of separate panels or mouldings. On rare occasions a split or breakdown of the joint may occur. If all other tests prove to be OK yet the leak persists, check all seals and joints thoroughly. Curing such problems can be tricky, but if encountered, small faults may be rectified by using epoxy glue to coat the affected section.

Box 14/15

If the fault persists at this point, re-inspect plumbing and ensure it corresponds with the *Basics – plumbing,* Chapter 7. If this should not prove to be at fault, Box 15 directs you to powder used. See *Common causes of poor washing results.*

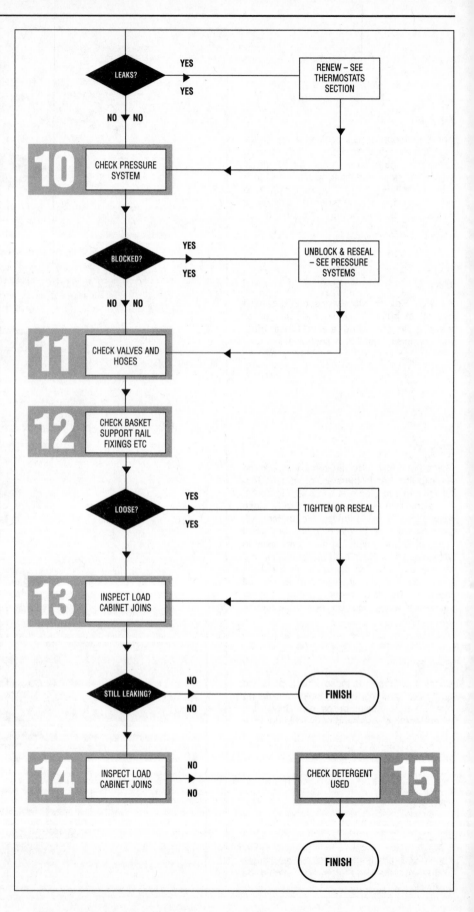

Chapter 19
Machine will not empty flowchart

This is one of the most common faults. Although inconvenient, it is usually remedied if the fault is approached in a logical manner. Before commencing with the following sequence of the flowchart, a few simple checks would be advisable. Make sure that the door has not sprung slightly open during the wash cycle, cutting off the power. Re-latch the door and check. Also check that the door micro switch has not failed as this would give a similar situation depending on where in the cycle it had failed. If you are happy that these simple checks are OK proceed with the flowchart.

The 'not emptying' fault can fall into three main categories. Blockage, Mechanical fault or Electrical fault.

Box 1

Follow the emergency procedure for removing the water already trapped inside the machine.

Box 2

Check the outlet and sump hoses, as well as the outlet filter. If a blockage or a kink is found, remove it and refit the pipe(s) and filter.

Box 3

The pump is located at the machine end of the outlet hose, and junction of the sump hose, or an integral part of the sump moulding (on some machines such as Zanussi the impeller is held on by a nut and both nut and impeller have to be removed before the pump body can be withdrawn). The small chamber should be checked for blockages. The impeller should be checked for free rotation, and that it hasn't come adrift from its mounting to the pump motor shaft. If the impeller is found to be adrift from the shaft, this would give rise to no water being pumped although the motor itself would run. A quick check at this stage would be to hold the shaft whilst trying to turn the impeller. If all is well they should only turn in unison. Remember to turn anti-clockwise, or the impeller will unscrew from the shaft. If a fault is found at this point, refer to *Pumps* Chapter.

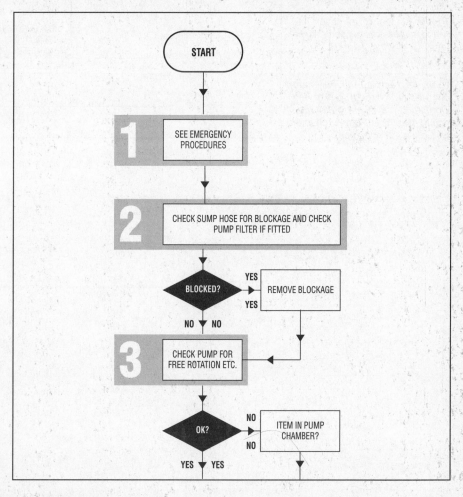

Box 3A

If NO blockage is found in the section above, and the bearings are not suspected, the stator continuity of the pump windings must be checked. Please refer to the chapter *Electrical circuit testing*. **Note:** *On some makes/models a mechanical or electrically operated non-return valve may be fitted in the outlet hose system after the pump outlet. Check both types for internal blockages. If it is of the electro-mechanical type check also the solenoid coil for continuity and for free mechanical action.*

Box 4

At this point, the outlet hose should be checked again. An internal blockage such as fat deposits can be very difficult to see. The best method of checking this is to connect it to the hose of a domestic tap, observing the flow of water.

Box 5

The final step is to check the wiring harness connection. Please refer to: *Wiring harness faults,* Chapter 36.

Note: *On machines that only have one motor for both outlet and circulation, similar faults can occur. See the* Pumps *chapter (Induction motor pumps).*

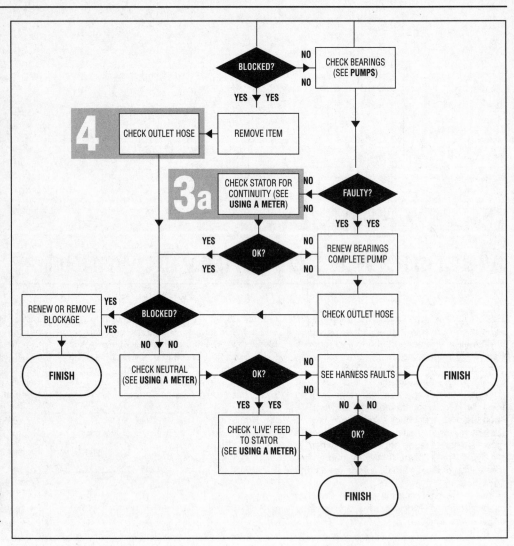

Chapter 20
Inlet valves

In addition to the following information on inlet valves reference to the chapter on *Flood protection systems* will be required as many modern dishwashers combine the inlet valve with flood protection devices. However, a thorough understanding of the electro-mechanical inlet valve will be required to fully appreciate the flood protection systems detailed later in this book.

Fault finding

We deal here with several of the most common faults reported: not taking detergent, not filling at all and not filling in certain parts of the programme. Please refer to the flowchart to be found later in this chapter.

Water inlet valves fitted to the dishwasher operate in the same way as those used in automatic clothes washers. A solenoid coil

of some 3 to 5000 ohms (3 to 5kohms) resistance when energised (i.e.: supplied with power), this creates a strong magnetic field at its centre. This field attracts up into the coil, a soft iron rod or plunger, and will hold it in that position as long as power is supplied to the coil. When power is cut off (de-energised) from the coil, a spring at the top of the plunger recess returns it to its resting position.

How does it work?

Shown here in detail are the two states of the water valve. With no power supplied to the solenoid coil (A) the soft iron core (B) is pressed firmly onto the centre hole of the flexible diaphragm by spring (C). As chamber (D) is only at atmospheric pressure and the water is at least 4lb psi (somewhat higher), pressure is exerted on the top of the diaphragm, effectively closing it tight. The greater the water pressure the greater the

Triple valve: Generally cold supply. May also have restrictor on one outlet for regeneration cycle

Single valve: Red for hot supply, white for cold supply. (Note: This valve has an earth tag)

Double valves: Cold supply only. Right side for main fill, left for softener regeneration cycle. (Note restrictor on left-hand opening)

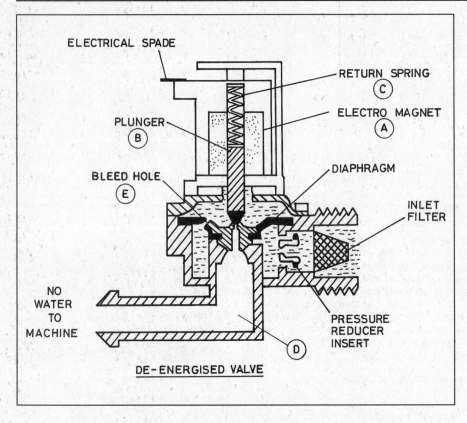

The de-energised valve (at rest – no power supplied)

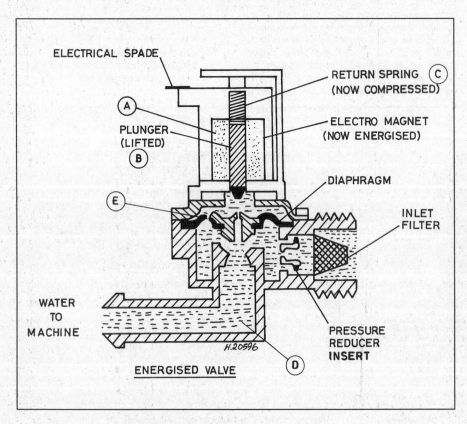

The energised valve (power supplied to it)

closing effect of the valve and therefore no water will flow.

The pressure on top of the diaphragm is via a small bleed hole marked (E). It is essential that this very small hole is not obstructed. Though very small, it is a major factor in the correct operation of these types of pressure operated valves.

When power is supplied to the solenoid coil, the resulting magnetic attraction of the coil overcomes the power of the spring (C) and pulls the plunger up into the coil centre. This allows an imbalance of pressure to occur by exposing the centre hole of the diaphragm. The pressure in the top chamber is lost due to the centre hole being larger than the bleed hole. The imbalance lifts the flexible diaphragm and allows water to flow into chamber (D), thus water flow into the appliance is achieved. **Note:** *It is easier for the water to lift the diaphragm than to balance the pressure by flowing through the very small bleed hole. Any enlargement or blockage of this vital bleed hole will render the valve inoperative.*

Main benefits of such valves

1 The higher the pressure supplied to it, the tighter the valve will close.
2 Cost is relatively low.
3 Very reliable to use.
4 Simple to change if faulty.

Typical faults to watch for

1 As with ordinary house taps, the valve seat may wear and allow a small trickle of water to pass even when de-energised. This will cause the machine to fill when not in use if the taps are left turned on over a long period of time and the machine will overfill, resulting in a possible flood. (see: *Flood protection systems*).
2 The valve, when de-energised, fails to allow the plunger to return to its normal resting/closed position. This problem will cause severe overfill and flooding (if the appliance is not fitted with a flood protection system). **Note:** *Turning off the machine will not stop the overfilling in such cases. Complete isolation of both power and water supply is required and, as with step 1, complete renewal will be necessary.*
3 The valve fails to allow water to flow due to open circuit in coil winding. See: *Electrical circuit testing (Using a meter)* and *Flood protection systems* sections.
4 The valve fails to allow water to flow due to

a blocked filter on its inlet. Carefully remove and clean. Do not allow any particle, no matter how small to escape past the filter as it could block the bleed hole.

Water valves come in many sizes and an assortment of shapes – single valves, double valves and triple valves or a combination of all three. On the double and triple valves, each solenoid operates one outlet from a common inlet. Unfortunately, a fault on one coil or one output will generally mean a complete renewal of the whole valve assembly, as individual spare parts are not available. **Note:** *Dishwashers with double or triple valves, will have a restrictor fitted to one of the valve outlets. It is important that any replacement valve has this internal restrictor fitted. The valve with the restrictor is for water supply to the regeneration side of the water softener unit, as it requires a slow flow of water to operate efficiently. See* Internal water softeners *chapter.*

The water requirement of a dishwasher differs little from the automatic clothes

Single inlet valve in situ on the rear panel of a dishwasher
Note: *This hose has a factory fitted 'crimp' fit type of hose clip. If removed for any reason you will need to renew the clip with worm drive version*

90 degree double inlet valve

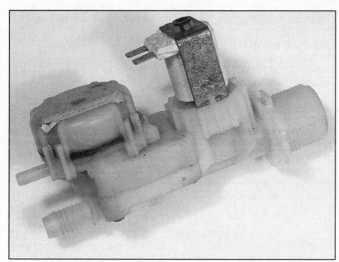

Water inlet valve with combined mechanical flood protection device. Refer to chapter *Flood protection systems* **for details of this type of valve**

A more compact version of a water inlet valve with mechanical (pressure operated) flood protection system

Flow sensing water inlet valves are essentially normal inlet valves with the addition of the following components fitted within the valve's entry point

A *Valve unit which may be single double or triple as in this instance*
B *Reed switch mounted within the valve's plastic fixing bracket*
C *Small permanent magnet clipped to the inner turbine*
D *Turbine body (free to rotate within the inlet)*
E *Turbine support*
F *Flow regulator (to maintain a flow rate of around 8 litres per minute)*
G *Inlet filter. Although small in size the components function the same as described for the larger independent version*

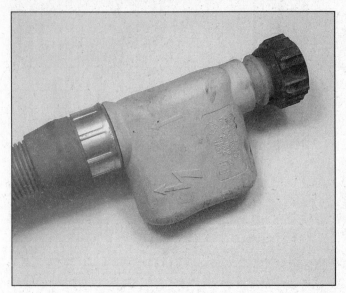

This particular version of Aqua-stop hose is a fully sealed system with no access to the water inlet valve housed within the white plastic block

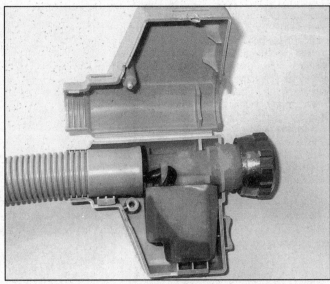

Internal view of a Siemens Aqua-stop hose showing the sealed inlet valve within the 'clip together' outer casing
Note: *This internal view is shown for information purposes only as faults with this type of system will require a complete new hose assembly*

Models with flood protection systems usually clearly indicate they have this useful feature

washing machine. However, it is generally agreed by most manufacturers that, unlike the hot and cold fill clothes washing machines, the dishwasher is best plumbed to cold water only, unless otherwise directed by the manufacturer. At first this may not seem a very economical way of operating your machine, but by using the cold fill only, (unless otherwise directed), your machine will function and operate much better, and will not waste your hot water for cold rinses. Another advantage is that hot water sprayed directly onto the wash load, prior to the detergent dispenser opening, will help fix soiling especially egg and other similar foodstuffs on crockery, etc.

The test, descriptions and flowcharts given assume that the machine will have been plumbed in cold supply only.

Verify the suspected fault

Note: *The following information and accompanying flowchart relate to dishwashers without flood protection valves/systems. If your dishwasher has a flood protection system you will need to refer to both the following information and that contained in the chapter* Flood protection systems *to fully identify and correct the problem.*

In this theoretical instance, the machine was loaded and a programme selected but failed to fill. Moving the timer/control to a pump out position confirmed that power was being supplied and that the door safety switch was working. See *Door safety switches* chapter

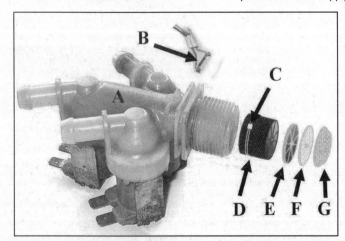

Water inlet valve combined with a flow sensing system. Details of which appear in the chapters *Water Level Control, Flood Protection Systems* and *Fuzzy Logic*

Independent flow sensing system. Details of which appear in the chapters *Water Level Control, Flood Protection Systems* and *Fuzzy Logic*

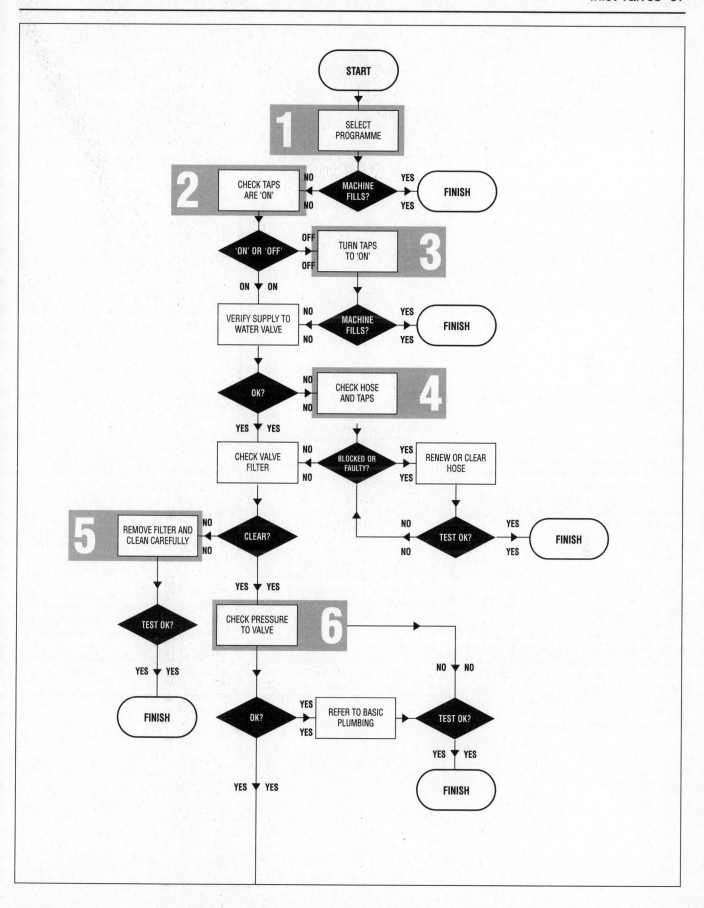

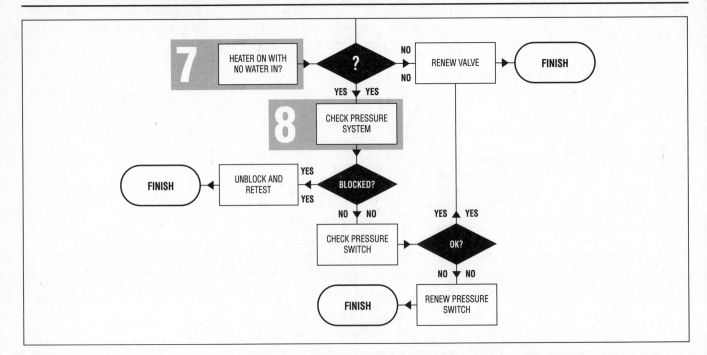

Box 1

Reselect wash programme to confirm that machine was originally set and turned on correctly. With the machine properly set.

Box 2

Confirms that, although the machine has electrical feed, no water is entering to begin the filling/washing action. Check that the appliance is not just filling very slowly due possibly to reduced water pressure or a blocked inlet filter.

Box 3

This may seem too obvious to mention, but many an engineer has been called out to find the taps were in the OFF position. This normally brings up the comment that the taps are never turned off, and in this case it must have been some other devious member of the family or innocent plumber that has done the dirty deed! This comment brings in the cardinal rule that all automatic washing machines and dishwashers should be turned off at their isolation taps when the machine is not in use. This may seem a quite pointless task, but the objective is simple. If an inlet

hose should split, or an inlet valve fails to close correctly, a quite disastrous flood could occur. However, if the taps were turned off, this could not happen.

Note: *If the machine has a float or pressure actuated flood protection valve as described in the chapters:* Water level control (float operation) *and* Flood protection systems*, it should be checked along with all pivot points and pressure hose connections.*

Box 4

By unscrewing the hose from the valve, the water supply can be easily checked by turning the tap, to which it is connected, ON and OFF, ensuring that the free end of the hose is resting in a suitable container. Failure of water flow could be due to a faulty tap or tap shaft or an internal fault of the supply hose.

Box 5

Checking of the water valve inlet filter can be carried out while the hose is removed for Step 4. Take care not to allow any particles to escape past the fine mesh filter and into the valve. Carefully clean the filter of all scale and

debris etc. and replace. **Note:** *The filter can be removed by gently gripping the centre with pliers and pulling it free of the main valve body.*

Box 6

Ensure that the water supply to the valve is adequate to operate the valve. See *Basics – plumbing* chapter.

Boxes 7 & 8

If the heater is found to be ON when there is no water in the machine, a pressure system fault is indicated and should be checked. Details of this process will be found in the chapter on *Water level control.* If the heater is in the OFF position when there is no water in the machine, the valve would appear to be suspect. The valve is easily changed by removing the fixing screws and detaching the internal hose/s from the valve. Making a note of the wiring and hose connections that are on the valve, remove them and replace with a new valve assembly by simply reconnecting the hoses and wires in a reverse sequence.

Chapter 21
Air break systems

What is an air break?

An air break is a device to create an unbridgeable gap between the water inlet to the machine (fresh water) and the water within the machine used for the washing and rinsing (soiled water). They are often part of a large plastic moulding called a matrix.

Where is it located?

The location of air breaks differs from machine to machine. The shapes and designs are also varied. Some are relatively simple air break systems while others combine the dual function of air break and steam vent in one unit. There are some makes and models that combine air break, steam vent, water softener and fill tank metering systems all in one large and complex matrix (these systems are shown in the Chapter on *Water level control*). To locate the air break system, follow the outlet pipe from the inlet valve or the separate softener unit. If necessary, you may have to remove a side panel of the dishwasher to do this. **Note:** *Not all makes of dishwasher have removable side panels. Access to air break systems in machines without removable side panels normally involves the removal of the large load compartment from the one-piece outer shell of the appliance.*

What are they for?

Air breaks are essential to create an unbridgeable gap between the clean fresh water from the domestic supply and the soiled water inside the machine. This gap prevents any soiling or wash detergent, etc. from going back down the inlet hose and into the house supply. This is a requirement of all water authorities and the air break ensures that this cannot happen under any circumstances.

How does it work?

Although the shape, size, positioning and complexity of air breaks vary greatly, they all use the same principle. The inlet, either direct from the fill valves for ordinary rinsing, or via the softener compartment etc. is formed into a jet of water at the inlet to the air break by its own pressure. The jet is directed across an air gap within the unit to a catchment point and then on by gravity to the load compartment. If

A more complex combined air break and water level pressure system. It is best to renew this type of system if internal blockages occur

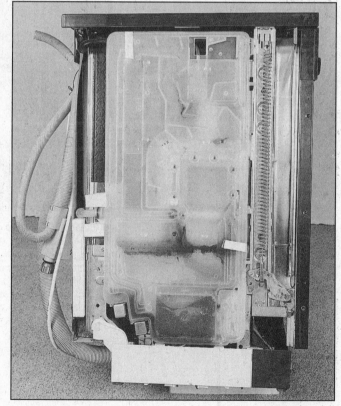

This large matrix combines, air break, steam vent, tank fill metering, regeneration tanks and water softener systems. For details of this type of system refer to chapters on *Water level control* and *Internal water softeners*

water were to be forced back in the other direction it would be slowed by the design of the unit and unable to jump the gap or be caught by the inlet jet. If the machine overfilled dramatically and reached the height of the unit, the air gap is so designed that it would vent the overfill to the atmosphere, i.e. to flood out of the air gap before making a bridge between the jet and the catchment area. In effect the air break system is designed to prevent the contamination of the water supply under any circumstances.

Problems with air breaks

Generally, basic air break units are very reliable if at first sight a little complicated. The units that are combined with the pressure vessel and steam vents seem especially complicated, but when studied closely are

relatively simple. The main trouble occurs with blocking and scaling in certain parts of the unit. Both faults can cause water to leak from the air gap. One such fault is at the water inlet points where scaling, although maybe only slight, can cause the jet to spray or become misaligned resulting in water escaping from the air break gap. Careful cleaning and regular checking of the system will prevent most if not all faults. The need to renew simple air break systems is very unusual, but if it becomes necessary is not a difficult task. Make sure all the hose positions are marked clearly before removal and that they are sealed securely when the new unit is fitted. Some machines may also combine water compartments for the regeneration cycle within the air break. These units are easily recognisable as they are of a much larger construction. For details of the more complex matrix systems containing water softeners and fill tanks refer to the chapters on *Water level control* and *Internal water softeners*.

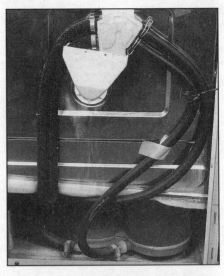

Typical basic air break system found in dishwashers

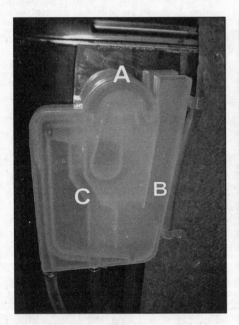

A plastic matrix with hose connections to the various chambers

A Air break for water intake
B Steam condensing chamber
C Regeneration reservoir chambers

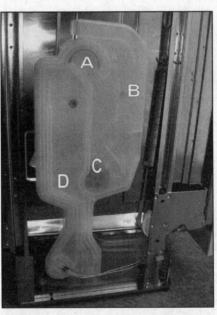

A plastic matrix that connects directly to the large plastic regeneration unit eliminating the use of hoses

A Air break for water intake
B Steam condensing chamber
C Load compartment vent
D Regeneration reservoir chambers

Plastic matrix with water inlet air break, steam condenser and regeneration chambers. This version connects to the water inlet valve and softener unit with flexible hoses

Note: *The tape which can be seen centre picture is part of the production process*

Chapter 22
Water level control

There are five ways in which the level of water within a dishwasher is controlled:

1 *Timed fills.* The timer allows the fill valve a pre-determined time of operation at the end of which it moves on to its next operation regardless of the level reached (such timed fills are often linked to other operations, e.g. pre-wash or rinse and hold).

2 *Pressure switch systems.* Similar to those used in automatic clothes washing machines, but operated at much lower trapped air pressures. There are two distinct versions of pressure operated systems – the mechanical pressure switch and the anologue electronic pressure detector.

3 *Float switches.* These are often used either independently or in conjunction with ordinary pressure systems or flow control.

4 *Tank metering.* This type of system may utilise float level control, pressure system level control or both. Unlike the first three systems tank metering level control systems do not come into direct contact with soiled water within the load compartment and therefore avoid many of the problems associated with those versions that do.

5 *Flow control.* In this system the flow of water entering the appliance from the inlet valve is monitored to achieve the correct level of fill for that particular programme function.

Many variations and combinations of level control can be found. What follows are descriptions of the various types of systems found in most, if not all of today's modern dishwashers. Your machine may contain one or more of the systems detailed and it is recommended that the whole of this chapter is read in order to gain a thorough understanding of the various types you may encounter.

What is a pressure system?

Pressure operated systems are the most common means of water level control in dishwashers.

Where are they located?

The pressure system has no standard design or location. It is identified as the large circular switch that has several wires and a plastic tube attached to it leading to a pressure vessel. Pressure vessels have two distinct designs, and are usually made of rigid plastic. The first type is an integral part of the plastic sump housing, the second is an independent unit usually located to the side of the machine or sump moulding. There is also a pressure hose system which does the same task as the pressure vessel, and is a part of the flexible sump hose. This will either be grommet-fitted to the lower part of the load compartment or between the outlet pump and the sump chamber.

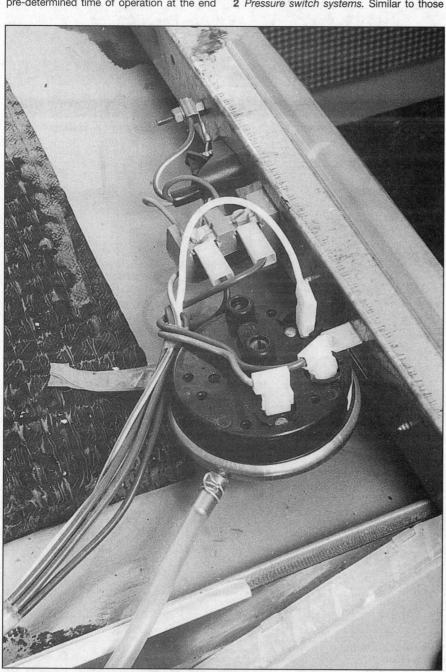

Early top mounted pressure switch. (Situated beneath lid of machine)

Base mounted pressure switch centre right-hand side (arrowed). Note: When machine is laid over for any reason, ensure that water does not enter the pressure tube. If in doubt always clear the pressure tube prior to testing. Failure to do this can result in incorrect level control

Remember that base mounted pressure switches normally require the pressure tube to be looped above the normal water level. Failure to do this can cause problems with water levels

How does it work?

The pressure switch does not actually come into contact with water, but uses air pressure trapped within the pressure vessel or pressure hose. When water enters the load compartment and the level rises, it traps a given amount of air in the pressure vessel. As the water in the load compartment rises, so the pressure of the air in the pressure vessel increases. This pressure is then transferred to a pressure sensitive switch via a small-bore flexible tube.

Machines with pressure switches fitted below the base of the load compartment (below water level) must have the pressure tube looped above water level height, usually at the side of the cabinet between the outer cover. This will ensure that the water cannot enter the switch even if failure resulting in overfilling occurs.

Checking a pressure switch

By blowing into the switch via the pressure tube, the audible clicks of the switches should be heard. This should also happen when the pressure is released. **Note:** *Do not blow too hard into a dishwasher level control pressure switch as they operate at very low pressures and damage may occur if blown too hard.*

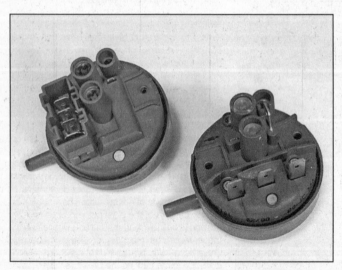

Typical small pressure switches that are used on many makes and models. The left-hand pressure switch has block connections and the right-hand pressure switch has individual terminal connections

Some pressure switches may have their tube connections on the rear plate. This is only a variation on the fixing type and does not impair the operation of the switch

If your machine uses a single level of water, one click will be heard, two levels of water will produce two clicks. Some machines may have an overfill level detection system which will activate the outlet pump should any excess water enter the machine for any reason. This system may simply be a second switch of the existing pressure switch, operated by the increased pressure of the overfill situation. Unfortunately, a system that uses the same pressure vessel for both normal and abnormal water level detection, may fail to detect overfilling if it is caused by a blocked pressure vessel or hose. A system using a separate pressure vessel and a separate pressure switch for detecting over-filling is much less prone to failure of this nature. Nevertheless, they still require cleaning and checking frequently. Refer to the chapter on *Flood protection systems* for further details.

On many dishwashers, a bleed tube is fitted below the pressure vessel and connected to the outlet pump or branch of the sump hose or to the sump chamber. This ensures that, as the water level in the machine drops, the level in the pressure vessel is not falsely held by a semi-vacuum within the top. Such retention of water would give a false level on the next fill. This type of bleed hose configuration can also have a cleaning effect in this vital area. When checking or overhauling the pressure system, make sure that all such hoses are completely clear of sediments, fat deposits, etc.

a) When the diaphragm becomes holed or porous, the switch can be operated and clicks heard, but will click back again without being de-pressurised.

b) The contact points inside the switch may weld themselves together. This will alter the number of clicks heard, as one or more may be inoperative. Movement of the switch may free the stuck points, although this will not be a lasting repair, as the switch will inevitably fail again.

Any of the above faults require the fitting of a new switch. The make, model and serial number of the machine should be stated when ordering, as pressure switches are internally pre-set for specific machines, although the external appearance is similar. Fitting is a simple direct exchange between the old and new.

Some machines may have a second pressure vessel with a pressure tube attached. This second pressure vessel comes into operation should the water level for any reason rise above normal (i.e. failure of valve on normal pressure system). This anti-flood system can operate the outlet pump via a second pressure switch (i.e. discharge the water constantly until over-filling has ceased), or operate a special pressure operated valve situated between the inlet valve and air break. This later system shuts off the internal water supply mechanically and not electrically. Such valves may also incorporate a mechanical float flood protection system. This system uses a recess in the base plate of the machine to catch any spilt water or leak. Any accumulation of water will allow a large float to be lifted and shut off the mechanical valve. This type of flood protection is more commonly found on built-in machines. Correct operation of such systems depends on the machine being level. Ensure that the installation is correct and check regularly. Refer to the chapter on *Flood protection systems* for further details.

On some dishwashers, the level of water can be adjusted simply by raising or lowering the pressure vessel or float chamber as the case may be. The reason for this is that the systems are actuated by the level of water in the machine and not its total volume. Take care and ensure that the machine is level and the pressure system is perfectly clean before making any adjustments. With adjustable pressure vessels or float systems, the amount

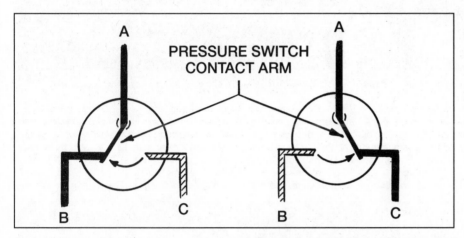

PRESSURE SWITCH CONTACT ARM

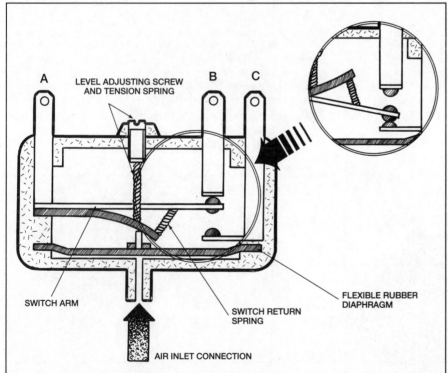

Diagrams illustrate the theoretical operation of a single level pressure switch. A Being the live supply. Point B is the empty position of the pressure switch, and in this position power supplied to A via the programme timer would be allowed to flow to the fill valve via B. When the preset level of water is reached, the diaphragm of the pressure switch pushes the contact arm across to contact C. Power to the fill valve is therefore stopped and transferred to connection C which in turn could supply the circulation motor and heater

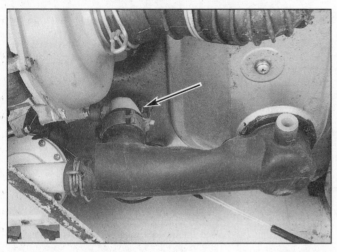

Arrowed is a sump hose mounted pressure vessel – early Indesit type prone to fat blockages

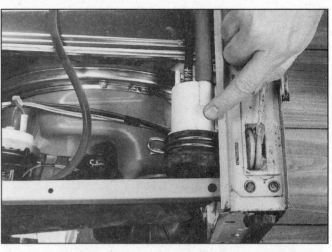

Pressure vessel of the type found on various makes

the vessel is raised or lowered is directly proportional to water level, i.e. a lowering of the vessel by 1mm will in effect lower the water level by 1mm. **Note:** *Do not make any adjustments to level switch systems without first making sure that they are clean and clear of any sediment or blockages.*

Possible faults in the pressure system

To create the highest pressure in the chamber of the pressure vessel, the vessel must be positioned as low as possible in the machine. Any sediment that is in the machine collects at this point and can therefore block the entrance. Similarly, because of its very small internal diameter, the pressure tube can also block easily. The pressure that this device creates is very small, and can easily be

blocked by a very small obstruction, such as a lump of powder or sediment deposits.

The seals and hoses of the system are also of great importance. These should be checked for air leaks and blockages. Any puncture or blockage would create a loss of

pressure, resulting in the incorrect operation of the switches, i.e. if the air pressure in the pressure vessel were to leak out, the vessel would fill with water. Thinking that the machine was now empty, the water valves would be re-energised, thus filling an already

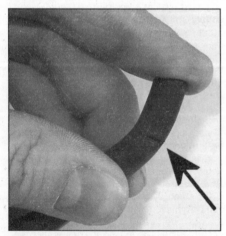

Check pressure tubes (especially rubber versions) closely for chafing and small porous cracks. Renew if suspect ensuring all connection points are sealed and that the route of the tube is correctly positioned and secured

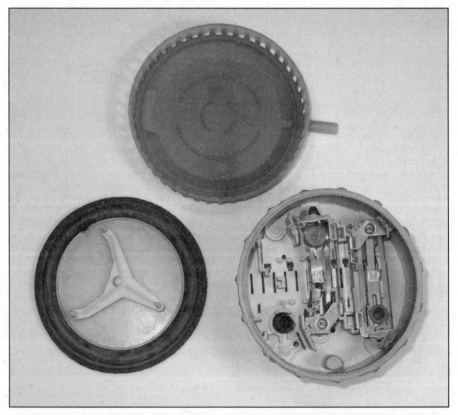

Shown is an internal view of a mechanical pressure switch. This particular switch was faulty due to a small hole developing in the internal rubber diaphragm. When first pressurised it would appear to work correctly but the pressure would slowly decrease during the wash cycle resulting in the appliance overfilling. If a functional test is rushed, this type of fault can be easily overlooked. The switch was taken apart only to confirm the fault within it. When faulty, pressure switches should be renewed and under no circumstances should repair or adjustment be undertaken full machine. The results would be obvious. **Note:** *Whenever the appliance has been laid over to gain access for repair or servicing ensure that the pressure tubes are free of blockages or restrictions. One particular fault that can occur is the ingress of water into the pressure tube. It takes only a small amount of water in the tube to create a restriction and therefore incorrect level detection. Some makes have clear neoprene pressure tubes and these will clearly show the capillary action of drawing water well into the tube. However all pressure tubes can be blocked in this way, ensure they are clear prior to allowing the machine to fill with water.*

The above example assumed that the air was stopped from getting to the pressure switch. If a blockage occurred whilst the switch was pressurised, the machine would work as normal until the machine emptied. The next time a programme was started the pressure switch would already be pressurised. Therefore the machine would not take any water, but proceed to turn the heater on. Although most heaters are now fitted with a TOC (Thermal Overload Cut-out) – see *Jargon,* this may not come into force until after some damage has been done, as many dishwashers have plastic components or liners. It is essential that the TOC or heater over-heat protector is not bypassed and if found to be faulty, should be renewed immediately.

Points to note

a) The pressure system should be checked at yearly or half-yearly intervals, depending on the water hardness in your area, (more often if large amounts of fatty foods are washed off in the water).
b) Dishwasher pressure systems are often affected regardless of water conditions. Fat deposits can block the pressure vessel, allowing the water level to rise to a leakage point.
c) Any hoses or tubes that have been removed must be sealed, and any clips tightened.
d) Blowing down the accessible end of the pressure tube may seem an easy solution to remove a blockage, but this may only be a temporary cure. Also, water may enter the pressure vessel before you can push the end of the tube back onto the pressure switch. This will render the pressure system inaccurate, if not useless.
e) When tilting or laying the machine over for repair or servicing, ensure that water droplets do not lodge within the pressure tube as they will cause incorrect operation of the pressure system.
f) The water level in some machines can be adjusted slightly by raising or lowering the pressure vessel. Early Candy machines are an example of this and certain other makes have similar adjustments. All such adjustments are limited.

g) A pressure switch should only be suspected when the system has been thoroughly cleaned, checked, sealed and re-tested.

Dynamic Performance Control DPC – what is it?

Some machines may be fitted with an extra hose connection on the main circulation pump chamber. This will be connected directly to a separate pressure switch and secured firmly with much larger clips than normally seen on pressure systems. This is no ordinary pressure switch – it is a 'high pressure' switch and cannot be tested simply by blowing into it and listening for the switch to actuate ('make'). The pressure to operate this switch is in excess of 26 times that of a normal level switch. Its purpose is to monitor the main pump pressure. If the pump 'hunts' and pressure drops in the chamber, the switch which is normally held open circuit, will close. This system is called DPC – Dynamic Performance Control.

How does it work?

DPC quite simply means that if dynamic performance of the pump (the energy transferred to the pump), drops below the preset limit, it is probably due to a lack of water getting to the pump from the sump. This may be caused by poor cleaning of filter, over foaming or most likely an item in the wash load incorrectly stacked which has filled with water therefore reducing the overall water level for circulation for the wash. On most machines this would lead to a poor wash result due to lack of water to the spray arms, etc. DPC counteracts this by sensing the drop in pump pressure and compensates by allowing extra water in until the pressure is high enough to operate the DPC pressure switch thus stopping the water inlet. You may think flooding would occur due to overfilling, but a normal overfill switch is fitted in the same circuit to prevent this happening.

The system appears to work well and in reality adds very little complexity to the machine.

Venturi systems

Some machines will have, in addition to the normal type of pressure system, a float device situated in the sump or centre section of the machine's base. This float device is not used for accidental overfill situations. Its purpose is to allow the machine to fill higher

than the level governed by the pre-set pressure switch. This is necessary to avoid unwanted tripping of the water fill valve which would occur when the main wash/circulation pump starts, thus reducing the water level by its operation. The higher level is achieved by a venturi effect of passing water past the pressure vessel base opening, thus causing a pressure drop within the chamber. The float is designed to float at the higher level and in so doing, it shuts off the flow through its base. This action then allows the level to rise quickly around the float chamber and for the level to equalise in the fill tube and load compartment. The slowing and eventual stopping of the flow past the pressure vessel base cancels the venturi effect and pressure returns to operate the switch with a slightly higher pressure than is actually required. In simple terms – if the pressure switch was used only to govern the water level, the following sequence would occur. When the pre-set level is reached and the main circulation pump starts, the water level would reduce so quickly as the circulation system fills that the pressure switch would sense the drop in level and re-energise the fill valve. If such a float and venturi system were not employed, the valve, pressure switch and motor would 'trip' several times.

Venturi float operation
See top illustration on p.66

As water flows along pipe 4 and through outlet 5 to the lowest part of the machine, a pressure drop in vessel 1 is created. This is maintained until the float 3 shuts off valve 2. With the flow now stopped along 4, the venturi effect is stopped and pressure is built up in vessel 1. This pressure is higher than would normally be created by this pressure vessel. Gravity then levels the water in both inlet and load compartment. The higher level alleviates the problem caused when the main circulation pump starts to operate and reduces the overall level slightly.

Simple float operation
See lower illustration on p.66

Like the illustration on pressure switches, A is the 'live' supply and B the empty position in this instance allowing a supply to the fill valve. When water level is reached as in diagram B the float rises and pushes the micro switch contact arm to the C position. This removes the power supply to the valve (stopping filling) and allows power to flow through contact C.

This is a simplified float system operation. The location of the float and micro switches will vary between makes and models. The float system is in many cases combined with

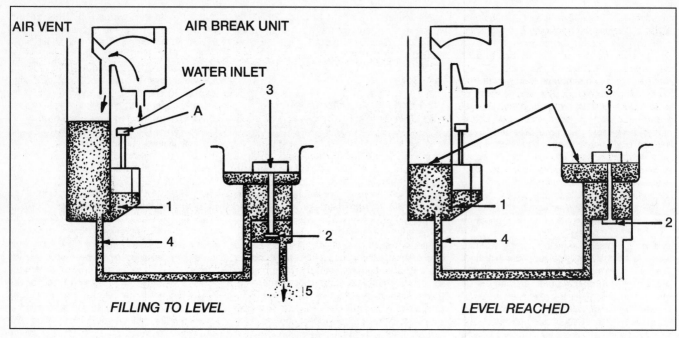

AIR VENT   AIR BREAK UNIT

WATER INLET

A

3

FILLING TO LEVEL

LEVEL REACHED

Venturi float system operation

the air break and steam vent mouldings situated between the inner and outer side panels. As with the pressure system, check for blockages and fat deposits. The micro switches can be easily tested. See *Electrical circuit testing.*

Float switch operation is quite simply what it says – as the water rises, a float is lifted and at the correct level actuates a micro switch with this action. The placing of both pressure vessels and float systems varies and can sometimes be an integral part of a complicated plastic moulding of both water inlet, air vent, steam vent and level systems. Due to their complex moulding, it is important that they are clean and free from blockages and fat deposits, etc.

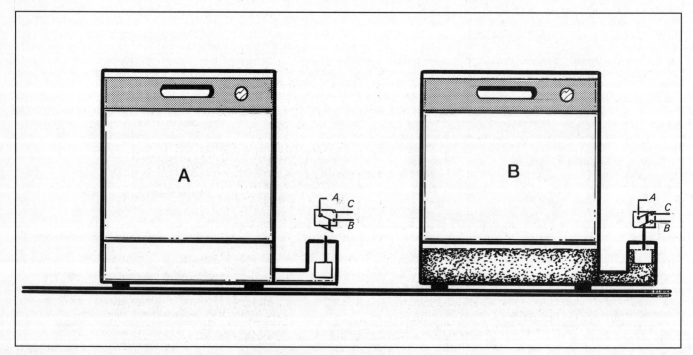

This simplified drawing shows the float switch operation

A Machine empty   B Machine at correct water level

Pressure system stripdown

This particular machine had only one pressure vessel and switch. Machines with additional pressure vessels and switches would require all hoses, etc. checking. Some modern machines have the hose and vessel situated near the pump to create a degree of self-cleaning to take place when emptying thus reducing deposit build-up.

Check and adjust level of the machine before functional test for water level.

Always isolate machine completely before any repair

Carefully lay machine over if necessary, to gain access to pressure system hoses. In this instance the side panel had to be removed

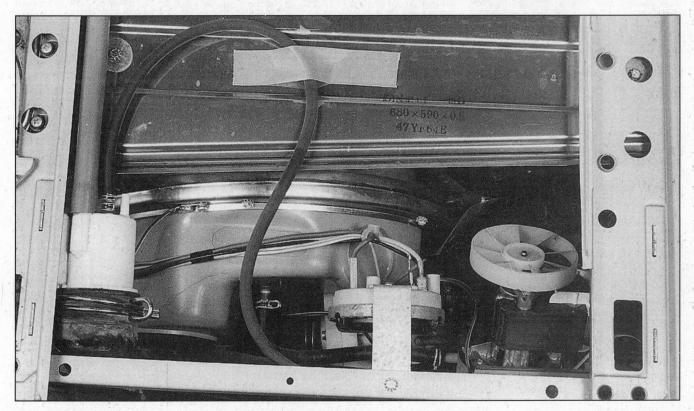

Both pressure vessel and hose were thought to be blocked

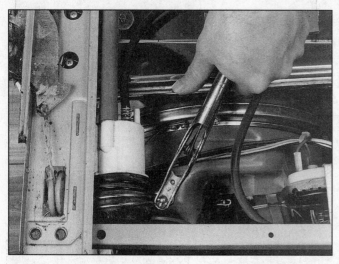

Remove clips and connections to pressure vessel

In this case a build-up of fatty deposits had collected in both vessel and hose. Thorough cleaning was required

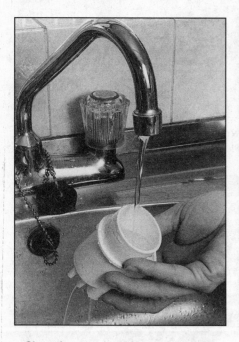

Clean the vessel and hoses thoroughly prior to reassembly

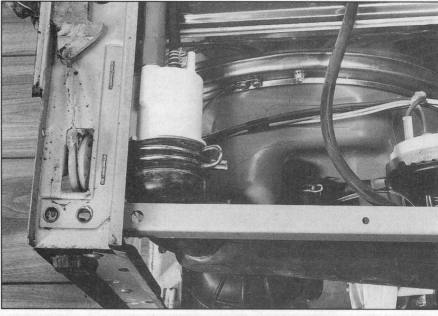

Seal and refit all hoses and panels securely

Electronic pressure switches/detectors

An alternative to the mechanical pressure switch which has internally operated switches is the analogue electronic pressure switch. The name is somewhat misleading as the item does not contain any switches and really should be referred to as an analogue pressure detector.

How do they work?

Electronic pressure detectors use the same types of pressure vessels, chambers, hoses etc. as the mechanical pressure switches described previously and as such are affected by the same problems of blockages, air leaks etc. However, they operate in a totally different way, having only three connection wires but are capable of accurately detecting even small changes in the pressure within the sealed pressure system. These features result in a wider range of water level control (more levels available) whilst at the same time being extremely accurate. Unlike the mechanical pressure switch an electronic pressure detector cannot operate on its own as the signal it produces in relation to the pressure it detecting needs to be fed to an electronic circuit. It is the electronic circuit (often part of the programme control PCB) that carries out the control (switching) functions.

Although smaller in appearance the construction, shape and outward appearance of an electronic pressure detector is very similar to the mechanical pressure switch but internally they are very different. As with the mechanical pressure switch air pressure in the sealed system distends a rubber diaphragm within the detector and the distension of the diaphragm is proportional to the pressure being applied to it.

The diaphragm is connected to a ferrite

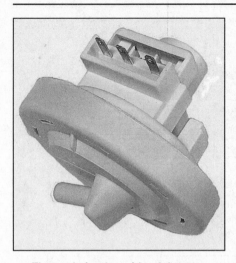

Electronic (analogue) level detector

core which is free to move within a coil of wire that surrounds it. In addition to the coil and ferrite core there is a small circuit board within the unit called an oscillator that feeds the wire coil with a set frequency. The position of the ferrite core within the coil directly affects the frequency due to a phenomenon called inductance and it is this change in frequency that is detected and used by the main circuit board (PCB) as the control signal for the programme routine.

The unit requires three wires – two being used to provide the low voltage power supply for the small internal PCB and the third is for transferring the frequency information to the main control PCB. **Note:** *Electronic level detectors are operated by low voltages of 5 volts or less and may be damaged by test meters that use a higher voltage during testing. Little can be gained from using a test meter on this type of item and may even result in damaging the unit by inadvertently applying too high a voltage during testing.*

As this type of level detector is generally only found on electronically controlled machines, fault identification is best left to reading the error code that the machine will display when a fault occurs. For further information on fault codes see chapter *Fault and error codes* and, prior to suspecting the electronic detector or main control PCB, ensure you have thoroughly inspected and cleaned the whole of the pressure system.

Microprocessor float system

Float control on some microprocessor controlled machines utilises a potentiometer system to achieve a range of fill levels. In these systems the float is connected to a potentiometer, the resistance of which changes with the position of the float. Specific resistances will be chosen by the manufacturer to relate to different levels of fill. For instance – 2kohms (2000 ohms) may equal empty, 17kohms (17,000 ohms) rinsing level and 22kohms (22,000 ohms) main wash level. The microprocessor will de-energise the fill valve when the required resistance is reached. This type of system is usually combined with the flow control system and other means of flood protection.

Flow sensing water level control

Flow sensing is the ability to measure the quantity of clean water entering the machine rather than reacting to the level of water collecting in the tub. In reality machines that utilise flow sensing normally combine this primary level control with water level pressure detection as a back up.

The way in which flow sensing works is very similar to the way fuel is metered into your vehicle's fuel tank at a petrol station or a water meter measures the amount of water you use in your home.

However, the system employed in dishwashing machines is essentially much smaller and more compact and can be an integral part of the water inlet valve or be an independent unit situated between the inlet valve and entry to the detergent dispenser/tub.

When the water inlet valve is energised (opened) to fill the machine to the required level depending on the type of system employed the water passes through or past a small turbine causing it to rotate. The number of rotations made during the fill period is proportional to the volume of water entering the machine. A small permanent magnet is embedded into the turbine and an externally mounted normally open reed switch closes each time the permanent magnet passes by it.

The opening and closing of the reed switch in relation to the magnets rotation create a series of pulses which are detected by a microprocessor housed on the main programme control PCB.

To fill to the required level for the selected programme the microprocessor simply counts the revolutions (pulses) from the reed switch. When the required number of revolutions (pulses) for the selected programme is attained the control circuit will switch off the inlet valve and continue with the programme sequence.

Metering the clean water intake in this way eliminates many of the problems associated with the pressure operated systems that simply measure the volume of water (dirty) within the outer tub unit.

However, even when measuring the clean water inlet into the appliance problems can

Independent flow sensing system

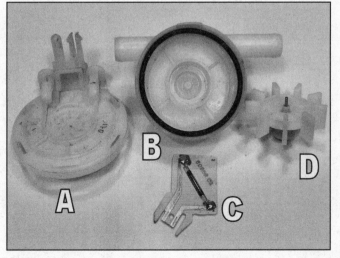

Internal component view of an independent flow sensing system
A Top cover   B Flow chamber   C Turbine
D Small PCB with reed switch

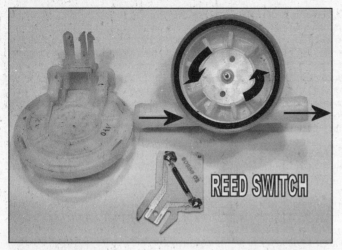

This diagram illustrates the action of the independent flow sensor unit. When the water inlet valve is energised water enters the flow chamber on the left and exits on the right. As it passes through the chamber the turbine with a permanent magnet mounted in the base is turned by the water flow. The reed switch mounted externally beneath the flow chamber is activated by the magnet's rotation

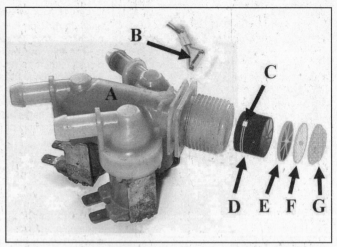

Water inlet valve combined with a flow sensing system. These types of inlet valve have miniature flow sensing systems mounted at the entry point to the valve and have all the same components as those described for the larger independent flow control system described previously

still occur and most if not all flow control systems will often have pressure operated back up systems. The primary being:

1 No flow through the valve due to no water supply (tap not turned ON), blocked inlet hose or inlet valve filter will prevent rotation of the turbine resulting in no pulses being generated. This will be detected by the microprocessor, the programme will be cancelled and an error code or alarm will be displayed.

2 Low pressure or partially blocked inlet filter may result in water entering the appliance but not turning the turbine (a pressure of at least 0.2 bar is required for correct operation). This will be detected by the microprocessor, the programme will be cancelled and an error code or alarm will be displayed.

3 Jamming of the inlet valve in the open position will result in the processor continuing to receive pulses even when the required number has been attained and the valve electrically turned off by the control unit. In this instance the microprocessor will cancel the programme and will power the drain pump to prevent a flood occurring. An error code and alarm will also be displayed.

4 Should the microprocessor develop a fault which results in leaving the inlet valve open i.e. fails to respond correctly to the above problems 2 or 3 the excess water entering the load compartment will be detected by the pressure operated back up level control system. This will normally result in cancellation of the programme and the

pressure switch directly powering the drain pump to prevent a flood occurring. An error code and alarm will also be displayed (see Chapter 31 *Fault and error codes*).

Tank metering systems

Dishwashers that use tank metering systems do not fill the load compartment with water directly from the fill valve. Unlike a standard dishwasher, when the fill valve is energised water flows into the load compartment via the air break, softener or directly and the valve is turned off when the correct level is detected. As the name implies, the tank metering

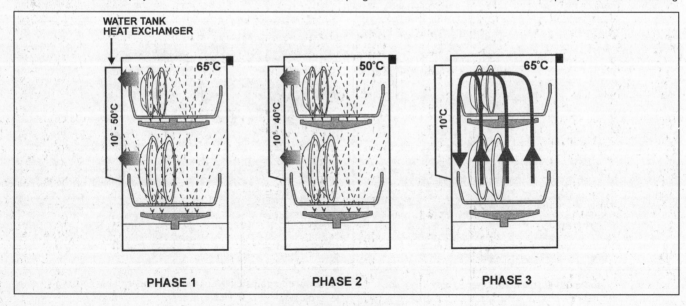

Tank metering diagrams

system fills tanks within the body of the appliance with a known volume of water. The water is then held within the tanks until the wash programme requires it. Transfer to the load compartment occurs by opening a simple solenoid (transfer) valve and allowing the water to transfer by gravity to the load compartment. Hence a metered volume of water enters the load compartment to be used for that portion of the cycle. Regeneration of the softener system occurs in a similar manner by the use of a second simple solenoid (transfer) valve. Regeneration allows one or a combination of up to three reservoirs (depending on water hardness and setting) within the side tank matrix to flow through the salt container and resin compartment.

At first the tank metering system may seem a rather cumbersome way to fill a dishwasher with water. However there are several benefits to this type of system.

1 The level control systems used within the appliance (float, pressure or in some instances both) only come into contact with clean water. This eliminates the problems associated with fat deposits, blockages, etc.
2 The water held within the tanks can be used as a heat exchange system to pre-heat the next fill of water prior to discharging the hot water currently being used.
3 By filling the tanks with cold water at the end of the heated drying cycle (the water is used for the first fill of the next programme) a condenser aided drying process is created within the load compartment to speed the drying process. All in all this system has many advantages and energy saving features.

Construction

The rear of the load compartment has a second panel welded to it on the outside to form a slim but large tank. The tank is in turn connected to a large plastic matrix housed between the outer panel and inner of the load compartment on the left-hand side of the appliance (see photo). The large plastic matrix houses the transfer valves (bottom left), air break system (top left), float level detection system (top right), regeneration reservoirs (centre) and in some models as in this instance the whole of the water softener system (centre right). There is also provision for pressure level detection by means of pressure vessel mouldings (bottom right inner face).

Heat exchange and condenser features explained

The diagram opposite illustrates the 3 phases of a typical tank metering system.

Phase 1. Shows the machine as it nears the end of its heated wash cycle having reached its required temperature (for this theoretical demonstration wash) of 65°. With the heater no longer in circuit the tank is filled with cold water via the main water inlet valve. The temperature of domestic cold water supply is normally between 10 and 12°. For the purposes of this theoretical sequence we have chosen 10° as the fill temperature. The programme continues with the wash process and heat is transferred by conduction from the 65° wash water heating the water in the tank to around 50°. At the end of the wash cycle the soiled water (now reduced to 50°) is pumped away.

Phase 2. After the wash water has been pumped away the preheated water from the tank is transferred to the load compartment giving a 50° rinse. The tank is then once again filled via the main inlet valve with water at 10°. During the rinse cycle the temperature of the water in the tank is raised to 40° by simple conduction. At the end of this rinse cycle the soiled rinse water is pumped away.

Phase 3. The tank water now at 40° is transferred to the load compartment for the final heated rinse prior to drying. As with most dishwashers the final rinse water will be heated to 65° to aid drying. However, the water taken at this point is already at 40° and therefore requires less energy and time to reach the required temperature. At the end of the heated final rinse the hot water is pumped away leaving the wash load to evaporate from the hot items. However, at this point the tank is once again filled with water at 10° causing the rear of the load compartment to cool. This creates a circulating air flow within the load compartment as the moisture in the warm air condenses on the cold surface. The condensate runs to the base of the machine and is pumped away leaving the load compartment free from steam. The clean water that remains in the tank is then ready for use in the next wash cycle. **Note:** *When servicing or carrying out repair work remember that the tank and matrix may be full of water.*

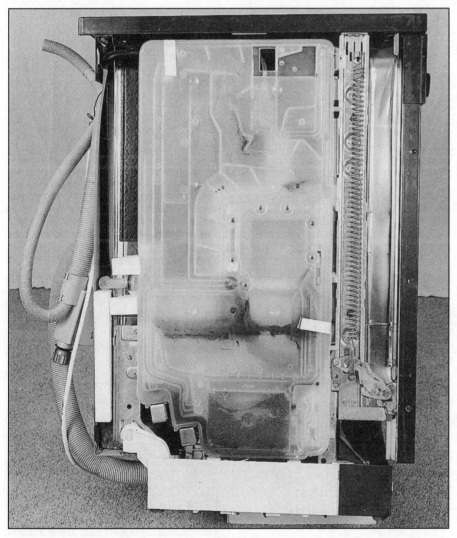

This large matrix combines, air break, steam vent, tank fill metering, regeneration tanks and water softener systems. For details of this type of system refer to chapters on *Water level control* and *Internal water softeners*

Further dishwasher drying systems

There are several ways in which a wash load can be dried:
- Standard drying – often referred to as 'passive' drying.
- Cool wall condenser drying (vented).
- Cool wall condenser drying (sealed) often referred to as 'active' drying.
- Cool wall turbo drying.
- Mixed air condenser drying.

Standard drying

Standard drying often referred to as 'passive' drying is the most simple of the drying systems and was all that was used in early models and is still used on the base models of many manufacturers.

This system simply directs the warm moist air (produced as the water evaporates from the hot wash load) through a vent on the side of the load compartment into the space between it and the outer case of the appliance by convection. From there the warm moist air joins that of the room. The technical term for this is vent to atmosphere.

In an effort to reduce the moisture content of the vented air the 'simple steam vent' some makes and models use a larger plastic labyrinth (maze like) structure through which the air has to pass before reaching the outlet. This can allow some of the moisture to gather on the internal surfaces and run back down into to the load compartment or sump via a hose.

Cool wall condenser drying (vented)

Vented cool wall condenser drying uses a similar plastic labyrinth as described previously. However, in this instance it is an integral part of a much larger combined air break, regeneration chamber reservoirs and vent unit.

Once again the system works by the warm moist air in the load compartment working its way through the plastic labyrinth to escape from the unit via the vent into the space between it and the outer case of the appliance. However, within this type of labyrinth the surfaces of the labyrinth are cool due to the presence of cold water stored within the regeneration chambers. The warm moisture-laden air passing over the cold surfaces of the labyrinth both speeds up and improves the condensing process. As a result the load dries a little quicker and the air vented from the unit has a greatly reduced moisture content. The condensed water (condensate) drains back into the load compartment or sump via a hose or direct plastic connection.

Cool wall condenser drying (sealed)

Sealed cool wall drying often referred to as 'active' drying uses a combined air break and regeneration chamber reservoirs plastic labyrinth but in this system both the inlet and outlet points are connected to the load compartment – one on the side wall of the load compartment and one on the top resulting in a sealed system. As the name implies this type of system does not vent any moisture into the cabinet void or atmosphere.

The warm moist air within the load compartment is drawn to the cold surfaces of the regeneration chambers within the sealed plastic loop and moisture condenses on the cold surfaces and drains back into the load compartment or sump via a hose or direct

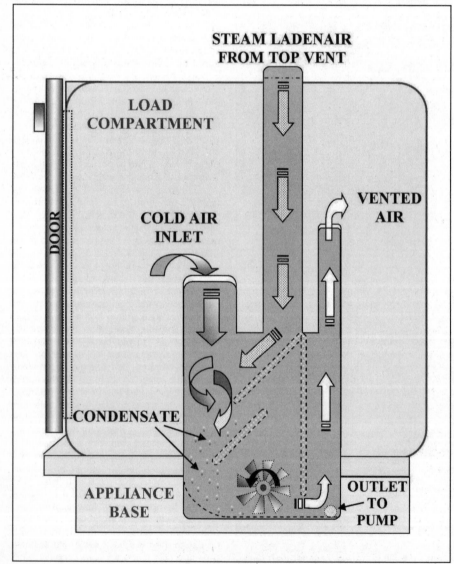

Mixed air flow drying diagram

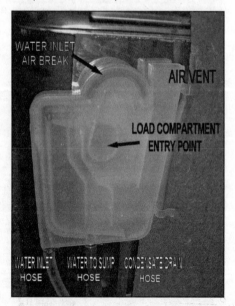

Typical standard drying system with combined water inlet air break and steam vent

Typical cool wall condenser drying system with direct connection to the sump and water softener unit

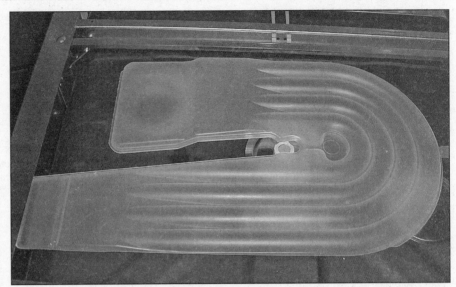

Removing the lid of this dishwasher revealed a large top condenser ducting

plastic connection. To further enhance this system some makes and models may also trickle feed a little water by a restricted flow inlet valve into the labyrinth chambers during the drying cycle.

Cool wall turbo drying

Cool wall turbo drying uses the same style of combined air break and regeneration chamber reservoirs plastic labyrinth as the sealed cool wall turbo drying system described previously. However, in this instance the condensing process is speeded up by the addition of a fan (turbo) to circulate the moisture-laden air from the load compartment through the plastic labyrinth and return the drier air back into the load compartment.

The fan and its small drive motor are usually mounted in the top ducting where it draws air from the load compartment and blows it through the labyrinth to re-enter the load compartment at a side mounted entry point. Some makes and models may also trickle feed a little water by a restricted flow inlet valve into the labyrinth chambers during the drying cycle. Moisture condensed from the air flow during this process drains back into the load compartment or sump via a hose or direct plastic connection.

Note: *As 'sealed cool wall drying' and 'cool wall turbo drying' use very much the same components models with 'Turbo Drying' often have the option to select between 'Turbo' or 'Active' drying. In such instances selecting 'Active' drying simply means the fan will not operate during the drying cycle.*

Mixed air condenser drying

As the name implies this drying system works by the mixing of different temperatures of air. A small fan usually mounted within the base of the appliance is connected to a large plastic chamber mounted between the outer of the load compartment and shell of the appliance. A duct runs from the top of the load compartment to the top of the plastic chamber where there are two openings at the top of the plastic chamber – one larger than the other. When drying takes place the motor turns the fan connected to the base of the chamber and creates a vacuum effect by blowing air out of the small vent. The effect of this action is to draw air back into the chamber from both the load compartment and the larger open vent.

The internal design of the chamber is such that both air streams meet within the chamber resulting in the moisture condensing from the steam-laden air as it meets the cooler air. The condensate produced by this interaction is then pumped away.

This system is simple and effective but the removal of water vapour from the load compartment air stream is dependent on the temperature of the ambient air being drawn in i.e. if the air in the room is warm then the condensing action will not be as effective and vice versa.

All the systems described in this section rely on water evaporating from the wash load after the last heated rinse has been drained away. For any of the drying processes to work effectively and produce streak and spot free results the water used for the last rinse requires the addition of 'rinse aid' refer to Chapter 27 for further details.

Chapter 23
Internal water softeners

What is a water softener?

A water softener is a means of removing excessive levels of calcium and magnesium in suspension within the ordinary domestic supply. Such levels vary considerably from region to region but your local Water Authority will advise you regarding the levels in your particular area.

Why have a water softener in the machine?

The reason why most dishwashers are fitted with water softeners is because of the way they wash and dry the load. The chemicals used for cleaning, combined with the water containing high levels of calcium and magnesium, would cause scale build up on the wash load, resulting in a rough, dull, opaque layer on crockery, glassware, etc. See *Common causes of poor washing results*.

Do you really need a softener?

A water softener is necessary if your water supply is 15 HF (hardness factor), or above. If a large domestic softener has previously been installed for all your household use, you need not fill the regeneration compartment in your dishwasher with salt, as further softening is not necessary. This may also apply for hardness factors of below 15. The machine will still fill via the softener device and no action to your machine needs to be taken to modify the machine in either case.

If you own a machine that does not have a water softener unit fitted (not all machines have them as standard fittings), and you are encountering the build up of a dull rough layer on crockery, glass, etc., check the hardness factor for your area. If the result is above 15 HF it could be worth finding out from the manufacturer of your machine if a softener kit can be obtained for your dishwasher. The lack of a salt compartment top within the base of the load compartment will confirm if a softener unit is not fitted to your machine.

How does a water softener work?

The water softener unit is made up of two linked compartments, one sealed and containing resin granules, and the other compartment is a fillable container for salt. Most dishwashers use softened water for the wash and end rinse cycles only, whilst others soften all the water used by the machine. Softening of the water is carried out by passing the in-coming water through the resin granules. The granules are designed to attract calcium ions (Ca++) and magnesium ions (Mg++). They do this by in turn releasing sodium ions (Na+). The emerging water is therefore softened by the removal of both calcium and magnesium by the loss from the resin of sodium. After passing through such a softener, water with a hardness factor of 40 HF will now be in the region of 7 to 10 HF. For the resin to work efficiently as a softener, it must be replenished with sodium ions. This operation is called regeneration.

With use, the resin granules become saturated with calcium and magnesium ions and possess few sodium ions. Regeneration

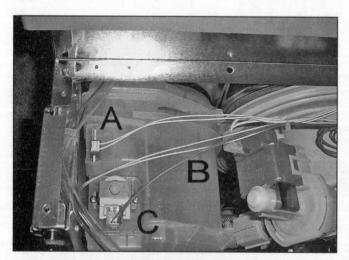

Typical under load compartment water softener unit
A Externally mounted reed switch which reacts to internally mounted floating permanent magnet
B Large salt container with access for filling within the load compartment
C Regeneration solenoid operated valve
The second chamber of the combined unit containing the regeneration granules is not visible in this picture

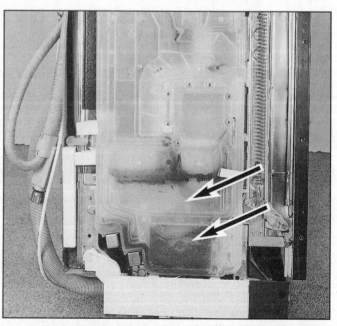

This large matrix also houses the water softener unit
Salt container and resin unit arrowed

On many makes and models water hardness adjustment needs to be carried out by turning a small dial situated within the salt container filling point on the base of the load compartment. It is not surprising that this important setting is so often overlooked. Check the instruction booklet that came with the appliance to find where and how to ensure that correct setting exists

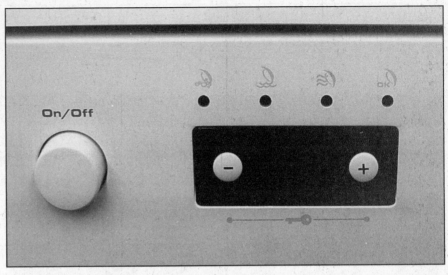

Water hardness on some models is set electronically – refer to the instruction booklet for your particular appliance as methods of setting differ greatly between the various makes and models

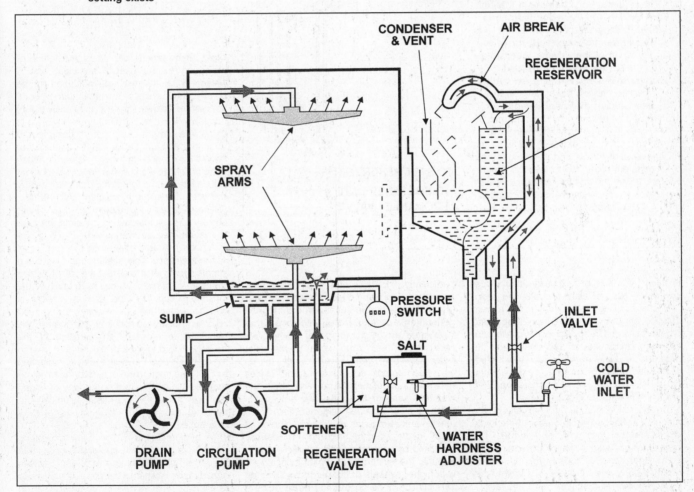

This diagram illustrates a typical inlet water flow. Water enters via a single cold inlet valve and passes through an air break system within a large plastic matrix. Most of the water continues on through the softener unit and into the load compartment, however, a small amount is diverted to fill the regeneration reservoir within the matrix. Regeneration occurs when the valve situated within the softener unit opens and allows the reservoir to drain through the salt container and softener unit by gravity. In this particular system adjustment for water hardness is made within the salt container

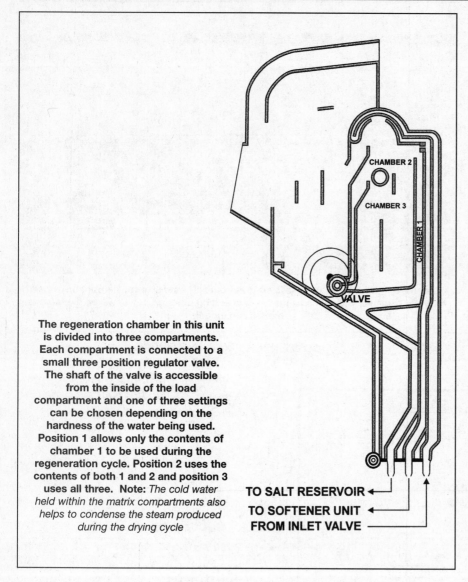

The regeneration chamber in this unit is divided into three compartments. Each compartment is connected to a small three position regulator valve. The shaft of the valve is accessible from the inside of the load compartment and one of three settings can be chosen depending on the hardness of the water being used. Position 1 allows only the contents of chamber 1 to be used during the regeneration cycle. Position 2 uses the contents of both 1 and 2 and position 3 uses all three. Note: *The cold water held within the matrix compartments also helps to condense the steam produced during the drying cycle*

TO SALT RESERVOIR ←
TO SOFTENER UNIT ←
FROM INLET VALVE ←

regeneration, i.e. 1 compartment – soft, 3 compartments – hard. Water is allowed to flow slowly, under gravity only, through the softener unit during the regeneration cycle.

The water softener will require filling with salt regularly as per the instruction manual. On average, a dishwasher will take approximately 2.2 kilogrammes of salt which under normal conditions is enough for between six and seven regenerations. The amount of salt consumption of a dishwasher is sometimes overlooked or ignored altogether, but such oversights can cause problems with the quality of the wash. Check regularly and top up the salt compartment to maintain optimum efficiency of this unit. The salt used for regeneration can be anti-calcium salt or unrefined cooking salt; but better still are the packs of salt in granular form sold especially for dishwashers. DO NOT USE TABLE SALT as it may have additives such as iodine which can cause problems to your machine.

Salt level indication

Most dishwashers will have a means of indicating to the user if sufficient salt is present within the reservoir. Indication can be by one of two ways or a combination of both.
1 A simple coloured sight disc (usually green) housed within the salt container cap. This is actually a simple hydrometer* designed to float in the high saline (salt) solution that should normally be in the salt reservoir. When there is sufficient salt in the container the float will be lifted to the top of the cap and seen by the user. If there is insufficient salt the float will not be lifted and the coloured disc will not show. Although effective in principle this type of system is easily overlooked.
2 A neon indicator situated on the front panel of the appliance. This system again utilises a simple hydrometer to detect the salinity within the salt container. In order to switch the indicator neon ON and OFF a magnet is housed within the hydrometer and a reed relay is positioned on the outside of the container to react to the position of the magnet. The presence of the magnet next to the reed relay will cause the relay to close and turn ON the neon to indicate that the reservoir requires filling. This is a better way of letting the user know there is insufficient salt but unfortunately even this system gets overlooked.

*A hydrometer is a device for measuring the relative density of a liquid. It consists of a weighted bulb housed in this instance within a guide tube in which it is free to move up and down. The bulb of the hydrometer used in dishwasher salt reservoirs is calibrated to float only when there is sufficient salt in solution within the reservoir. Water with salt in suspension has a higher density than plain water.

is done by simply passing salt water (water containing sodium (Na+) through the resin, therefore allowing the resin to absorb a fresh supply of sodium (Na+), so becoming regenerated and ready for use. To allow an optimum interchange of sodium ions on the regeneration cycle the water flow is restricted, i.e. slowed down to around 1 litre per minute, to allow a thorough regeneration and interchange to take place.

Regeneration is done automatically by the machine at the beginning or end of the cycle depending on the make and model. The frequency of regeneration is governed by a small knob on the switch that is set to correspond to the hardness of the water in your area. Not all machines have this facility. The time taken to regenerate can be twenty minutes or more, allowing time for the transfer of sodium ions back into the resin. It is, therefore unwise to restart the machine unless twenty minutes or more have elapsed,

particularly if the indicator is set for a hard water area. The water used for regeneration is pumped away by the outlet pump during the generation cycle. **Note:** *Machines that regenerate at the beginning of every cycle take much less time than those that regenerate only after several wash cycles have been completed.* The amount of cycles between regeneration is governed by the hardness selector i.e. soft water selected – more cycles between regeneration. With machines that regenerate at the beginning of every cycle, the regeneration is usually governed by passing a fixed volume of water through the system. The volume increases with higher settings of the hardness selector. This can be done on a timed basis or by a mechanical system which is combined into the air break unit. Three compartments of varying sizes within the air break fill whenever the machine operates and it is a combination of these that governs the strength of

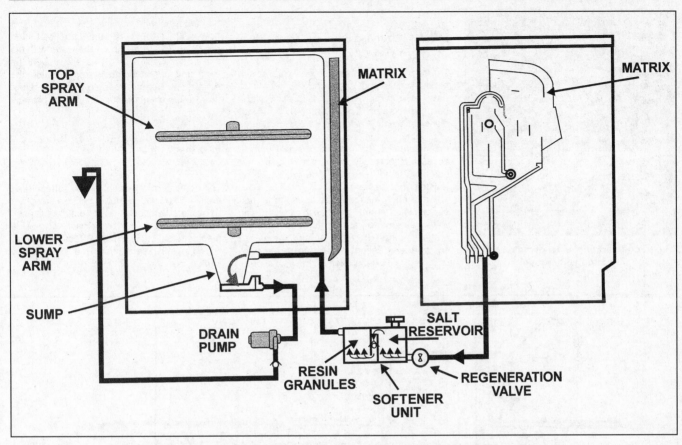

Top Spray Arm, Matrix, Matrix, Lower Spray Arm, Sump, Drain Pump, Resin Granules, Salt Reservoir, Softener Unit, Regeneration Valve

This diagram illustrates the regeneration water flow of the diagram opposite

Length of Regeneration	Hardness	Parts per million P.P.M.	Mg/L CaCO$_3$	Grains per British Gal. (Clarke) degrees	German degrees	French degrees	Grains per U.S. Gal.
NO SALT REQUIRED	S	0	0	0	0	0	0
		25	25.17	1.75	1.41	2.52	1.5
	MS	50	50.33	3.5	2.82	5.03	3
		100	100.66	7	5.64	10.07	5.8
	SH	120	122.23	8.5	6.84	12.22	7.0
		150	150.99	10.5	8.45	15.10	8.7
	MH	200	201.32	14	11.27	20.13	11.7
NORMAL REGENERATION	H	260	258.84	18	14.49	25.88	15
		300	301.98	21	16.91	30.20	17.5
	VH	350	352.31	24.5	19.73	35.23	20.4
		400	402.64	28	22.54	40.26	23.3
LONG REGENERATION		430	431.40	30	24.15	43.14	25

Water hardness comparison table

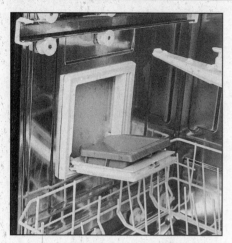

Load compartment view of matrix side-mounted softener unit

Water hardness

The degree of hardness can be expressed in various ways and each country seems to have a different way of expressing the hardness factor. The handbook for your dishwasher may give the factor in figures applicable to the country in which it was manufactured. The table shown will help in assessing correctly your particular water hardness factor which may be expressed on a different scale.

Water can be supplied to the softener unit at point (I) for normal filling and softening. The water is forced to pass through the resin and out at point (H). Flow through the salt compartment cannot occur due to the non-return valve. Regeneration of the resin is done by supplying water to the unit via (E). Water flows slowly first through the salt and dissolves a little as it does. The water with the salt in suspension then passes through the resin and out at point (H) regenerating the resin granules as it does so. The non-return valve (F2) prevents water escaping at point (I).

The non-return valve with the softener unit

The non-return valves within the softener unit are simply a shaped rubber seal (see diagram opposite). Water entering at point (1) will push open the valve. If a back pressure or reverse feed occurs (2), the resulting pressure at point 3 and 4 effectively closes the valve tightly shut.

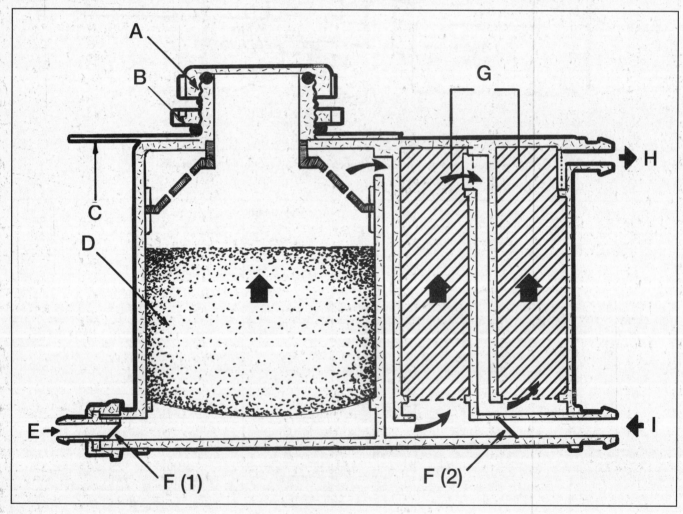

The softener unit

A Salt container top (may contain float indicator)
B Retaining nut and rubber seal
C Load compartment base
D Salt
E Regeneration water inlet
F1&2 Non-return valves
G Resin granules
H Outlet to load compartment for both softened and regenerated water
I Main inlet for water to be softened prior to use in machine

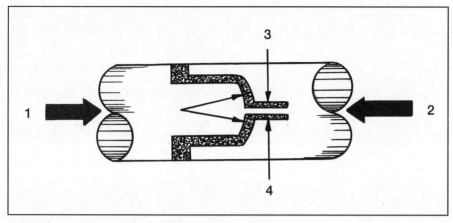

Non-return valve

A complete base-mounted water softener unit removed from a dishwasher showing clearly the two containers: left – the salt reservoir and right – the resin container, and various pipe connectors

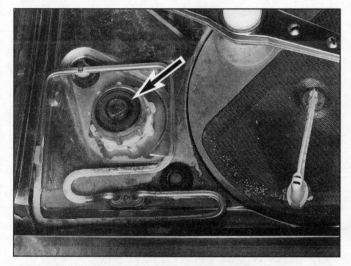

All that is normally seen of the softener system. Check regularly that the salt indicator is working

Softener unit in situ viewed from underside of the load cabinet

Area guide to water hardness in the U.K.

Due to a new grid system for water, hardness may vary considerably in times of shortage. Details shown are therefore only an indication of normally expected hardness.

	Parts per million as $CaCO_3$	Degrees Clarke	Degrees French
Soft	0 to 50	0 to 3.5	8 to 5
Moderately soft	50 to 100	3.5 to 7.0	5 to 10
Slightly hard	00 to 150	7.0 to 10.5	10 to 15
Moderately hard	150 to 200	10.5 to 14.0	15 to 20
Hard	200 to 300	14.0 to 21.0	20 to 30
Very hard	over 300	over 21.0	over 30

Area	Authority	Water Hardness
Argyll	Scotland	S
Ashborne	Severn - Trent	MS - H
Ayrshire	Scotland	S
Birmingham	Severn - Trent	S - VH
Bolton	North West	S
Bournemouth	Wessex	H - VH
Cambridge	Anglia	SH - H
Carlisle	North West	MS
Cheshire - Mid	North West	MS - H
Chester	North West	SH - H
Chiltern	Thames	VH
Clyde - Lower	Scotland	S
Colna Valley	North West	H - VH
Corby & District	North West	H
Cumbria South	North West	S - MH
Cumbria West	North West	S
Derbyshire - North	Severn - Trent	S - H
Derbyshire - South	Severn - Trent	MH
Derwent Valley	Severn - Trent	S
Dorset	Wessex	H
East Anglia	Anglia	H - VH
Eastbourne	Southern	SH - VH
Eden	North West	S - MH
Essex	Anglia	S - VH
Exeter	South West	S - H
Fife & Kinross	Scotland	S - VH
Folkestone & District	Southern	S - VH
Fylde	North West	S - SH
Gloucester	Severn - Trent & Thames	MH - VH
Guernsey	-	SH
Hampshire Central	Southern	H
Hampshire North	Southern	H
Hampshire West	Southern	H
Hartlepool	Northumbrian	H - VH
Invernesshire	Scotland	S - MH
Ireland Eastern	-	S - H
Ireland Northern	-	MS
Ireland Southern	-	S - VH
Ireland Western	-	MS
Isle of Wight	-	SH - H
Jersey	-	MH
Kent	Southern	H
Kent East	Southern	H
Kent Mid	Southern	SH - VH
Kent West	Southern	MS - H
Lakes & Lune	North West	S
Lambourne	Thames	SH - VH
Lanarkshire	North West	S - VH
Lancashire	North West	S - VH
Lee Valley	Thames	VH
Leicester	Severn - Trent	MH - VH
Liverpool	North West	S - SH
Loch Lomond	Scotland	S

Area	Authority	Water Hardness
Loch Turret	Scotland	S
London - Metropolitan	Thames	MH - VH
Lune Valley	North West	S - SH
Macclesfield	North West	MS - H
Makerfield	North West	S - MH
Manchester	North West	S
Mersey Valley	North West	S - VH
Montgomery	Severn - Trent	S - MH
Newcastle & Gateshead	Northumbrian	MH
Nottingham	Severn - Trent	MS - MH
Northumberland & Tyne	Northumbrian	SH
Nuneaton	Severn - Trent	SH - VH
Pennine - West	North West	S - MS
Plymouth	South West	S - SH
Preston & District	North West	S
Rickmansworth & Uxbridge Valley	Thames	H - VH
Salop	Severn - Trent	H
Scilly Isles	-	MH
Scotland - Mid	Scotland	S - MH
Scotland - North	Scotland	S - VH
Scotland - North East	Scotland	S
Scotland - South East	Scotland	S - H
Scotland - South West	Scotland	S - MH
Sherwood	Severn - Trent	MH - VH
Somerset	Wessex	S - VH
Stafford	Severn - Trent	H - VH
Staffordshire - South	Severn - Trent	H - VH
St. Helens	North West	SH
Stockport	North West	S
Sunderland & South Shields	Northumbrian	MS - VH
Surrey East	Thames	MS
Surrey North	Thames	H - VH
Sussex	Southern	H
Sussex East	Southern	MS
Sussex Mid	Southern	S - H
Sussex North West	Southern	MS - VH
Sutton District	Thames	SH
Tees	Northumbrian	S - MS
Tendring Hundred	Anglia	H
Truro	South West	S - SH
Vales	Thames	MS - VH
Warwickshire	Severn - Trent	MH - VH
Wear	Northumbrian	S
Wiltshire	Thames	H
Wolverhampton	Severn - Trent	SH - VH
Worcestershire - North	Severn - Trent	S - VH
Worcestershire - South	Severn - Trent	MS - H
Wrexham & East Wrexham Denbighshire	Welsh	SH
York	Yorkshire	H
Yorkshire North	Yorkshire	S - VH

Chapter 24
Heaters

There are three main types of heating systems used in dishwashers. The exposed element located within the load compartment and the remote element and through flow types located out of sight below the load compartment.

Where is the exposed type of heater located?

This type of heater is located on the lower part of the load compartment or inside the sump well of the machine. Size and shape of heaters vary enormously from manufacturer to manufacturer. Some are used only when immersed in water whilst others operate immersed for wash cycles and for a very short period when uncovered to help dry the load at the end of the cycle.

Removal and refitting of the heater

To remove the heater: Make a note of the connections and remove them, the heater can then be withdrawn from its position by removing the centre nut, and fixing plate. Next lift the heater free from any retaining clips inside the load compartment.

Refitting is a reversal of these instructions, ensuring that all securing clips are refitted and good contact is made with overheat thermostats, etc. Care should be taken that the centre nut is not overtightened, as this would cause a distortion of the metal plate.

Main faults with heaters

One of the most common faults with any type of heater is that of open circuit, i.e. no current flows through the heater, therefore no heat is produced, and the machine will fail to move off the wash programme as the impulse via the thermostat will not be produced. This can be due to a broken or loose connection to one of the heater terminals. This then overheats, leaving an obvious discoloration of the connection or terminal, resulting in a break of the circuit at that point. Alternatively, the break in the circuit can occur within the element itself. This can be tested for continuity, as described in the chapter

Electrical circuit testing. **Note:** *Remote heaters will also have additional protection switches/thermostats that will need to be checked.*

Another fault that can occur is that of low insulation. In this case please refer to chapter *Low insulation.* Accompanying the low insulation fault is that of the short circuiting of the heater, caused by a complete breakdown of insulation. This results in the machine blowing fuses or earth tripping.

Should any of the above faults occur, a complete replacement of the component is required. This is so, even for the double element heaters and remote versions. If one of the two elements should fail, a complete element replacement is needed.

Some machines have plastic or nylon load compartments and are fitted with overheat protectors. These are essential and are linked in line with the live feed to the heater. They are fitted for safety reasons, for if a pressure switch or pressure system were to fail, it is possible for the heater to be engaged with no water in the machine. In a machine with a metal load compartment and exposed type of element, this would be most unwelcome, but only minor damage would be caused. If this were to happen in a machine with a plastic/nylon compartment or remote heating

unit, the result could be extremely dangerous. **Note:** *Under no circumstances should any overheat protection be removed or bypassed.*

The overheat protector that is used on some machines may be an integral part of the heater and is similar to a capillary thermostat switch. Some versions can be reset by pressing the reset button on the unit. A protector which is found to be open circuit or tripped, would result in no heating of the wash water and would also cause the machine to 'stop' i.e. fail to move through the programme. If this item is found to be 'open circuit', check the pressure switch and system prior to renewing or resetting the overheat device.

Another problem that can affect the heater and its safety cut-out is scale build-up or a covering of food sediment. This can cause the heater to be, in effect, insulated from the water surrounding it and unable to transfer its heat quickly enough to the water. Such overheating of the element causes the safety cut-out to operate. In this instance, a thorough cleaning of the element would be required and a check on why the build-up had occurred (possibly lack of filter cleaning, under-dosing of powder, failure of softener system, etc.). A similar fault is caused by too little water for circulation, exposing the element during main circulation motor

Shown is an early Whirlpool cylindrical through flow heater and overheat thermostat. This one-piece unit has a stainless steel tube with the heating elements wound round and welded to the outside. Note: *The heating element does not come into direct contact with the water flowing through the tube*

operations. Check levels and listen for the pump 'hunting' during the wash as the pump will, for a second, run out of water to circulate.

Incorrect or poor quality detergents can also cause 'hunting' and premature heater failure due to excessive foaming.

Remote/through flow heaters

This type of heating system is becoming more popular. There is no visible evidence of a heater in the load compartment or sump unit. It is mounted in line with the sump unit or hose, and links directly to the circulation pump inlet or outlet.

There are two distinct types:
1 The through flow type has an element which is externally wound around a stainless steel tube which transfers heat to the water via this tube. The makers of this type of heater state that it cannot fur or scale up in any way

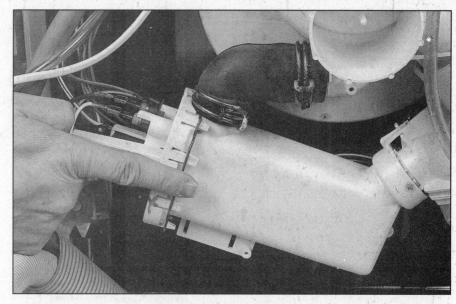

This is a remote heating unit. The heating element is housed within this container beneath the load compartment. The element in this type of system is in direct contact with the water as it flows through the chamber

Base-mounted heater

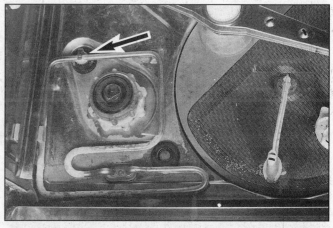

Overheat thermostat position on heater (self-setting version)

Badly scaled element caused by hard water area and infrequent salt container filling

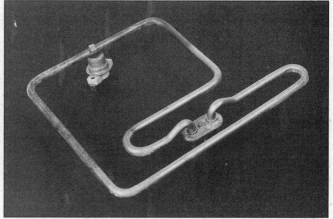

Normal condition of element after use. Pictured here with overheat thermostat fitted

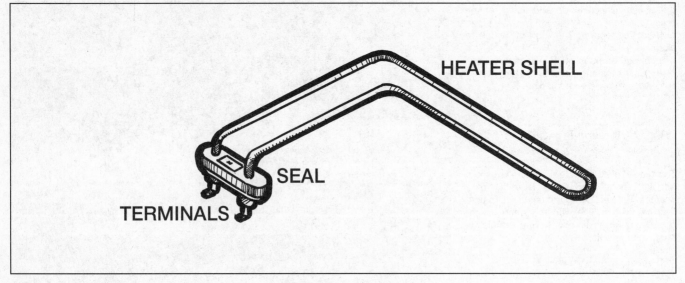

Typical exposed type heater

and technically they are correct as the heating element does not come directly into contact with the water. However, scale can and does form in the tube in certain circumstances (i.e. not using salt, etc.). Also, being in line with the pump inlet, the water flowing through the heating tube is drawn through the filter giving rise to problems if the filter is not cleaned regularly and thoroughly. The heater unit is fitted with a TOC (Thermal Overlead Cut-out) but often it is not a self-setting one. If the TOC has tripped, make sure of the reason for it having done so and rectify the problem prior to resetting, i.e. clean filters thoroughly or, in the case of scaling, remove the unit and clean it thoroughly. Take care if using descaling chemicals and follow the manufacturer's instructions for use. Identify also the reason why the unit scaled up in the first place and rectify the problem. As with any repairs – ensure the machine is isolated before removing any panels. Taps off and plug out.

2 Remote type. With this type of system the heating element is housed within a container located beneath the load compartment. The heating element within the unit is in direct contact with the water as it flows through the unit. The remote heating chamber is mounted between the outlet of the main circulation pump and spray arm feed connections. During the circulation process water is forced through the unit by the circulation pump. Within the unit is a flexible rubber seal which rests against an externally mounted micro switch. The micro switch is a normally 'open' switch and only when water flows within the unit creating sufficient pressure will the rubber seal press against the micro switch with enough force to close the switch and allow the heater to operate. Due to the plastic construction of the chamber and high

wattage of the heater the unit will also have additional thermal protection devices (TOCs). Problems that can and do occur are similar to those described previously with addition of micro switch failure caused by constant switching (nuisance tripping) due to

restricted water flow through the unit. **Note:** *As this type of unit works under pressure it is therefore essential that all seals and connections are in good order. Ensure correct refitting and renew any worn or defective seals.*

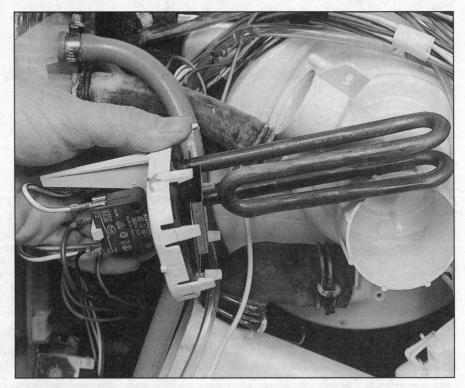

The end of this remote heating unit has a flexible rubber seal on the inside. On the outside is a micro switch which is connected in series with the heating element. Only when water flows within the unit and creates enough pressure will the rubber seal press against the micro switch with enough force to close the circuit and allow the heater to operate

This remote heater often referred to as a heat exchanger or through flow heater has a heating element wrapped around the outside of a metal tube which heats the water as it passes through

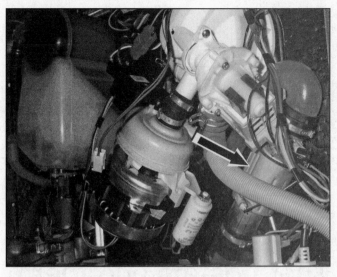

Remote heater in situ in the base beneath the load compartment

Using a simple multi-meter to check a heating element. With the connections removed the heating element should indicate continuity i.e. in most instances a resistance of between 20 and 30 ohms would be found for wattages between 2000 and 3000 watts

Note: *The wattage of a heater is often marked on the securing plate (the higher the resistance the lower the wattage). Using Ohm's law (voltage divided by the resistance) to calculate the wattage from its resistance will not result in an exact match to that displayed on the heater. This is due to the resistance when cold being different from its resistance when it is hot*

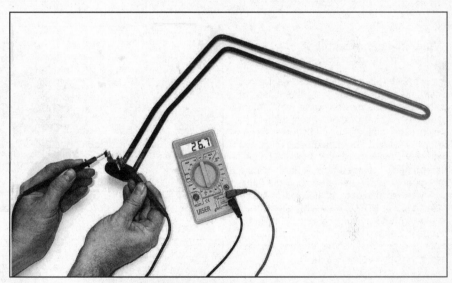

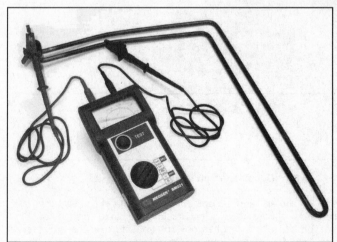

To conclusively test a heater for 'low insulation' (a very common problem) you will require an insulation test meter like the one shown

A typical through flow remote heater unit. To the top is an overheat protection thermostat – if this has tripped check the circulation system for blockage including scaling of the heater tube

Chapter 25
Thermostats and thermistors

What is a thermostat?

A thermostat is a mechanical device for detecting temperature. In the case of dishwashers this can be water temperature or the direct heat of the heating element (in which case, acting like a TOC, see: Chapter 24, *Heaters*). The thermostat (stat) will also either 'make' or 'break' a circuit at a pre-determined temperature. Temperature ratings are usually marked around the metal perimeter on the back of the stat and also marked NO or NC, i.e. normally open contact – closing and making a circuit at given temperature, or normally closed – opening at given temperature. Some thermostats can and do contain both variants.

Where are they located?

Thermostats are located anywhere the need to detect temperature is required.

Most thermostats are located under the bottom panel or base of the dishwasher, in direct contact with the metal base or door liner, or grommet fitted through holes in the panels to come into direct contact with the water or heater. Access to thermostats will vary depending where they are located.

Many thermostats are grommet fitted, i.e. fitted into a rubber seal and then in turn fitted to a hole in the machine's metal base or plastic sump moulding. Always ensure a watertight fit. The use of a little sealant is advisable to assist stat fitting to grommets. See *Useful tips and information*. In addition to the grommet they may also be held in position by metal clips or clamps, and again, make sure of a good seal and check that the clips or clamps do not trap or touch wires or connectors.

Single thermostat

Double thermostat

To avoid the need for holes and grommets many manufacturers choose to mount thermostats in direct contact with the metal lining of the load compartment. In these instances the detection of temperature is by conduction as the temperature of the metal lining of the cabinet rises and falls in line with the water being circulated within it. This type of fitting has obvious benefits over the grommet fit type thermostats. There are some makes that have metal plates moulded into the sump hose to accommodate this type of thermostat system.

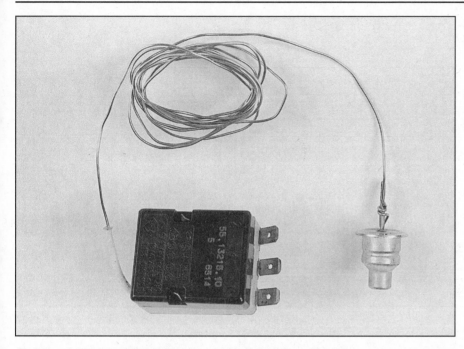

Pod type thermostat currently rarely used on dishwashers. This type can have a greater range of temperatures from just the one probe

How do they work?

A diagram overleaf shows a typical thermostat, in this instance a 50°C (NO) normally open contact and an 85°C (NC) normally closed contact. The latter is a safety thermostat which operates if overheating should occur within the machine. Normal operational temperatures of dishwashers are much lower with a maximum rating rarely exceeding 65°C.

The diagram illustrates the position of a thermostat at rest. Bimetal discs are mounted directly behind the metal front cover of the stat and are preset to distort at a given temperature (in this instance 50°C and 85°C). They are linked to contact switches by push rods. Any corresponding distortions of the discs, either make or break the corresponding contacts as shown.

When removed from the machine, the thermostat's operation can be tested by placing the metal cover in contact with a known heat source, e.g. radiator, hot water, etc. which matches or slightly exceeds the required temperature. Allow a little time for the heat to warm the stat and bimetal discs. Testing for closing or opening of the

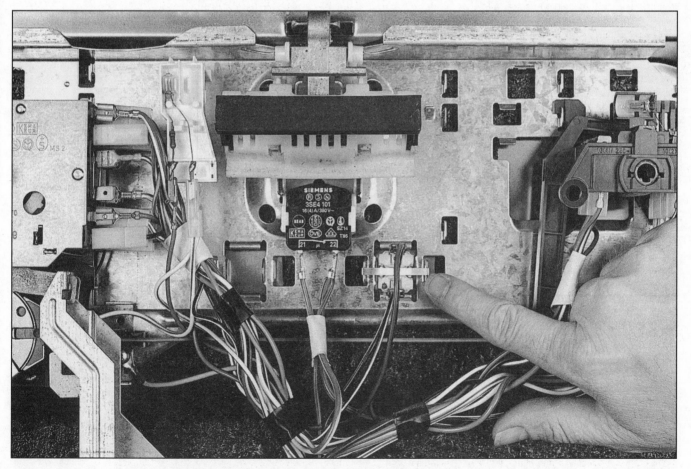

This thermostat detects the temperature of the water circulating within the load compartment by being pressed into contact with the metal inner liner of the door. This type of contact fitting allows for easy removal and refitting

thermostat can now be carried out as shown in the chapter *Electrical fault finding.*

Check temperature with a household thermometer and allow a few degrees either way of the marked temperature on the outer rim of the stat, and remember to check if the stat is normally NO or NC. When cool, check that the seat returns to its normal position as indicated on the rim, i.e. NO or NC.

Removing and refitting a grommet thermostat

Warning: *Before attempting to remove or repair any component from the machine, isolate the machine from the main electrical supply by removing the plug from the wall socket.*

To remove

Make a note of the position, orientation and connections of the thermostat and then disconnect the wires. Insert a small flat bladed screwdriver between the inner rubber lip and the metal front plate of the stat and prise the stat from the grommet. Care will be required if sealant has previously been used as this will have glued the stat into position. When refitting, it is advisable to smear a little sealant on the grommet to avoid leaks.

To refit

See Diagrams C, D and E.

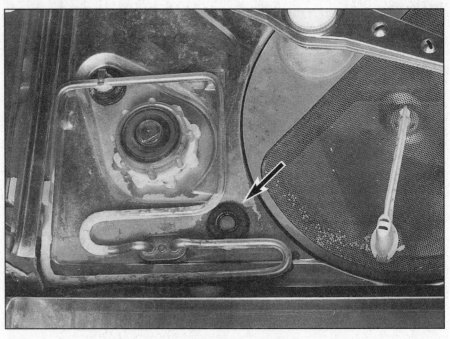

Base of load compartment of this Candy machine shows the position of grommet fitted double thermostat (arrowed)

Locate the metal lip in grommet recess (C) and with the aid of a flat bladed screwdriver ease the outer lip over the metal lip of the stat (D). Sealant will help locate and seal the thermostat into position (E). Ensure that the thermostat is securely located into the grommet and that the outer lip is not trapped.

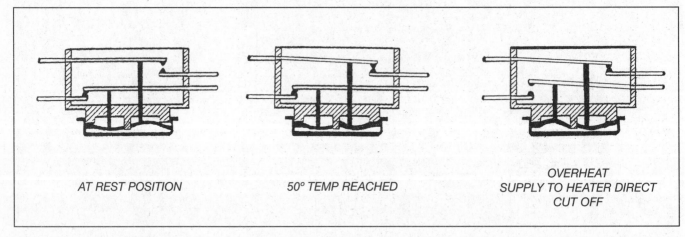

AT REST POSITION   50° TEMP REACHED   OVERHEAT
SUPPLY TO HEATER DIRECT CUT OFF

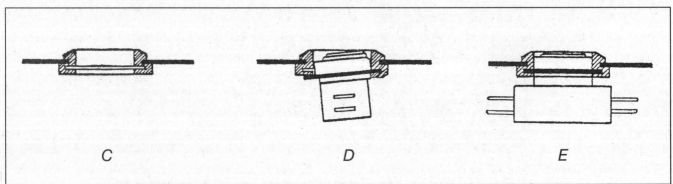

C   D   E

Thermostat operation flowchart

Using the following flowchart, trace the sequence of events:

1 The machine is turned on.
2 The timer impulses, fills the machine with cold water and turns the heater on.
3 to 4 The thermostat 'waits' until the heater has heated the water to 40°C.
5 to 6 When the thermostat closes (i.e. the water has reached 40°C), the timer washes for two minutes. The timer starts the washing action for two minutes. (At this point the heater is still engaged.)
7 to 8 The above operation is repeated, again with the heater engaged. When the two minute wash has ended, the water will be at 45°C due to the extra four minute heating.
9 to 11 The timer then moves to the next position, which disengages the heater, and would then be ready for the programme to continue as required.
12 For the purpose of this flowchart, the wash will end here as we are only concerned with the operation of the thermostat at this time.
Note: *This is only used as an example to illustrate the use of the thermostat, and does not actually represent the way in which a wash is formed. For further information regarding the timer, see Chapter 29: Timers (programmers).*

This way of using preset thermostats can give a greater variation in wash temperatures.

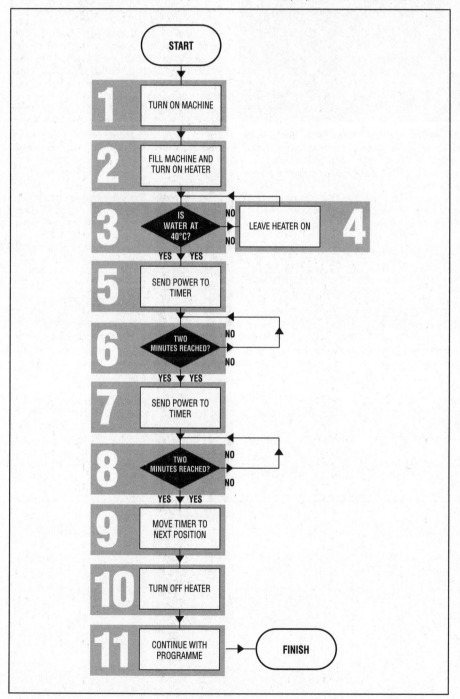

What is a thermistor?

A thermistor is a solid state device used in place of a fixed or variable thermostat. Thermistors' particular properties allow them to be used as infinitely variable temperature sensors that have no moving parts. They are also incapable of going out of calibration, i.e. giving incorrect temperature resistance values, but occasionally they can and do go 'open circuit', or connections to and from them may short circuit. Both are faults which will inevitably give rise to temperature sensing problems.

Where are they located?

Like all temperature sensing devices, it must come into direct or indirect contact with the substance that needs monitoring. Its location is therefore similar to the thermostats detailed previously.

How do they work?

Unlike other temperature control devices the thermistor cannot work alone. It is an electrical resistor, the resistance of which varies in relation to its temperature. There are two ways in which it varies depending on manufacturer, and the requirements of the finished product. Thermistors can be positive or negative temperature coefficient. In simple terms, this means a positive coefficient thermistor's resistance increases as its temperature increases and conversely, a negative coefficient thermistor's resistance decreases as its temperature increases. Thermistors are therefore rated as PTC or NTC respectively. The NTC type of thermistor is the version most often used in temperature sensing circuitry in electronically controlled dishwashers. A theoretical operation of a thermistor control circuit is shown. It is essential that only the correct version of thermistor is used which conforms to the rating requirements of the machine and its circuitry.

The variation in resistance to temperature change forms part of an electronic circuit, the output of which controls the advancement of the selected wash programme, in either mechanically (some machines may have a control PCB) or electronically controlled machines. On electronically controlled machines, i.e. those without mechanical timers, the resistance of the thermistor is monitored directly by the main programme circuit board or sub-module. However,

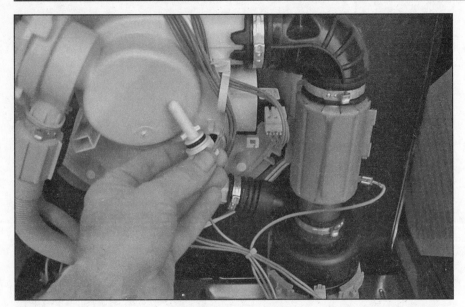

Sump unit mounted thermistor. This particular thermistor is 'bayonet' fitted into a hole in the sump moulding and sealed by a small 'O' ring at its base. The term 'bayonet fit' refers to locating lugs on the item locating into slots in the moulding which lock into and out of position when twisted – clockwise and counter clockwise (similar to a UK light bulb fitting)

Note: *To remove a thermistor (or thermostat) from a grommet fixing carefully insert a small flat bladed screwdriver and ease it free. Do not attempt to remove the grommet with the thermistor (or thermostat) still in position*

thermistors can be found on machines with mechanical timers/programmers and the way in which they work in this instance is as follows. The resistance of the thermistor forms part of a temperature control circuit by means of a separate module solely for this purpose. A theoretical operation of such a system follows.

In this instance the output voltages at D & C are used to control a triac (an electrical component within the circuit). The triac in turn switches the thermostop coil on a mechanical timer or impulse to the control panel of a computer control machine.

Being an electronic circuit in either mechanical or computer controlled machines, the operating voltage within this portion of circuit will be low (5V DC). Therefore, any electrical testing of the thermistor must be with a low voltage test meter as voltages of over 5V will damage the thermistor or module circuitry.

The two resistors Ra and Rb are of the same value. A 5V DC voltage supplied to point A will take one of two routes depending on the resistance opposing it, i.e. A.C.B. or A.D.B. Route A.C.D. has within it four resistors each of which can be switched in and out of the circuit in relation to the programme selected and temperature required for that wash cycle. The diode at point E eliminates reverse supply to the triac. The route A.D.C. contains the thermistor in its second leg D.B. If we assume that the water within the machine is cold, then the thermistor resistance will be high. This will

allow a current flow from D. to C. thus energising a thermostop or holding the programme on the heat cycle until the predetermined temperature (governed by the switchable resistors) is attained. Releasing of the thermostop or impulse of the programme is as follows. As the water temperature increases, the resistance of the thermistor decreases (N.T.C.). At some point the

resistance in both sides of the circuit will be equal and at this point, no current will flow between D. & C. and the triac will switch off. This in turn will release the thermostop on mechanical timers or allow impulse to the next stage of the programme on electronically controlled machines. Variations in temperature are gained by switching in or out the required resistors in the C.B. leg of the circuit, thus altering the point at which equilibrium is reached within the circuit. All switches open = all resistors in circuit RC + RD + RE + RF would result in high resistance, therefore a cooler wash of say 30ºC is achieved. Quick wash switch closed = resistor RF bypassed, i.e. lower total resistance gives wash of say 40ºC. Switch 1 closed = two resistors in circuit RC & RE may relate to 50ºC with option of quick wash switch to further reduce temperature (and time) if required by user. Switch 2 closed – three resistors RC, RD, RF in circuit may relate to 80ºC with option of quick wash switch to further reduce temperature (and time) if required by user. All switches closed = this will leave only RC in circuit at this point, and a high temperature of say 90ºC would be achieved, again with option if required. **Note:** *The temperatures shown are used to illustrate the operation of this type of circuit and do not relate to any specific make or model of dishwasher.*

Note: *The option to alter the temperature selected by the set programme, i.e. by pressing a quick wash or short wash option button on the control panel, may be bypassed itself by the timer on some programmes. This means that although in the theoretical operation detailed above, each setting could be further affected by the quick wash switch, in reality, this may not be the case as a quick wash may not be suitable for certain types of wash loads.*

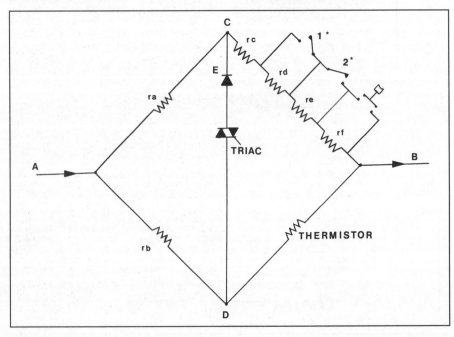

Chapter 26
The steam vent

The steam vent can be part of the more complex moulding of combined pressure system, float system, water inlet and air break or a much smaller unit for steam venting only (see chapter *Water level control* for further details). Whether combined or separate the function of the unit is the same. Water heated during the wash and final heated rinse naturally forms water vapour (steam). If this were allowed to simply vent in to the kitchen, it would condense on other surfaces and be most unwelcome. To alleviate this problem, the steam vent unit simply condenses the water vapour and returns it to the sump to be pumped away during the empty cycle.

The unit is usually mounted on the side of the load compartment between the inner and outer cover. Only the small inlet (A) is visible. This leads directly into compartment (B) which is much larger and it is this larger area that condenses most of the steam back into water to be drained by outlet (C).

In this picture the extra position (D) is in fact the water inlet to the load compartment from the softener unit. Many machines combine inlet and steam vent to cut down on entry points into the load area.

In most cases, it is necessary to remove the side panel to gain access to the main body of the unit. As with all repairs, isolate the machine prior to any repair or adjustment: plug out and taps off.

Problems with vent systems are usually rare and are mainly caused by blockages or cracking of the moulded unit. When the steam vent is combined with inlet or other systems, ensure all hoses are noted prior to removal and refit all hoses, clips and seals securely.

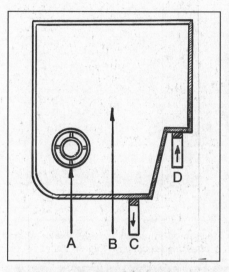

A small steam condenser vent unit

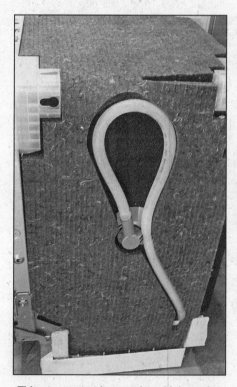

This steam vent has a tube which carries the moisture-laden air to a large plastic matrix on the opposite side of the appliance

The steam vent tube enters the large plastic matrix at point A. The matrix holds cold water for both tank metering filling of the load compartment and the regeneration sequence. When the moisture-laden air meets the cold surfaces within the matrix condensation occurs effectively drying the air prior to it being vented from the top of the matrix at point B

Chapter 27
Detergent and rinse aid dispensers

Detergent and rinse aid dispensers can be found in many different shapes, sizes and configurations. They can be individual or combined into one large rectangular unit. Whether they are individual or combined the following information can be used to identify and correct faults that may occur.

Detergent dispensers

For dishwashers to work correctly the detergent (in liquid, powder or tablet form) must be added at the correct point of the wash programme. If it is added too early it will be flushed away on the pre-rinse, too late and it will not have sufficient time to act on the wash load.

The way in which the detergent is added to the wash water (dispensed) is by means of a

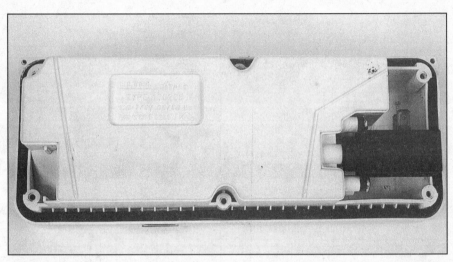

Most modern machines now use combined detergent and rinse aid dispensers like this one. Unfortunately a fault in either section will normally require a complete new part

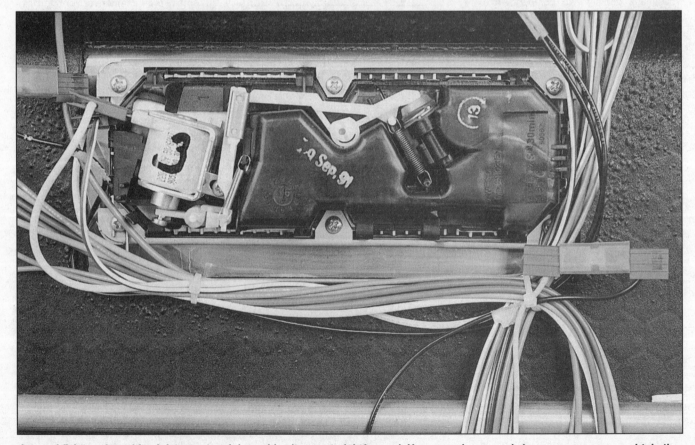

Internal fixings of combined detergent and rinse aid units are straightforward. However, shapes and sizes vary, ensure you obtain the correct one for your machine

container with a latching lid or cover which can be opened at a predetermined point in the wash cycle, the contents of which will be flushed out by the spray action. This achieves a quick and thorough mixing of the detergent and water at the correct point in time of the wash programme.

Three versions of dispensers are commonly found – the simplest being a small drawer type container in which the detergent is placed and flushed into the load compartment during filling for main wash. The other two versions each have a spring loaded cover or slide that is manually latched shut by the user and unlatched by the machine by means of:

a) A purely mechanical operation linked directly to the timer cam. At a set point in the programme the cam pushes a connecting arm and unlatches the dispenser cover (this type of system often controls rinse aid dispensing in the same way but at a different point in the programme).

b) Electro-mechanical operation of the dispenser cover. Three variations of electrically-operated dispensers can be found:

1 A small heater wound around a bimetal strip. When energised, the bending of the bimetal strip unlatches the dispenser cover.

2 A solenoid and magnet latch system. When closed a permanent magnet holds the cover in position, when power is supplied to the solenoid coil, the magnetism induced in the coil cancels the permanent magnet's field therefore it can no longer hold the latch in position and the dispenser cover opens.

3 A solenoid coil that electro-mechanically

unlatches the dispenser cover when the solenoid is energised. This particular type of system is the most popular version currently in use.

All are one shot devices and require the lid/cover to be re-latched by the user after they have refilled the detergent container ready for the next wash cycle.

Care must be taken with all dispensers as they are easily jammed or strained. When loading with detergent powder or tablet, try to keep the load central to avoid straining or fouling the catch or slide. Avoid problems associated with clogging by only filling the

detergent dispenser immediately before starting the wash programme and keep all stored detergent dry and safely away from children.

The most common problems with detergent dispensers are sticking shut or breaking of the cover (especially on flap dispensers). Some manufacturers will supply new covers, but other faults such as open circuit of coils or heaters will require the renewal of the whole unit. This is a relatively simple task, which necessitates the removal of the outer door cover, which will give access to the dispenser unit and its fixing screws. As

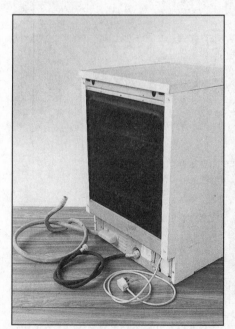

As always, before any repair completely isolate the machine

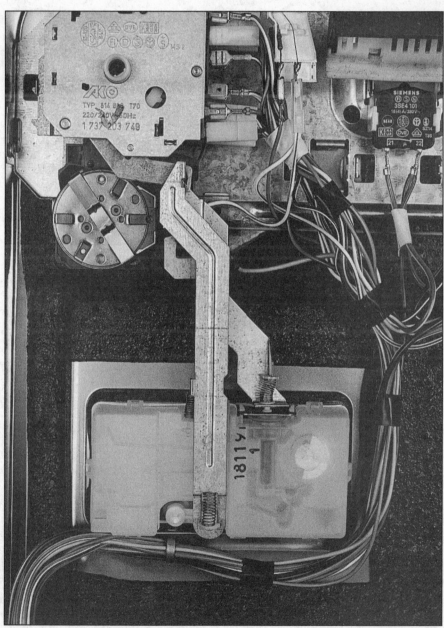

These dispenser and rinse aid systems are operated by a series of mechanical links connected to the timer cams. Ensure you make a note of the position of all the parts prior to removal or stripdown as the correct settings on these types of system are critical

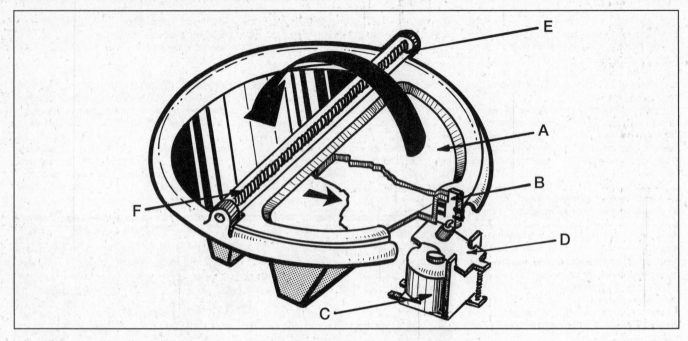

Electro-mechanical dispenser

with any repair or service isolate the machine completely before starting.

Machines with mechanically linked timer and dispenser will need to be reset if either the timer has been removed or incorrect dispensing is suspected. Most work on a tappet type action. Correct operation depends on a tappet clearance of between 1 and 2mm, usually attained by an adjusting screw. This operation can be checked by turning the timer manually and observing the movement of the mechanism at the correct part of the cam cycle. As before, all adjustments and work should be

done with the machine completely isolated – not just switched off but with plug pulled out!

The illustration shows one of the many variations of powder dispensers used in dishwashers. This is a latch operated unit. The dispenser is filled with the correct amount of detergent and cover (A) is closed and held in

position by latch (B). At the correct point of the programme, solenoid (C) is energised and in this instance attracts plate (D) by electromagnetism. This movement is transferred to latch (B) and releases the latch. Return spring (E) and hinge (F) flips cover (A) open and exposes the detergent to the wash water to be dispersed by the wash action.

This early circular dispenser is similar to the diagram but has a sliding compartment cover and latching is by a magnet. When the solenoid is energised, the permanent magnet latch is cancelled out and the return spring slides the compartment open

This early Candy dispenser was one of the most simple. At the correct part of the cycle, water is flushed through the unit, effectively mixing and dispensing the powder or liquid. It dispenses liquid detergent as easily as powders. With no moving parts this unit is easy to maintain. The removable drawer also acts as the measuring cup for detergent usage. More modern Candy machines now use the combined detergent and rinse aid unit which is housed in the door

Typical complete rinse aid dispenser

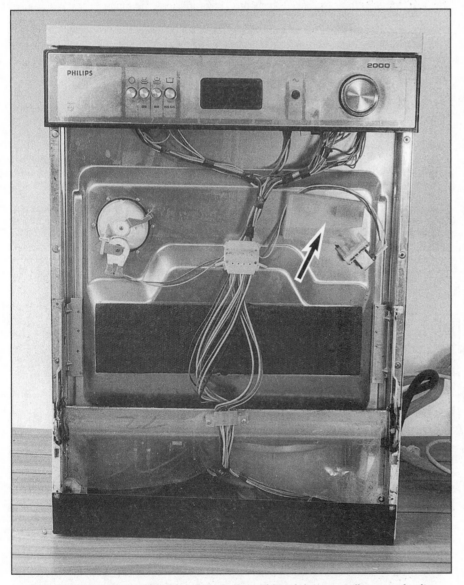

Early inner door assembly with separate rinse aid and detergent dispenser in situ

Rinse aid dispensers

What is rinse aid?

Rinse aid is essential for the final rinse cycle of all dishwashers. It comes in a concentrated liquid form. Most dishwashers have a reservoir to hold approximately 140cc of the liquid and at the correct stage in the rinse cycle, it will dispense a pre-determined amount. Rinse aid in this concentrated form is very powerful and care should be exercised when filling the rinse aid reservoir. Avoid contact with skin or eyes, also general spillages. However, in the event of accidental splashing or spilling, flush the area with water, but if the liquid has been swallowed, seek medical advice immediately. Remember: Keep all detergents and chemicals out of the reach of children.

Normally, only a small amount of rinse aid is required as it is highly diluted as described.

Why use it?

Rinse aid is used in the final rinse to reduce spot marks and streaking when the water evaporates during drying. The drying process is helped greatly by rinse aid leaving the well washed crockery, pots and pans with a clean sparkle.

How does it work?

When mixed with a very large quantity of water the 1 to 5cc of concentrate rinse aid reduces the surface tension of the water to stop droplets forming on the wash load. The warm load will then dry more easily as most of the water will have run off the load's surfaces.

The reduction in water surface tension works in a similar way to normal hand washing. Detergent and rinse aid also look very similar, but under no circumstances must the two be confused. Rinse aid is a very concentrated liquid and formulated to be anti-foaming. To use an ordinary liquid detergent would cause foaming and flooding.

If the rinse aid compartment or valve fails and allows excess rinse aid into the machine or weeps rinse aid into the wash cycle, over foaming will occur. Look for the tell tale runs from the discharge point and ensure that the cap is refitted correctly and securely after each fill. Once filled, the rinse aid compartment will not require filling again for sometime and does not need topping up for every wash. If continuous filling proves necessary, the unit should then be checked.

Most rinse aid compartments have a means of indicating when topping up is necessary. Some machines have an indicator on the front of the control panel. This is usually a simple neon light which may be activated in one of two ways.

1 The timer after a given number of washes.

2 A reed relay and floating magnet system (see: *Internal water softeners* for further details) may be employed to switch the neon ON when the level of rinse aid drops.

However, the most common system is a simple visual system and again there are two versions:

a) A simple extension of the filler cap which acts like a car dip-stick. Simply unscrewing the filler cap and checking if the probe is in contact with the liquid will indicate if topping up is required.

b) A sight glass that changes colour as the level of rinse aid drops. The indicator can be a separate sight glass or again, part of the filler cap.

As a guide, a 140cc reservoir with an adjustable rinse aid setting will disperse between 1 and 5cc per cycle. This will give around 28 rinses at the highest setting and 140 rinses at the lowest setting. Adjustment will be required to individual machines, corresponding to the varying wash conditions. Too much rinse aid can be as bad as too little. Read the chapter on *Common causes of poor washing results* to assist in the correct setting.

The rinse aid dispenser unit

The rinse aid dispenser has two basic styles. One has a combined filler cap/cover and discharge point for the rinse aid dose. More

FULL   TOPPING UP REQUIRED   EMPTY

commonly found is the version where the filler cap/lid and discharge point are separate. The latter having a meshed cover to allow the rinse aid liquid through. The tank or reservoir is made of plastic and may vary in shape and style.

There are two ways in which the rinse aid may be discharged

a) A purely mechanical operation linked directly to the timer cam. At a set point in the programme the cam pushes a connecting arm that actuates the dispensing chamber (this type of system often controls detergent dispensing in the same way but at a different point in the programme).

b) Electro-mechanical operation of the dispensing chamber. Two variations of electrically-operated dispensers can be found:

   1 A small heater wound around a bimetal strip. When energised, the bending of the bimetal strip actuates the dispensing mechanism.

   2 A solenoid coil that electro-mechanically actuates the dispensing mechanism (once) when the solenoid is energised. This particular type of system is the most popular version currently in use.

Some very early dishwashers are not fitted with automatic rinse aid dispensers and you have to add the rinse aid by hand on the last rinse, (approximately a half teaspoonful).

Where is the rinse aid unit found?

Most machines have the reservoir mounted between the inner and outer skins of the door, and only the fill and discharge points are visible on the inner surface of the door.

Some compact or work-top machines will have the reservoir mounted inside the load compartment as the door is single skin and therefore unable to house the unit.

How does it work?

The following sequence details the operation of a separate rinse aid unit. The information is also applicable to the combined detergent and rinse aid versions as only the volume of the reservoir is different.

Within the refillable reservoir of fixed volume (E), a smaller and adjustable chamber can be seen (B). Adjustment (G) to this chamber varies from type to type (F) i.e. manufacturers may fit more than one make to their range of machines. Sizes and fittings are generally standard although slight variations of dispenser may be found.

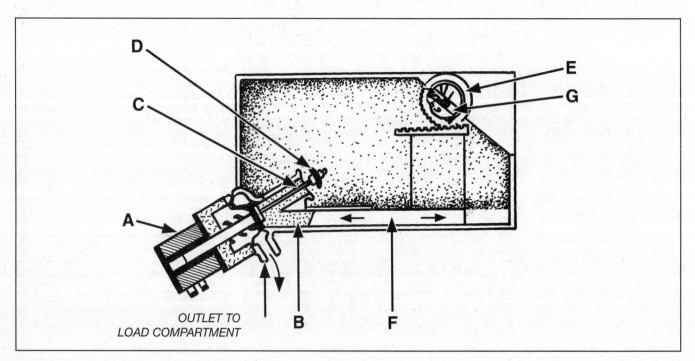

OUTLET TO LOAD COMPARTMENT

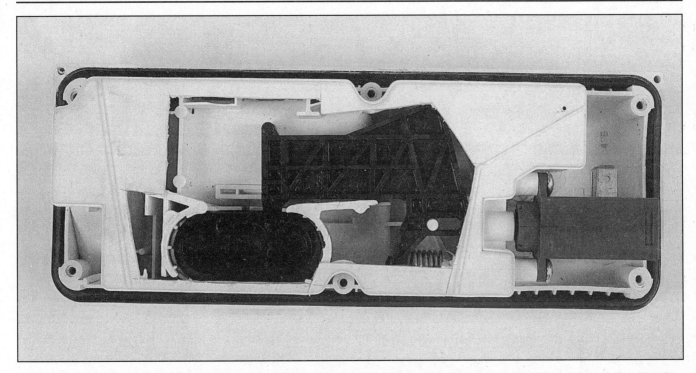

This combined rinse aid and detergent dispenser with the outer casing cut away has only one solenoid to operate both functions by means of a clever latch mechanism (shown for illustration purposes only)

Connected to the main body, linking both reservoir and chamber is a solenoid (A). This solenoid is similar to that used on water valves. When energised, the solenoid will discharge the contents of the variable chamber (B) by gravity only. When de-energised, the discharge section of the valve (C) closes and the fill valve (D) opens to refill the variable chamber in readiness for the next programme. **Note:** *Only one operation per wash cycle takes place and other means of actuating the discharge mechanism may be employed.*

Problems with rinse aid units

a) A leaking tank, caused by a split can sometimes be sealed, otherwise fit a new unit. **Note:** *The tank/reservoir has to have an air bleed hole on top to allow air in and out when filling and discharging. Do not block or obstruct this small hole in the tank.*

b) A fault with the solenoid coil or actuating mechanism will give similar symptoms to that of a faulty fill valve and can give rise to too much or too little rinse aid being dispensed.

c) Valve unit may stick or wear. Such faults may simply require strip down and cleaning.

d) Most faults with the unit will require a full renewal as most manufacturers supply complete units only, no matter what the fault. Strip the unit and clean before opting for renewal. Also test the solenoid as described in *Electrical circuit testing*. With a little care, it may be possible to repair the unit instead of replacing it.

Rinse aid repair

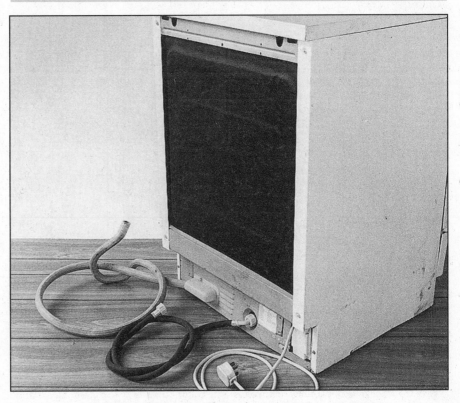

Isolate the machine from the power supply before any repair

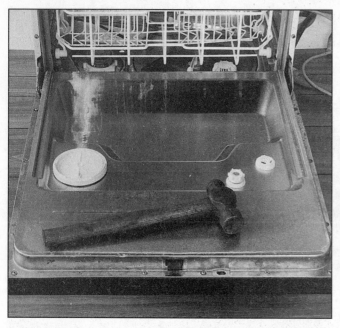

Place a weight on the door inner to hold it in the open position

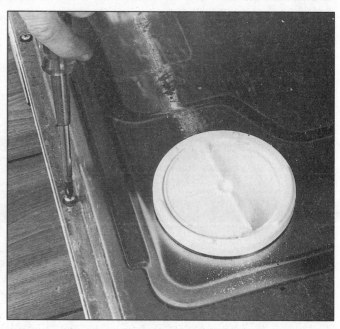

With door lowered and counterweighted remove the outer cover fixing screws

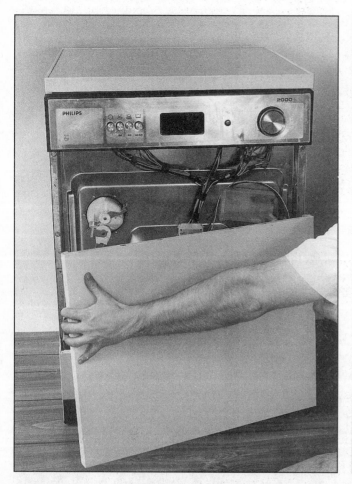

With the door raised, carefully remove the outer door cover to expose the inner section

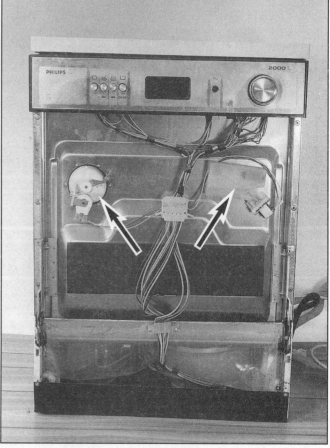

Both rinse aid and detergent dispenser are now clearly visible on this early machine

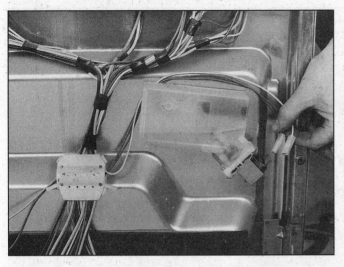

Note and remove the wires to the rinse aid compartment

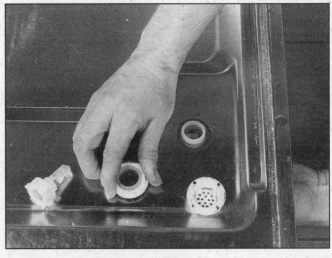

Support the rinse aid container and carefully unscrew the plastic securing collars. Take note of any seals

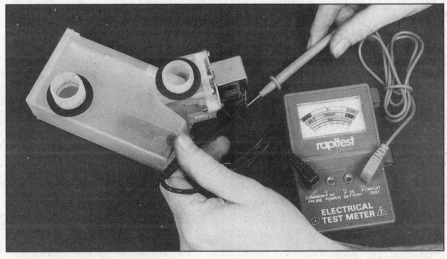

In this instance a blockage was suspected as the solenoid coil checked out OK

With the container removed from the door, drain any remaining liquid into a suitable container. (Avoid direct contact of the concentrated liquid with skin and eyes)

Mark the position of the solenoid and screws prior to removal

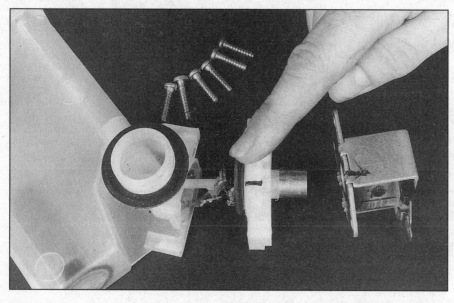

Carefully ease the valve system apart. Lay the parts out in order and clean thoroughly.
(Note the large blockage on this valve rubber)

Flush tank thoroughly and clean all the
chamber carefully

Clean valve slide thoroughly to remove
solidified rinse aid and particles of dirt,
etc. Usage of a good quality rinse aid
would reduce these faults from occurring.
Refitting of the rinse aid compartment
was a simple reversal of the stripdown
procedure. Take care to refit all the seals
and not to overtighten the plastic
securing collars

The method of actuating this rinse aid
container was by the use of a solenoid valve
similar to a water fill valve. An alternative to
the solenoid system may be found such as a
bimetal strip with a heater coil wrapped
around it. When power is supplied to it the
coil heats and the bimetal strip bends. This
movement is directly linked to a plunger
within the body of the container that
dispenses one measured shot of rinse aid
liquid per operation.

Faults with this system are identical to the
solenoid type. Open circuit element results in
no valve operation as would a blockage as
shown in the photo sequence.

The wiring and fixing remain identical. Both
versions are generally interchangeable.

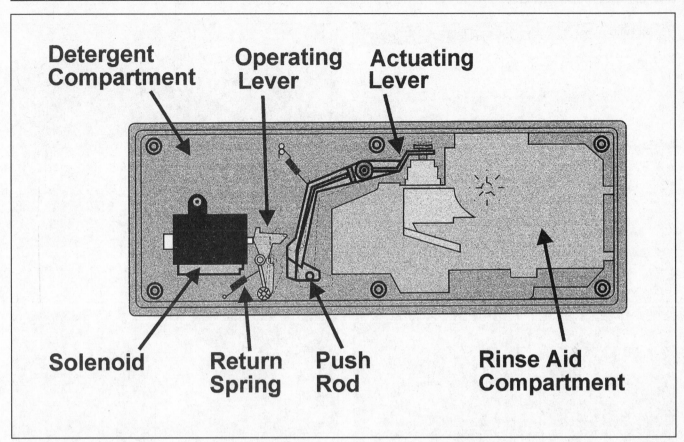

Detergent Compartment

Operating Lever

Actuating Lever

Solenoid

Return Spring

Push Rod

Rinse Aid Compartment

This style of detergent dispenser uses only one solenoid to operate the detergent dispenser latch and rinse aid dispensing chamber. Operation of the unit is as follows: When the solenoid is energised for the first time the operating lever passes behind the actuating lever unlatching the detergent cover and the lower push rod. Unlatching the push rod allows the actuating lever to drop back slightly. When the solenoid is energised for the second time (end of the rinse sequence) the operating lever pushes directly on to the actuating lever and a single shot of rinse aid is dispensed. At the end of this second sequence the push rod resets the mechanism ready for the next cycle

Counterweight the door prior to removing the front panel. This prevents the door closing when the panel is removed

Remove the lower outer fixing screws only

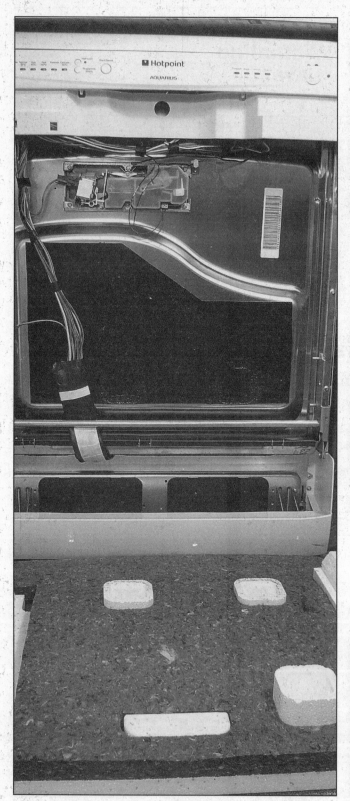

Pressing a small plastic tag on this wiring connector allowed it to be carefully eased from its position

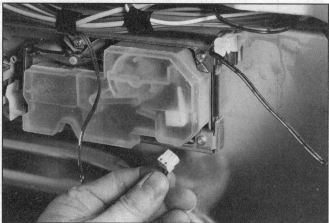

As this dispenser unit had a rinse aid level detector (small internal magnetic float and external reed switch) a small printed circuit board edge connector was carefully removed
Note: *Do not pull on the wires of wiring connections to remove them. Ensure you grip the connector and carefully ease them free*

Carefully removing the front panel, foam support and sound insulation material in this instance (on the floor in the foreground) provides excellent access to the dispenser and its fixings
Note: *Ensure that protective gloves are worn when removing and*

With the wiring connections removed the retaining screws can then be removed

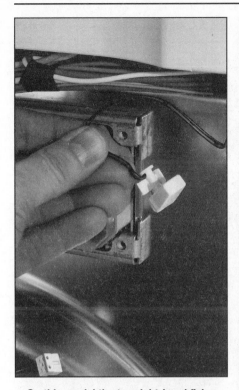

On this model the top right-hand fixing screw has a small bracket which holds a thermistor in contact with the door inner lining. Refer to Chapter *Thermostats and thermistors* for further details

Removing the three lower fixing screws released the lower fixing bracket. Removing the two remaining top screws and bracket releases the dispenser unit

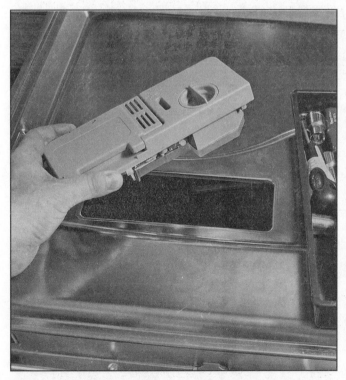

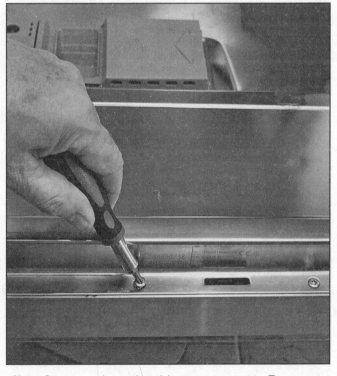

When all internal door fixing are removed, the dispenser unit can be eased out of its position from the outer surface of the door

Note: *On some makes and models you may encounter Torx screws like the ones shown here*

Chapter 28
Pumps

Dishwashers in general have two pumps, one large pump called the circulation pump which is used during the wash process to continuously circulate the wash/rinse water and create pressure to drive the spray arms.

The second pump is smaller and less powerful. Its function is to discharge the water from the machine at the end of each wash or rinse cycle.

In some machines however, only one large pump motor may be found which is used for both the circulation and the discharge of water. There are two ways in which both wash and draining with one motor can be achieved.

a) With the aid of a specially designed impeller, pump chamber and reversible induction motor both wash circulation or emptying can be selected from the same unit. When running in one direction the pump will circulate the wash water through the spray arm system. However, reversing the main circulation motor will create a lower force discharge (pumping action) therefore eliminating the need for a separate outlet pump. **Note:** *Most motors with this dual function are mounted vertically in the sump moulding. This unfortunately allows water to run into the motor windings when the shaft seal begins to fail.*

b) An electro-magnetically operated valve system can be used to eliminate the need for two pumps or for the circulation motor to reverse. When emptying is required, the circulation motor runs as normal, but a valve positioned on the outlet of the pump chamber opens and allows a bypass to the normal spray arm feed, and the water will then discharge. **Note:** *Specific problems associated with this system are failure of the drain valve in either the open or closed position, and blockages due to potential restriction of the water flow at that point.*

Circulation pumps in greater detail

The main circulation pump is easily recognised by being much larger than the drain pump motor. It can be a single-phase asynchronous induction motor or large permanent magnet motor which is similar in construction and operation to its smaller counterpart used to drain appliances. The pump chamber may be bolted directly on to the motor front-end frame with the rotor shaft through its centre or is an integral part of the sump moulding. On the back plate of the pump chamber, the rotor shaft passes through a rubber shaft seal, which is combined with a spring-loaded carbon, or ceramic face seal. A corresponding counter face seal is secured on the impeller to produce a watertight rotating seal. The impeller may be fixed permanently or internally threaded and directly screwed onto the rotor shaft. Alternatively a stainless steel bolt (usually left-hand thread) or plastic domed nut may secure it to the motor shaft.

Induction motor pumps

Currently the most popular type of motor used in today's dishwashing machine is the induction motor, which is used because of its quietness and general reliability. However the permanent magnet (PM pump) is becoming increasingly popular with dishwasher manufacturers.

The induction motors in use fall into three categories:

1 Asynchronous induction used for the main motor.
2 Shaded pole induction used for the outlet pump.
3 Permanent magnet pumps often referred to as synchronous. Most people seem to understand a little about universal motors (motors that require a wound armature and brush gear, etc.), but very little about induction motors of any type.

The asynchronous induction motor is in fact quite simple and uses the absolute basic principles of electricity. Its apparent complexity stems from the need to use extra windings to control its speed. Although modern electronics have allowed for variable control, we are dealing here with the basics of asynchronous induction motors and those

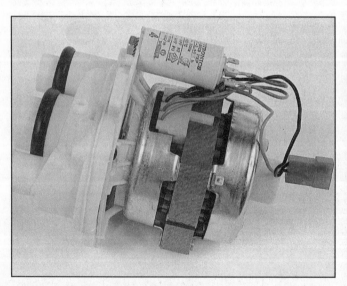

Main circulation pump motor. Typical asynchronous induction motor. Styles may vary along with size and water outlet points

Internal view of a main circulation pump chamber. Shown is the main shaft seal and ceramic face of the seal on the impeller

used without module control as only simple single speed induction motors are used in dishwashers.

Single phase induction motors consist of two main items – an outer wound coil called a stator (see diagram 1 and 1A) and a rotatable core (called the rotor) made of high grade cast aluminium with internal metal laminations which are slightly skewed to aid torque for starting purposes (see diagram 2). The rotor is isolated from the windings and receives no power at all.

The most simple stator would consist of two sets of windings 180° to one another (see diagram 1). Two windings are needed to induce the rotor to turn by their magnetic fields when power is applied. One coil would not induce movement, though if the rotor were started by mechanical means, it would continue to turn as long as power was being supplied to the stator coil. In reality, the motion/starting is induced by placing one set of the windings 90° out of phase with the other. This can be with the use of a relay, but more usually by the use of a capacitor, the rating of which is matched to the windings. The rating is given in microfarads (µF) on its casing. Being out of phase due to the delay caused by the capacitor/relay, a rotating magnetic field is created causing the rotor to turn up to speed at which point the start windings, as they are known, could be switched out if required. Reversal of the motor is quite simply a reversal of current flow through the start winding or the run winding, but not both.

When a motor, supplied with 240V at 50Hz. (i.e. mains voltage), a 2 pole motor mimics the phase cycle and rotates at 50 revolutions per second – i.e. 50 x 60 secs = 3000rpm, 4 poles 1500rpm, 8 poles 750rpm, 16 poles 375rpm, variable speeds resulting in complex stator windings and expensive motors. Ensure that faults with motors are checked and rectified promptly. A loose motor block connection may allow power to one winding only and cause overheating and failure of the whole motor. A faulty capacitor or a malfunction of the programme switches or internal TOC (thermal overload cut-out) of the motor can also have the same result.

Main drawbacks of induction motors

a) As all of the work is done by a complicated set of windings in the stator, this motor is generally not repairable and must be changed for a new unit.
b) Capacitor failure often results in the motor failing to run. This often results in burn-out as the rest of the motor windings are receiving power and therefore rotation is not possible. Overheat is inevitable, even when TOC protected.

Main benefits of induction motors (capacitor/relay start)

a) Generally reliable.
b) Quiet.
c) Can be made to run in both directions.

Warning: *When checking for faults, the machine must always be isolated from the mains supply. Turn off at the wall socket and remove the plug. THE CAPACITOR(S) MAY STILL CONTAIN A CHARGE ALTHOUGH THE MAINS HAS BEEN ISOLATED. THIS MUST BE DISCHARGED BY USING AN ELECTRICALLY INSULATED SCREWDRIVER.*

Using this, 'short' the terminals of the capacitor with the shaft of the screwdriver ensuring that you are only in contact with the insulated handle. IT IS NOT SAFE TO PROCEED FURTHER UNTIL THIS HAS BEEN DONE. If the stator windings of an induction motor are faulty, it may continue to run, although appearing sluggish and getting extremely hot even when used for a short time. Therefore if you have been running the machine to determine the fault, proceed with care as the motor will remain hot for some time. If the motor appears to be very hot, the motor winding may be faulty and the unit should be replaced.

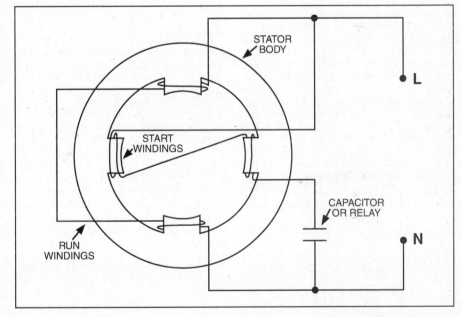

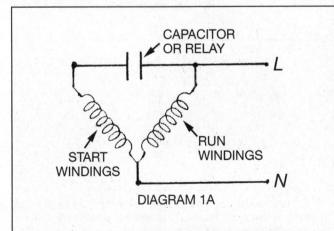

DIAGRAM 1A

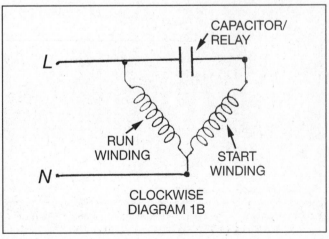

CLOCKWISE
DIAGRAM 1B

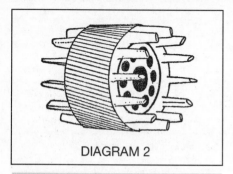

DIAGRAM 2

The capacitor

What is it?

The capacitor in a dishwasher is a unit that enables the asynchronous circulation pump motor to be started.

What does it look like?

Capacitors used in AC machines can have either metal or plastic outer casings with an insulated top with two terminals.

How does it work?

What follows is a simplified version of what happens within a capacitor in an AC circuit.

The two terminals of the capacitor are in fact completely insulated from one another.

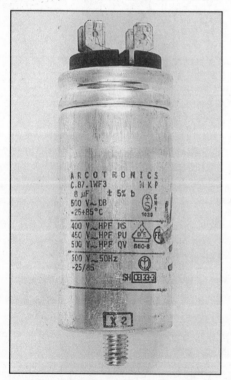

Typical capacitor for use with induction motors. Do not confuse capacitors with suppression units. They may look similar, but their functions differ

Internally they are connected to two sheets of metal foil and between this foil is an insulator. This package of large surface area is rolled into a tube formation, which fits into the shell of the capacitor. If the two terminals and their connected sheets of foil are insulated from one another, you may ask how do they pass a current when in use? The answer is that as the voltage supplied to one terminal is in fact alternating, (i.e. at 50 times per second 50 Hz), therefore so is the polarity of its connected foil. An opposite movement of electrons is produced in the other foil even though they are insulated electrically. This effect causes a delay in the electrical path at this point, and this, in the case of an asynchronous induction motor gives the out of phase feed to the start winding.

The storage capacity of a capacitor is measured in microfarads (µF) and is displayed on the shell. Any replacement must be of the same µF rating.

The relay

What is it?

A relay is an electro-mechanical device used in this particular instance for induction motor starting in place of a capacitor.

What does it look like?

The most common relay consists of a plastic moulding with three terminal tags – two at the top and one at its base. On the centre section is a wire wound coil.

How does it work?

The main aim of the relay in the context of asynchronous induction motors is to cause a delay in the start winding supply, similar to the capacitor. The main difference is that the relay achieves this operation mechanically. The wound coil section is connected in series with the run winding. When power is supplied to the motor, the current to the run winding

passes through the coil and on to the motor run winding. This current induces a magnetic force in the coil which in turn attracts the metal core of the relay. The metal core is linked to an internal contact switch and when 'made', allows current to pass to the start winding (see top diagram p.105). This operation gives the required delay to induce starting of the induction motor.

When power is switched off, gravity resets the relay core. It is, therefore essential that the relay be in its correct position and the machine upright for this item to function correctly. **Note:** *To avoid the start winding being in circuit after rotation has been achieved and effectively slowing the motor, relays are normally designed to operate only under the initial starting surge and drop out of circuit when the motor runs up to speed. Like capacitors relays are matched to the motor they are connected to, ensure only the correct replacement is used.*

Faults to watch for are: open circuit of the coil, metal core sticking (in either position), and contact points failing. Renew any suspect relay immediately as the failure of this item can lead to motor failure as with the capacitor.

If you have to renew a damaged stator coil or motor and it is relay started, it is wise to change the relay at the same time as it may (a) have caused the original motor fault or (b) have been subsequently damaged by the motor failure.

Induction motors with variable flow rate washing and rinsing

Variable flow rate is a feature of some electronically controlled dishwashers which allows the flow rate of the water being circulated through the spray arms to be varied. Dishwashers that have this feature use asynchronous induction motors similar to those used in a standard dishwasher. However, although the basic structure of the motor is identical in having a rotor surrounded by the start and run windings of the stator

A relay may be placed in circuit to cause the phase displacement necessary to start the induction motor. This is a mechanical delay as described and it is essential that the relay is upright when energised

these motors have an additional component called a tacho generator. The tacho generator and the motor's winding are connected to the main control circuit board and this combination allows the speed of the motor to be varied according to what the selected programme requires.

How does it work?

A circular magnet is fixed to the rear on the main circulation induction motors rotor and revolves in unison with it. Encircling the magnet but not in contact with it is a coil of wire (this may be encased in plastic), which is called a tacho generator.

Whenever a magnet is rotated next to or inside a coil of wire a voltage/frequency is produced which is proportional to the rotational speed of the magnet. Therefore, the faster the motor is running the more voltage is produced or the higher the frequency. This voltage/frequency is fed to the motor speed control circuitry as a reference voltage/frequency and is used to monitor the speed of the motor by comparing the relative speed of the motor with a known voltage/frequency via a comparator circuit.

If the reference voltage/frequency is found to be lower than the comparator, the module will increase the pulse rate, therefore increasing the speed of the motor. If the voltage/frequency is found to be high, the pulses are slowed, therefore decreasing the motor's speed and vice versa. This monitoring and adjustment happens many times a second, and is undetectable.

The rotating magnet of the tacho unit produces an alternating voltage and frequency both of which are proportional to the speed of rotation. The speed control can therefore be designed to respond to either the voltage or the frequency produced.

The speed control circuitry reacts to information from both the programme input and the motor. If for example the programme selected requires a more gentle wash or rinse pressure the circulation pump motor will be supplied with less voltage via the speed control circuit by selecting the appropriate resistor circuit. In the simple example shown in the diagram there are two resistors, therefore three speeds can be achieved, i.e., no resistors, one resistor, both resistors. Dishwashers that have the ability to reduce flow rate in this way usually have three flow rates.

Checking a tacho magnet and tacho coil

a) If the magnet is loose or broken, this would result in incorrect speeds.
b) Severe damage or complete loss of the magnet would cause the motor to run at full speed on all positions.
c) A break in the coil or wiring to and from the main circuit board would result in the motor running at full speed even if a low speed were required. This is because a 'good' coil is

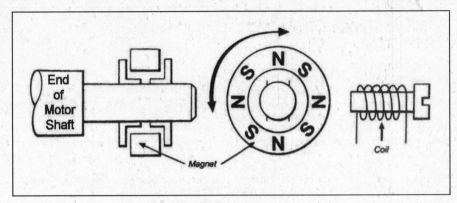

Tacho generator

usually about 200 to 1600 ohms resistance and a break in the coil would result in an infinity resistance. Quite simply such a fault would result in the tacho generator not returning any voltage or frequency to the speed control circuitry and therefore the circuitry would increase voltage to the motor. However, the increased speed would not be transmitted back to the control circuitry, so the process is repeated ad infinitum. **Note:** *The motor control circuit on most if not all appliances have in-built tacho circuit tests to prevent such an occurrence.*

If a motor of this type runs but only at one speed (does not vary when required to do so) and checking the tacho coil and wiring to and from the main circuit board prove to be OK then it is likely that the fault lies within the

main control circuitry. This can only be rectified with a new unit, ensuring that the correct type is purchased. To fit, make a note of the connections, remove them and replace them on the new unit. It is important that the multi-block edge connectors fit tightly on their connection points. If found to be loose connections directly to the printed circuit board edges can be closed slightly by inserting a small screwdriver between the back of the tag and the plastic housing. Care should be taken not to close it too far as this may result in the tag not making contact by being pushed back into the connector.

As with all inspection and repair the appliance must be isolated from the mains. Turn off at the wall socket and remove the plug.

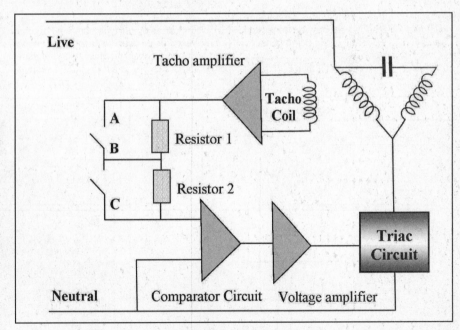

Low speed: A-B and B-C closed therefore bypassing both resistors, resulting in a low flow rate
Medium speed: A-B open, B-C closed therefore one resistor in circuit, resulting in an intermediate flow rate
Full speed: A-B and B-C open therefore both resistors are in circuit, resulting in a high flow rate which is equal to basic dishwashers without speed control options

The shaded pole induction motor

The shaded pole motor is the most simple of all induction motors and is similar in basic format of rotor and stator (see bottom diagram opposite). However, only one stator coil is used to create the magnetic field. Obviously this alone would not induce rotation of the rotor, only a constant magnetic field. To start rotation, an imbalance in the magnetic field is required. Copper band inserts at the pole ends of the stator laminations are used for this purpose. The copper bands within the mild steel stator laminations distort the magnetic field in a given direction, therefore inducing rotation in the stator. Reversing the supply to such motors does not effect any change in motor direction as this is governed by the direction of the fixed shaded poles. These motors do not have a high starting torque and because of the magnetic imbalance being fixed, heating of the stator occurs if run for long periods even if a cooling fan is fitted. However, under normal conditions heating creates few problems and to avoid overheating when faults occur most stator coils are protected by TOCs for safety.

Main drawbacks of induction motors (shaded pole)

a) Can be used in one direction only. This is governed by the positioning of the pole bands.
b) Due to the permanent imbalance described, excessive heat may be generated if used for long periods or the pump jams.
c) Low starting power.
d) If subjected to overheating for long periods, the motor will eventually fail – even if TOC protected.
e) Generally NOT repairable.

Main benefits of induction motors (shaded pole)

a) Very cheap.
b) Very reliable.
c) Very quiet.

Note: *TOC = thermal overload cutout. If the safe working temperature is exceeded, this device will sever the power supply through the motor. Most TOCs are now self resetting, resulting in constant heating up and cooling down of the motor. If the fault is not spotted quickly, the TOC itself will fail, therefore causing motor failure or more serious problems.*

Permanent magnet (synchronous) drain pumps

Smaller versions of this type of motor have for many years been used to power the timing and advance mechanism of washing machine programmers/timers. However, larger versions are now used to drive the outlet pump. It is the most simple of electric motors, quiet to run and cheap to produce. It also avoids some of the more common pump problems, especially the common shaft seal leak of the shaded pole pumps. Consisting only of a wound circular coil fixed around a permanent magnet rotor and supported at both ends by simple sleeve bearings, this motor can be made extremely small and at a low cost. As with all induction motors, its simplicity of construction limits it for use to AC supply only. The PM rotor is housed within a sealed plastic chamber, but is still free to rotate by the alternating current (AC) supplied to two externally mounted stator poles. The rotor drives the impeller of the pump in the normal way, only the motor of the pump differs.

A circular multi-pole permanent magnet forms the rotor of the motor and two series wound coils are attached to a laminated steel stator. Simply supplying AC power to the coils induces rotation of the magnetic rotor. However, rotation can start in either direction. This ability to run in both directions is utilised to its full extent when this style of motor is used to drive an outlet pump impeller. Should the impeller of the pump come into contact with an item that would normally jam/stall a

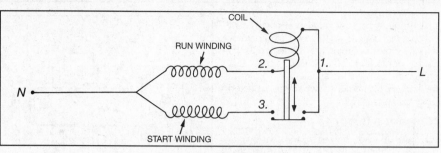

Relay operation

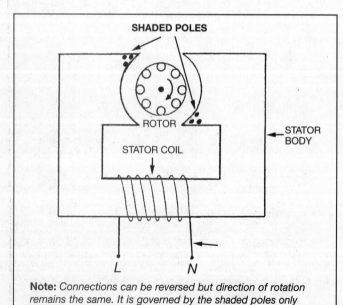

Note: *Connections can be reversed but direction of rotation remains the same. It is governed by the shaded poles only*

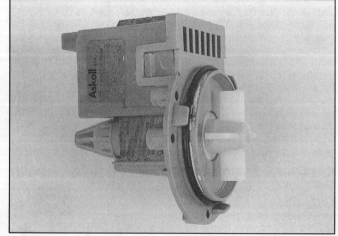

A typical permanent magnet pump. Note: *Unlike the shaded pole pump the rotor of this type of pump will not rotate freely when turned by hand. It will appear difficult and springy to turn due to the magnetic attraction between the multi-poled rotor and metal lamination of the stator*

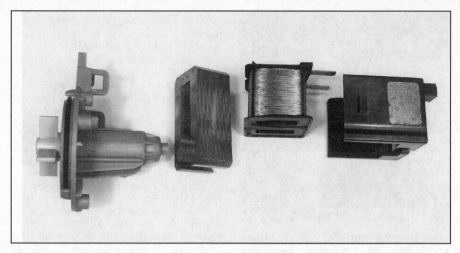

This dismantled pump shows the parts of a PM pump unit. However, only complete pump units are available as replacement items

Permanent magnet drain pump with non return flap on the inside of the pump chamber inlet

normal shaded pole motor, the motor may be nudged into revolving in the opposite direction and clear the blockage or continue to pump whilst being able to run in the opposite direction.

The construction of the PM pump helps alleviate the problems of shaft seal leaks and bearing failure which are common to shaded pole versions. Problems to look out for are open circuit of the start windings, water ingress into the sealed rotor chamber taking dirt with it, and the rotor popping out of the sealed rotor chamber. This latter fault normally occurs when water that has entered the sealed rotor chamber is heated and expands forcing the rotor out of position. This fault is often accompanied by a chattering noise when the pump is energised and tries to run. The pump may work but inefficiently. **Note:** *If a shaded pole stator is inadvertently fitted back to front, it will cause the main motor to run in the opposite direction and therefore reduce the pump's efficiency. Always note its orientation prior to strip-down.*

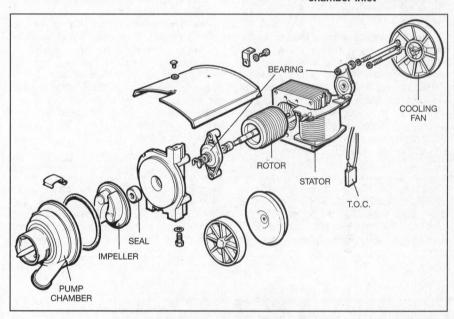

Typical shaded pole induction motor pump

Shown is a shaded pole induction motor stator. With the stator removed, the copper banding can be clearly seen

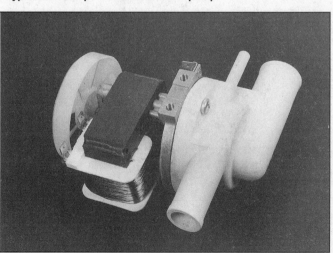

Typical outlet/drain pump. Large end is the water inlet and the smaller is the outlet. The very small connection on the top is used to flush a small amount of water around the pressure vessel base to help reduce the chance of blockages

Permanent magnet main circulation pumps

Permanent magnet main circulation pumps are essentially just larger versions of the permanent magnet drain pump motors described earlier. At present only few makes and models employ this type of motor to circulate water for the wash action. However, being a self starting motor (they do not require capacitors, relays or any other starting device) combined with their relatively simple construction and operation it is likely that this type of motor will become increasingly popular with manufacturers of dishwashers. As with their small drain pump counterparts when faulty these large permanent magnet circulation pumps are only available as complete units.

Drain pumps

The drain or outlet pump is a vital part for the correct functioning of the machine and prone to various faults. Leaks from the pumps may not be apparent, but the resulting pool of water usually is. So here are a few points to look out for. Remember which symptoms apply to the fault you have will depend upon which type of pump is fitted to your machine, i.e. shaded pole or permanent magnet.

Firstly check all clips on the hoses to and from the pump and tighten if they are loose.

If the leak remains, the pump's shaft seal should be checked. This is the seal that forms a watertight barrier on the rotating shaft of the motor directly between the impeller and the front motor bearing. The seal can be broken by a scale build-up or food deposits forming on

Large permanent magnet main circulation pump unit which is easily recognised as it has only two wiring connections (plus an earth connection), no visible rotor, no start capacitor or relay and is smaller than a typical dishwasher induction motor. The construction, function, testing and problems of this type of permanent magnet motor are the same as their smaller drain pump counterparts
Note: *The use of this type of motor has currently been discontinued by Whirlpool and its associated brands. Failure will require the fitting of the earlier 'standard' induction motor and capacitor described within this chapter*

the rotor shaft behind the impeller, thus distorting the rubber seal. To check if this is happening, remove the pump chamber, by removing its securing clips or screws, and whilst securing the rotor of the pump motor, turn the impeller clockwise to undo it from the shaft. (**Note:** *Impeller and rotor are generally*

left-hand threaded.) Having done this, remove any scale adhering to the shaft and refit, ensuring the pump chamber seal is in position. If the seal still leaks, then it is either worn or softened. On most machines, this means the complete renewal of the pump (not so costly as you may think, as many genuine and 'pattern' pumps of good quality are now available at very low cost: see *Buying spare parts*). This may seem drastic for such a small seal, but the fact is that water containing detergent would have been entering the front pump bearing long before the leak became obvious. This means it will probably be damaged itself and next in line to cause trouble.

If the rotor shaft was found to be worn, even slightly, e.g. roughness/scoured, it would probably be easier and quicker to fit a complete pump, to avoid any further trouble. In fact this could be the least expensive remedy.

Other leaks can be attributable to the pump, due to impeller damage, that is to say blades of impeller broken off or badly worn away by a solid object lodged in the pump at sometime, (bone or glass fragments are common causes).

Tight bearings may also cause the motor to run slowly.

Any of the above will result in poor water discharge, i.e. slow draining. This in turn may lead to faults such as poor wash results or machine retaining excess water (causing odours). Some machines may leak at certain points on programmes due to filling to too high a level especially those that have a timed fill action at certain stages of the programme.

Checking the impeller and bearings can be done at the same time as checking the seal.

Below is a simple illustration of the outlet pump chamber and impeller. Water from the sump enters from the front. The rotation of the

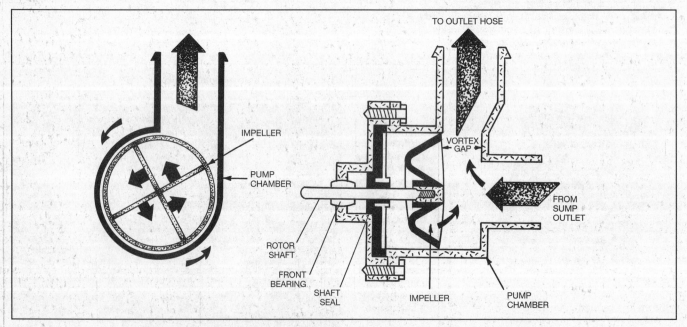

Vortex style pump. Dynamic force is exerted on the water in the direction of the outlet

impeller lifts the water in the direction of the narrower outlet hose. Some machines are fitted with a non-returnable valve system on the outlet hose. Watch out for blockages at that point. There are two types of impeller: one is simply a paddle type and more prone to blockages; the second is like the one illustrated and called a vortex pump. This type of impeller is more of a flat etched disc that allows a gap between itself and the pump chamber. This gap lets particles pass through easier than the bladed impeller version. The vortex impeller applies lift to the water as shown in the smaller version, the action is similar to the rotating vortex created when a bath empties.

Typical outlet pump replacement

Note: *Ensure that the machine is isolated before attempting any repair on your dishwasher.*

In the following sequence, we show the location of the outlet pump assembly on a Hoover dishwasher and its removal and subsequent renewal. This is then followed by a similar repair to a main circulation pump that illustrates the similarities across the whole range of dishwashers. Only the machines with one pump for both circulation and outlet have any significant differences.

The machine was leaking badly when inspected, but was in fact still working. When questioned, the user admitted that the machine

Ensure that machine is isolated and disconnected. Protect the rear and lay the machine carefully on its back

had been leaking for quite some time, but now more water seemed to be leaking out than ever before. As you may see, this is obvious in the pictures, by the degree of corrosion to both pump and mounting bracket. This level of corrosion would have been avoided by earlier detection/report of the initial, much smaller leak.

Shown in pictures are variations of pumps that may be encountered on this type of machine. The pictures also show the further

stripdown of the pump. In this case, it was thought best to renew the pump completely due to the amount of water and detergent damage to both the bearings and metal laminations of the stator. Again this may have been avoided if the initial leak had been dealt with earlier.

The complete pump was fitted, and the shell and mounts were coated with anti-rust compound prior to the fitting of the pump. Care must be taken that the anti-corrosion liquid does not come into contact with any rubber hoses or seals.

After replacing all hoses and connections (a simple reversal of the removal procedure) the machine was put into its correct working position and reconnected to the water and power supply. A short pre-wash programme was selected to ensure that the new pump functioned correctly, ensuring that the repositioned clips were watertight and that no other leaks were present.

At this point, the user was advised of the unnecessary danger (and damage in this case) caused by using the machine when it obviously had a fault that was ignored. **Note:** *In most modern machines, the pump has to be changed as a complete unit for even the smallest of problems. This is no excuse for turning a blind eye to such faults. Such behaviour is false economy.*

The anti-corrosion coat mentioned can be one of many types available from DIY care centres and hardware shops. Please use as per manufacturer's instructions, taking care not to allow any contact with rubber hoses or plastics. When using anti-corrosion gel or

Machine back protected and carefully laid over. Position of both pumps now clearly seen

Note and remove the hose clips and connections. Corrosion was found on the mounting. Treat with anti-rust compound prior to refitting

Support pump whilst removing securing bolts and support bracket fixings

Remove pump carefully from its position

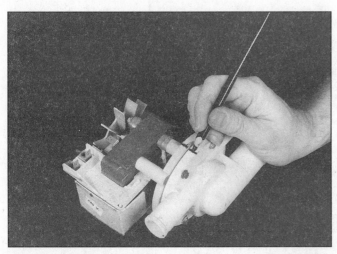

Mark the position of the chamber. Remove the screw holding the pump chamber in position (some machines may have clips)

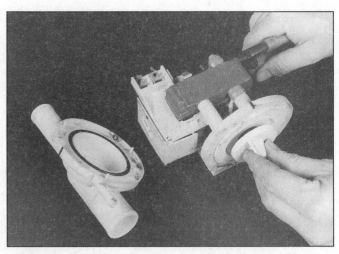

Whilst holding rear shaft securely turn impeller clockwise and remove. (LH thread in this instance)

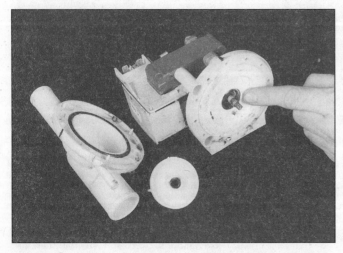

Rear seal exposed. In this case it is badly worn by a build-up of scale upon shaft

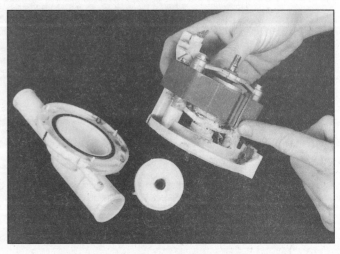

Water had penetrated the front bearing of this pump

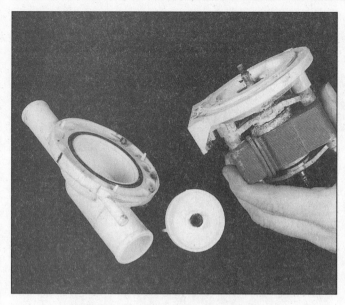

The stator laminations are also badly corroded

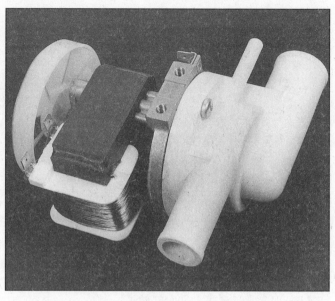

A new pump is required for this particular fault

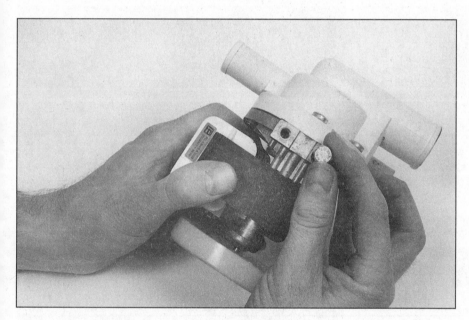

When fitting a new pump as in this instance, check the bolt sizes. Not all come with bolts as this one did. When reconnecting the terminals, make sure that, if the pump has an earth tag, it is a good fit as with all connections. When the hose and clips have been refitted, the machine is ready for testing on the rinse cycle. Make sure all panels are refitted before commencing functional testing

Main circulation pump fault

The machine was isolated prior to repair as usual. The reported fault was poor wash and very noisy. As the filters were clean, a faulty circulation pump was suspected, possibly bearings

The machine was carefully laid on its back to gain access to the large circulation pump motor unit

Checking the motor and pump required the removal of the whole unit. First the rear fixing screws

Next the clips securing the hoses were released

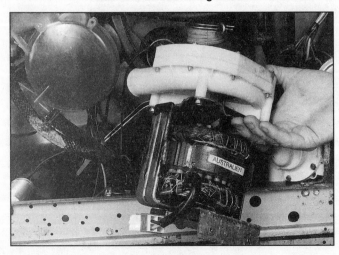

After making a note of all connections and hoses etc. the pump was removed

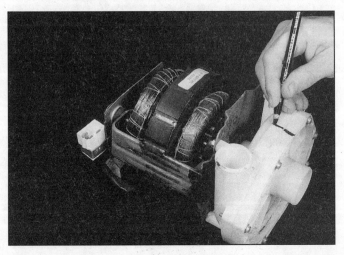

The pump chamber was marked to assist when the time came to refit it. After marking, all the securing screws were removed

As before the pump chamber cover was removed to expose the impeller. What was also revealed was the cause of the trouble. A plastic spoon had lodged in the chamber

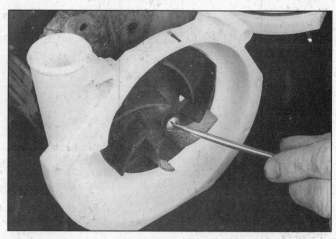

A check was made on the impeller and no damage had been done, but it was thought best to check the face seal at this point so the impeller was removed

The shaft seal and face seal proved to be OK. Only cleaning was required prior to rebuild

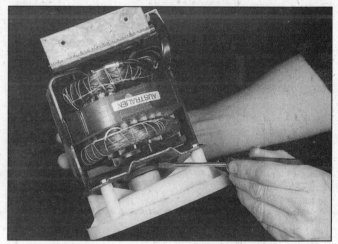

A check on the inner side of the seal confirmed it had not leaked or weeped

rubber sealant indoors, care should be taken to protect the floor from spillage, and ensure that adequate ventilation is available.

Refitting was a simple reversal of the stripdown procedure and testing identical to the outlet pump sequence described earlier.

The user of this machine was extremely lucky. If the impeller had jammed solid, the motor would have burnt out and a complete renewal at a very high cost would have been required. This style of motor is of a solid welded construction and cannot be repaired. Even a small bearing fault caused by a weeping seal would require a complete motor unit. Most manufacturers seem to adopt the complete unit change philosophy and only supply shaft seals and impellers as service items. If the motor bearings fail and the motor is of the non-welded type which can be stripped down, a trip to the local bearing stockist with the old bearing should result in new ones being obtained with very little trouble as they are generally a common size.

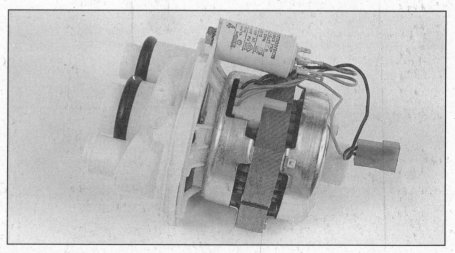

This style of pump can be completely stripped down for repairs unlike the welded motor shown in the photo sequence. Although the bearings would not be supplied by the machine manufacturer, they can be obtained locally from a bearing stockist by quoting the bearing number

Chapter 29
Timers (programmer/control)

The programmer or timer, as it is more commonly known, is the component normally located at the top of and within the door cavity, directly behind the selector knob on mechanically controlled dishwashers. Electronically controlled dishwashers may have selector switches, touch pads or selector knobs. The control circuitry/programmer may be split into two or more circuit boards, often referred to as modules.

When a programme is selected, in either mechanical or electronic versions, the timer follows a pre-determined sequence switching components on and off (i.e. heater, pump, valves) for various lengths of time. Due to the apparent complexity of this component, it wrongly tends to be regarded as a 'no go' area.

The intention of this manual has been to show that the dishwashing machine is not so mysterious, and when broken down into its constituent parts, its simplicity of operation is

revealed. To describe the workings of the timer/programmer in any particular dishwasher we would need to know the make, model number, date of manufacture and the timer number itself. These are needed to ascertain which variation of timer and associated variation of programmes that your particular machine has. In their most infinite wisdom, the manufacturers have seen fit to change their timers, numbers and wiring colours, etc., with regularity.

The timer/programmers used in dishwashers are similar to those used in automatic washing machines. They are generally more compact and contain fewer switch banks or control functions due to the less complicated wash actions carried out by the dishwasher. They have fewer specialised programmes than their clothes washing counterparts. Though smaller and less complex their replacement cost is often higher than the automatic washing machine.

To give detailed information about the unit that is in your particular machine, a book several times the size of this one would be needed. What follows is a general description of how timers work, some of the most common faults and their symptoms. The following information is split into two main sections – mechanical timers and electronic timers.

Mechanical Crouzet timer

Mechanical timers fall into two categories – edge cam and face cam although face cam timers are now rarely encountered.

A description of both variations follows.

How an edge cam timer works

This is the most common version of mechanical timer to be found in dishwashers and programme selection can only be made by turning the selector knob in the clockwise direction (no attempt should be made to force the selector knob in the opposite direction. The term edge cam timer, simply means that each switch within the timer is operated by its own cam on a central rotatable barrel. This allows switches to be dropped or lifted into different positions at the same time. This operation can be likened to that of the old style pianola or musical box that played a tune with the aid of a cylinder. If the cylinder were to be changed, a different tune would be produced. The same principle applies to the mechanical timer. Although the external appearance of the timer does not change, a simple change of the central barrel will give the manufacturer a different switching sequence and therefore a different machine to put on the market. Because of this, when changing the timer it is important that the correct version is used, i.e. one with the same central barrel. This is shown by the serial number on the timer.

On the central barrel there are several cams, with each cam having one or two switches resting upon them. The barrel is rotated by the cam advance motor, which is energised by impulse commands such as that from the thermostat. i.e. if the selected temperature is reached, the thermostat closes, thus causing the motor to run. The motor will continue to run until a cam position is reached that breaks the impulse path (motor circuit). The barrel is then in the correct position for the next sequence of instructions.

Mechanical timers are normally a 60 step cycle. This means that on one complete

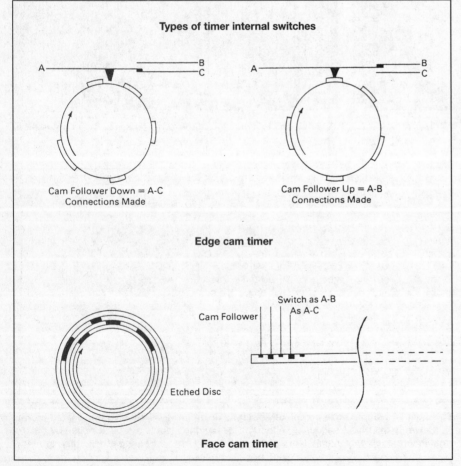

Types of timer internal switches

Cam Follower Down = A-C
Connections Made

Cam Follower Up = A-B
Connections Made

Edge cam timer

Switch as A-B
As A-C

Cam Follower

Etched Disc

Face cam timer

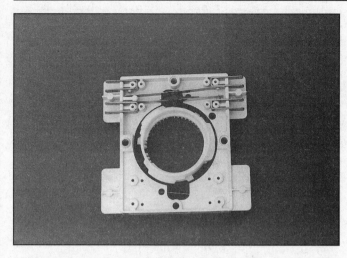

Internal view of switch bank. Note switch movements and cam position (Crouzet timer)

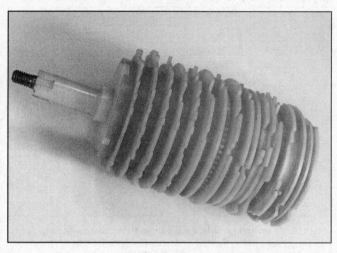

Internal view of cam barrel. Each row is for one switch block and has three levels

revolution of the cam, it will have initiated 60 different switching variations (60 'clicks'). There are variation to this, such as 45 or 56 step cycle timers. There are two distinct variations in the way the cam barrel is advanced: a) timers with two drive motors on the rear of the timer unit and b) a single drive motor system. A description of both types is as follows:

a) This type of timer is easily recognised by the two small drive motors on the rear of the timer. Each has its own function, one of which is dedicated to cam advance as described earlier and is called the cam advance motor.

Next to the advance motor is the timing motor, which times all of the functions of the machine. i.e. washing, emptying, etc. The timing motor drives a timing cam which turns one revolution every minute via internal gearing. Therefore a six minute wash consists of six, one minute timing requests.

An emptying cycle would consist of supplying power to the outlet pump for one minute and moving to the next cam position. Most dishwasher timers use a one minute time cycle, unlike their counterparts in automatic washing machines which use two minute time cycles (due to the larger quantity of water used and variations of wash times required).

Cams operate the switches within the timer. For example, at the correct point in the programme, the cam on which the heater switch rests will allow the switch to make, therefore engaging the heater. The cam will also engage the correct thermostat switch for that programme. When the correct heat is reached and the timer has timed out, the thermostat then impulses the cam advance motor. In English, this is read as 'When the temperature is reached, finish timing and then impulse (move) onto the next cam position.'

b) An alternative to the two motor Crouzet, is the one motor version, where the one motor does both of the jobs via the cams. This version is common in the Indesit, Zanussi, Candy, etc.

With a little imagination, it should be quite

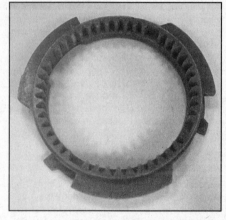

Typical three level profile of a cam barrel

clear how a programme actually works, not by some mysterious phenomena, but by a sequence of simple movements that combine to form a complete operational programme.

How a face cam timer works

The same basic edge cam timer principles apply, only the switches are operated by an etched disc that allows the switches to drop in and out of the recessed positions on its face. Face cam timers are of the one motor variety as described above. The timers are easily identifiable by the fact that an edge cam timer is much longer and deeper than the face cam. This is because the face cam timer is much slimmer as only one disc is used to operate all of the switches. The slim lines of face cam timers make them more popular on door mounted machines.

Problems and renewal

The main drawbacks of timers:
a) Units cannot be repaired. Complete unit changes are needed for timer faults.
b) Without detailed information of the switching sequences of the faulty timer, faults

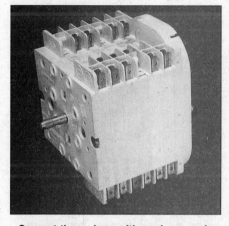

Crouzet timers have either a large code number on the top of the timer or a smaller, longer number on the left-hand side. When ordering a new item all numbers that are on the timer should be quoted together with the make, model and serial number of your machine

are difficult to trace as a combination of switches may be used.
c) Units can often be difficult to fit. (Unless a logical approach is used!)
The main benefits of timers:
a) Modern timers are very reliable.
b) New units are relatively low in cost.
c) Dishwasher timers are easier to fit than those of the automatic washing machine as they have fewer switch banks and connecting wires, i.e. much smaller harness.

It must be remembered that when a fault is suspected, it is not always the most complicated component that can cause the most trouble. If a process of elimination is used and all other parts of the machine are found to be working correctly, it is only then that the timer should be suspected. (Unless of course in the case of obvious failure, such as a burn out or damage to the timer.) **Note:** *Ensure that the*

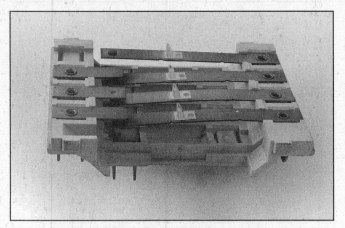

Edge block switch bank showing clearly the switch arrangement and cam followers. Switch operation is the same, only the style of mounting is different

Early Indesit Crouzet timer with one switch block removed showing cam barrel

power is turned off and that the plug is removed from its socket at all times. Do not remove the timer from the machine at this point.

The removal and subsequent exchange of the timer can be a long and tedious task. Allow enough time to complete the job – do not rush.

Do not remove any wiring as yet, but thoroughly check for any overheating of the connections to and from the timer spades (connections) i.e. If a fault is suspected in the heater switch, trace the wire from the heater to the timer. This gives the location of the heater switch, and should be examined for any signs of burning or being loose.

Having decided that the timer is at fault, a note should be taken of all the numbers that are on the timer, together with the make, model and age of your machine.

Armed with this information, you can obtain an exact replacement. See *Buying spare parts* chapter.

When the replacement has been obtained. visually check that they are identical, as timers will not be exchanged by any known company once they have been fitted. (You have been warned!) Having confirmed that it is the correct replacement, and that any accompanying instructions have been read thoroughly, you can proceed to swap the wiring. The only way that this can be done is by placing the new timer in the same place as the original, swapping the wires on a one-to-one basis. Although this is very time consuming, it is by far the safest method. A mistake at this point would be almost impossible to rectify without a wiring and timer diagram. When all connections have been successfully exchanged, the timer can be fitted into position, ensuring that any parts that are connected to salt indicators, etc. are positioned correctly. Once fitted into position, and the covers have been refitted, the power can be turned on, and a test programme can

be implemented. **Note:** *Some timers have small metal clips that join/link terminals together. These do not come with the new timer. Ensure they are swapped from the original. To avoid the possibility of error, detailed notes or drawings should be made prior to removing any connections or wiring. Unmarked wires should be tagged with their switch bank number.*

Mechanical timer variations

The mechanical timers shown are a small selection that are used in today's automatic dishwashing machines.

A manufacturer may have numerous variations of the same timer. For instance, although the timer in your dishwasher is an edge cam timer, your neighbour may have the same machine with seemingly the same timer in it, but in fact, it may be a variation of the same timer. These variations are identifiable

Early Indesit timer unit with individual wiring connection tags

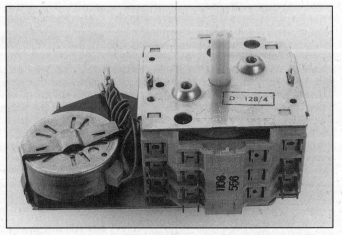

This is an early Zanussi timer. It has a very simple one block connector that is easily fitted. Take care that connections within the harness block do not slide out when it is pushed on timer. The timer motor is located beneath the unit and drives the cam via an elongated gear system. This saves on overall depth of the unit

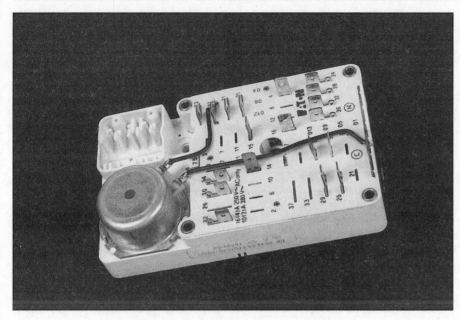

Typical face cam timer (terminals on rear)

The drive motor of this timer is internally fitted into the cam barrel to keep size to a minimum. It is also fitted with edge block connector for the single switch bank

by the slight difference in serial numbers shown on the timer. This illustrates the need to obtain the exact number of your timer and machine when a replacement is to be obtained.

Some machines have push buttons only to select the required programme and no visible selector knob. The switch/button bank usually consists of an 'ON/OFF' button, a series of selector buttons for various wash types and combinations, and a start button. On this sort of machine, the timer is of a similar type to those described earlier and can be of the face or edge cam variety.

The buttons act as bypasses to sections of the programme, for instance, the selection of a pre-wash cycle will allow the timer to advance to that position missing out all the steps before and after it when the start button is pressed. Sometimes a combination of switches can be used but all act as 'impulse' or 'bypass' depending on the length and type of wash required by the user. In reality, the buttons select the required programme in place of the user manually turning the timer shaft via the selector knob.

Pre-selector/jog dial timers

Unlike the mechanical timers described previously where programme selection can only be made by turning the selector knob clockwise, programme selection on pre-selector/jog dial timers can be made by turning the selector knob either clockwise or anti-clockwise. Such units are a combination of the mechanical timer and the electronic push button (electronic) programme selection units – a description of each is as follows.

Pre-selector controls are electro-mechanical. However, selecting a programme on this type of control does not directly turn the cam barrel of the mechanical timer as described earlier, it merely selects at which point the barrel should start from by closing a switch that corresponds to that point of the sequence. When the programme is then

Early one motor edge cam timer in situ. Size of timer is not important on this model as the timer is fitted beneath the top of the machine, not in the door

Edge cam timer shown with cover removed to highlight similar cam operation, this time with two banks and simple tag connections

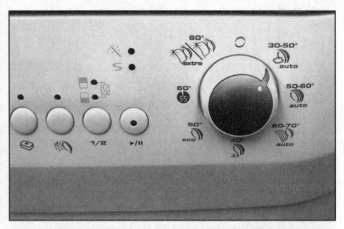

Like many modern dishwashers this computer controlled version has a wide range of programme options

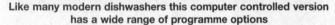

Some electronically controlled models use 'jog dials' and buttons for programme selection as in this instance

started the cam barrel advance motor is energised and runs until the cam barrel reaches the pre-selected point which open circuits the selector switch and commences the programme from that point. In essence the pre-selector system turns the mechanical cam barrel to its starting position, rather than the user.

A jog-dial control uses a light-action dial to select the required programme, which is stored electronically rather than mechanically. As the dial is turned an electronic display panel indicates the various programmes and you simply stop turning the dial when the required programme appears. As the system is purely electronic the selected programme will commence as soon as the start button is pressed.

In addition to basic programme selection, both types of control will generally have additional selection switches/buttons for features such as half-load, economy selection etc.

As it is only the way in which the programmes are initially selected when problems occur, you will need to make reference to either the mechanical timer or computer controlled sections of this chapter.

Computer-controlled machines (electronic timers)

The functional parts of electronically controlled machines, i.e., circulation pump motor, heater, drain pump etc., are essentially the same as machines with conventional selector knobs and mechanical timers. Microprocessor-controlled machines are easily recognisable by their digital displays used to indicate the programme in use and buttons or touch pads for programme selection. Most have the ability to display an error code when faults occur which relate to a table in the handbook. For a range of popular fault codes refer to chapter *Fault and error codes*. Faults within microprocessor timer circuitry can be difficult to locate as the complex circuitry board components cannot be easily checked.

It is best to eliminate all other possible causes of faults before suspecting either the power module or programme unit. If all the other checks prove satisfactory, then check all connections to and from the control boards (microprocessor machines generally have two – one low voltage board for the microprocessor, selector panel and display, and one power board with transformer, relays and triacs to operate the mains voltage switching which the processor cannot do directly). Some models may split the PCBs into three individual boards – a low voltage display board, a low voltage selector board and a mains voltage power board. The connections to printed circuit boards are prone to oxidisation resulting in poor electrical contact especially on the low voltages used by the programme boards. Check closely for poor connections.

If the fault remains after all other components have been checked and found to be satisfactory, the only option left is to change one or, in some instances, all of the circuit boards. Due to the way in which the power board functions (see following paragraph), it is most likely to be a failure in

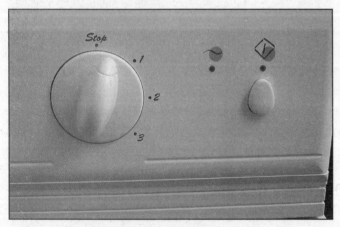

Typical mechanical jog wheel programme selection dishwasher

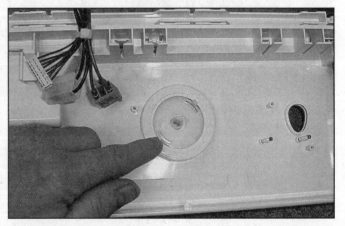

The programme selector knob is a simple push fit 'D' shaft type of fitting to the programme selection board. The knob itself can be removed by carefully pressing the two plastic latches

Unlike purely mechanical timers this programme selector knob (jog wheel) can be turned in either direction to select a programme and does not move on as the programme progresses. Programme position is displayed on a separate LCD or vacuum fluorescent display panel. Basic programme selection by turning the knob can be further enhanced by pressing various buttons on the facia of the appliance

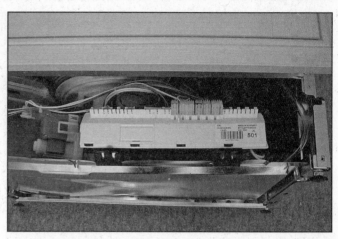

The main control PCB is mounted within a plastic holder beneath the load compartment and accessed by removing the lower front panel

this circuitry or its components at fault. Do not touch the processor board's components at all as they are sensitive to static electricity and are easily damaged by careless handling. The power boards are more robust but care must still be exercised when handling them. The power board is generally much bulkier than the programme board and may house a large transformer to drop the voltage to the processor and low voltage components. Due to its size and function power boards are usually housed in a plastic moulding beneath the load compartment. Electronic circuit faults occur more often with power boards as the mains switching operating the circulation pump, inlet valve, heater, etc., are switched mechanically by relays or electronically by triacs operated by the lower voltage supplied from the programme board, i.e., processors

themselves cannot directly switch mains power and use mechanical relays or triacs. Try to isolate if a mechanical fault is suspected (e.g. heater not receiving power, maybe a sticking/faulty relay, etc.).

It is not uncommon for items that short circuit and blow fuses to damage their respective control relay or triac. For instance, a common fault such as the heater failing internally if the inner wire is touching its earthed metal casing would result in a direct short circuit. Such a fault on a machine with a mechanical timer would blow the appliance fuse in the plug and rectification would be a relatively straightforward case of renewing the heater and fuse and checking the appliance prior to running a functional test. However, the same fault on a microprocessor controlled machine is likely to damage the components

of the circuit board used to switch the heater supply, resulting in a much more expensive repair. **Note:** *To prevent this particular problem causing damage to the power board some makes and models use a heavy duty relay which is not part of the power board and is mounted elsewhere in the appliance. The power board then controls the external relay by sending a low voltage to the relay's coil which creates a magnetic field which in turn closes the high voltage heater switch. This means that when an over current caused by the heater short circuiting to earth results in damage to the relay it can be easily changed and no damage is done to the power board.*

The programme input board and display board may be combined into one unit or be two separate but linked boards housed within the door cavity. They differ from the power

With the main control PCB removed from its plastic holder components such as: A transformer, B triacs and C heater relay etc. are clearly visible. **Note:** *To avoid static damage to sensitive components only handle printed circuit boards by their edges ensuring that you do not make contact with the printed circuit or board components*

This large PCB has a series of edge connectors which are keyed to prevent incorrect positioning. However, as a precaution it is wise to mark all connections before removal as not all manufacturers key connections

Typical LED programme indication with time delay short stroke selector button and programme sequence indicated by LEDs. The large button on the right is the On/Off switch

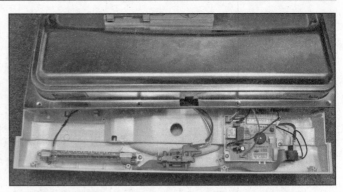

Internal view of LED programme indication components

module in that they are generally much slimmer than the power board and lack the larger components such as relays, transformers, etc.

Obtaining individual board components from the machine manufacturers is not possible as only complete boards/modules are supplied as spares. The control microprocessor is normally located within the circuitry of the board but may, on some machines, be included within the power board circuitry. As explained previously, the microprocessor takes the place of the cam barrel used in mechanical timers. The mechanical action of the cam barrel of physically switching components on or off is now carried out electronically by the solid state processor, i.e., no moving parts (although moving part relays may be required elsewhere), and the timing of each sequence is governed by a quartz clock chip, similar to that used in watches, within the board's circuitry.

The way in which the processor operates is very similar to the cam barrel of the mechanical timer in that it is programmed with unalterable predetermined functions, i.e., steps. The main difference is that the amount of steps can be (and usually are) much greater and the response from external sources 'feedback' can be utilised to monitor the processes being carried out, for instance to automatically check the time of fill, power consumption of motor, etc. Like the mechanical barrel, a predetermined set of functions is stored within the main chip in a similar way to the individual cam positions of the mechanical timer. The main difference being that a greater amount of 'positions' can be stored and accessed in any order unlike the fixed sequence of the mechanical version. The way in which a full wash programme is compiled is by electronically overriding or omitting the sequences not required. In this way an extremely variable and flexible wash programme can be built up with information obtained from the various wash selection

Typical LCD panel with short stroke selector buttons to the left and bottom of the display. Top right is where the larger On/Off button is positioned

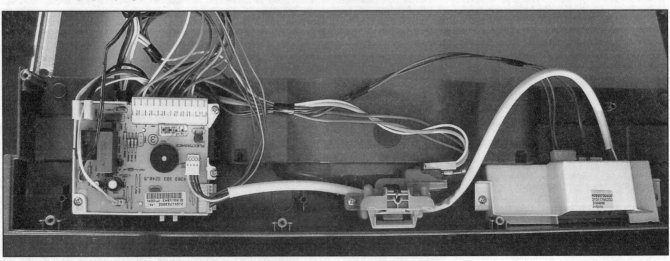

Internal view of LCD display panel

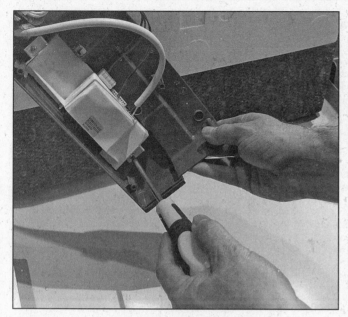

Internal view of LCD display panel

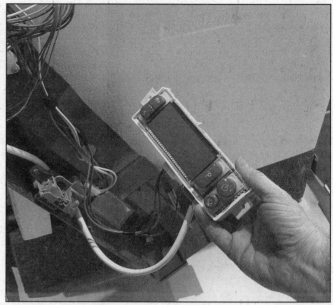

Internal view of LCD display panel

buttons operated by the user and combined with fixed sequences to suit the type of wash load.

The various wash options finally selected by the user and then held in volatile memory, i.e., held short term only for as long as the machine is switched on, but will be lost when turned off.

Note: *Some degree of memory retention is incorporated (approx 5 to 10 seconds) and varies from make to make. Most machines also have a set sequence of wash programmes plus the ability to store several user defined variations in a volatile memory that will only blank if the machine is unplugged for a long period of time.*

Faults within the components or circuitry of the board are extremely difficult to trace and as with the power board, only complete units are supplied by the manufacturer. Before contemplating a board fault, ensure all other components within the machine are satisfactory and that all connections to and from the printed circuit boards are in good condition and are firmly pushed into place. Check thoroughly all connections, wiring and all protective covers especially at the entry point of those that enter the door inner void. Wiring entering the door is subject to extensive bending and flexing each time the door is opened and closed and this can result in breaking of the inner conductor of the wire leading to permanent or intermittent open circuit problems. See chapter *Wiring harness faults.*

With the machine isolated, look closely at all connections that carry mains voltage when in use, as loose connections can cause overheating and interference which can affect the processor chips. Include all earth path connections in the wiring checks and renew any

that are loose, have cracked covers or show signs of damage, for example, overheating. Do not forget to include the plug connections.

With a persistent or unusual fault, e.g. intermittent operation, random displays, working for short periods and then blanking memory, etc., check the condition of the supply socket. If a poor connection exists between any pin of the plug and its supply connection, again interference will be present which may corrupt the processor, see *Basics – electrical*. Renew if suspect.

A faulty suppression unit may also be the cause of such random and difficult to trace faults. Ensure the unit is securely earthed, see *Suppressors* chapter.

If all the aforementioned checks prove satisfactory, then it is most likely that the processor chip is corrupted or the board has a fault within its circuitry. Such faults will require a replacement unit. Carefully note all connections to and from the unit and keeping in mind the paragraph regarding handling of the unit, remove it from the machine. Inspect it closely for dirt or debris which may be affecting the circuit or its components. If any dirt is present, it should be blown free (do not use metal items such as screwdrivers).

Check the board for cracks or possible moisture damage due to faulty covers, etc. Before finally accepting that a new unit is needed, it would be wise to inspect the printed circuit board's soldered connections to verify that they are sound. Loose or poor connections (called dry joints) can often be easily rectified and if all these checks prove negative, a new unit will be necessary. Take care to fit the unit correctly on all its mounts and ensure all covers and connections are sound. Take particular care to avoid direct contact with the components of the unit.

Do not touch the processor board's components at all as they are sensitive to static electricity and are easily damaged by careless handling. The power boards are more robust but care must still be exercised when handling them.

Note: *All checks must be carried out with the machine isolated in the usual manner: taps off, plug out! Under no circumstances should you try to test the processor board even with a low 9 volt or similar tester because the microprocessor chip can easily be damaged. Use of the 1.5 volt tester shown in the photographs is recommended for continuity testing of the wiring between the module units. Try to leave the block connectors in place and using the probes of the tester, check for continuity between exposed printed circuit points close to the connector blocks. This will test both the wiring between the modules (often ribbon cable) and the connection to the printed circuit board.*

On computer-controlled machines faults that develop may be indicated by a code which is displayed on the front of the machine. Codes differ from machine to machine so refer to your handbook to ascertain the meaning of each code. For a range of popular fault codes refer to chapter *Fault and error codes*.

Fuzzy Logic

With the availability of microprocessor control systems an extremely wide range of logic control options became available. However, in recent times another new option has emerged, that of Fuzzy Logic. An introduction to this relatively new form of processing is given in the chapter *Fuzzy logic*.

Additional features of electronic control

In addition to the standard features of programme control common to both mechanical and electronic timers, i.e. timed cycles, temperature control, detergent dispensing, etc. the use of electronics allows for a wider range of programme options such as delay start facility, countdown timer to inform you of the remaining time left to complete the wash, etc. The use of electronics can also allow a range of additional sensing features to be employed to monitor specific areas of interest during the wash cycle. The information obtained is constantly fed back to the microprocessor and used to adjust the current programme in many ways, i.e. to modify the current programme, inform the user that problems have occurred or if the problem warrants it abort the programme altogether. The use of microprocessors allows a range of interaction that cannot occur with mechanical programme control. A selection and description of some of the most popular sensors follows. However, it must be remembered that not all electronically controlled dishwashers will have these features, much depends on the manufacturer and which model you have.

Optical sensors

This type of sensor is used to detect the turbidity (cloudiness) of the water passing through the sensor. Refer to Chapter *Fuzzy logic*.

Opposed mode sensing is the most popular system used in a dishwasher and is often referred to as direct scanning. In simple terms this means that a light source and light sensitive receiver are positioned opposite each other and the wash water is allowed to pass between them. The intensity of light reaching the receiver is dependent on how much soiling is in suspension in the water passing between the two points. For instance, if sensing was to take place after the pre-rinse stage the response from the receiver would be passed to the microprocessor for a decision to be made on whether the water can be used in the wash cycle or rather pumped away and fresh water taken in. The parameters for the decision are contained within the microprocessor's memory. If the level of cloudiness was deemed acceptable the water would be used for the wash, the result being a substantial reduction in water consumption for the programme. The way in which the information from an optical sensing device is used on any particular machine will depend upon the design features and requirements of the manufacturer.

Thermistors

In electronically controlled dishwashers, thermistors are used to detect the operational temperature of the water (although fixed thermostats may also be used for certain functions). Thermistors are used because they can very accurately detect an infinitely variable range of temperatures. For a detailed explanation of thermistors refer to the chapter: *Thermostats and thermistors.*

Pulse generator

In dishwashers a pulse gererator can be used to detect the rotation of the spray arms to monitor whether or not they are rotating correctly. If problems are detected the user can be prompted (audible bleep or visual indicator) to check the loading of the baskets as the most common fault that prevents rotation is items protruding above or below the load baskets.

The system works by the lower spray arm having a small permanent magnet embedded into it and an externally mounted normally 'open' reed switch fixed to the outer of the sump moulding. The normally 'open' reed switch will 'close' and then 'open' each time the permanent magnet passes over it.

The opening and closing of the reed switch in relation to the magnets rotation creates a pulses which is detected by the microprocessor housed on the main programme control PCB. If the spray arm fails to rotate for any reason no pulses are produced and the processor will indicate a jammed spray arm fault.

Note: *Due to difficulties in detecting top spray arm rotation (i.e. positioning of a reed switch) most makes and models with this feature only have lower spray arm detection.*

The use of sensors and microprocessor control produces machines that have the ability to adapt to changes and customise each programme cycle automatically if required. Refer to Chapter *Fuzzy logic.*

Chapter 30
Fuzzy logic

At present this technique of programme control is used only on a limited range of makes and models, however, due to the benefits of such an intuitive system of operation it is certain to become common place. This brief overview of Fuzzy logic has been included to provide the reader with an insight into this latest technical innovation. It is not an in-depth study of this new science, rather an interesting insight into what the present has to offer on some models and what the future holds for all models. Reading this chapter should help complete your knowledge and understanding of machines past, present and future.

Most of today's dishwashers, either mechanically or computer controlled, are based on simple logic. For instance, take the action of a fixed thermostat, it is either 'open' or 'closed'. The timer simply waits for the signal to proceed to the next step in the predetermined wash programme. As humans we know that the water being heated is not simply the right or wrong temperature (cold or hot) but warm, fairly warm, etc. When we wash dishes by hand we do not simply take the temperature of the water into consideration, we access a wide range of both precise and imprecise information such as – what type of items make up the load, the degree of soiling, what type of soiling it is (greasy, baked on etc.). All of these factors and more ultimately affect the way the load should be cleaned, how long the wash should

be, how much detergent will be required for the level and type of soiling, how warm the wash water should be and how much rinsing is required, etc. Unfortunately a thermostat cannot detect this range of imprecise approximations and the control unit can only respond to precise logical inputs.

However, with a combination of microprocessor control, additional sensors and a new way of programming, the purely logical approach may not be with us for much longer. This new way of looking at the washing process is called Fuzzy logic and some makes and models already have varying degrees of this type of control system. The essence of Fuzzy logic is to produce a machine that can react and adapt the wash process as a human would – to look at a wide range of variables and to make informed decisions based on all of the available information both precise and imprecise. To do this, additional sensors are required to supply the processor with the information for the decision process. The wash programme is therefore not just a series of predetermined sequences it has the ability to respond and react to information it receives, in essence Fuzzy logic thinks the problem through and arrives at a solution based upon the whole range of both precise and imprecise information. In other words it has the ability to mimic the way we ourselves would react.

Some of the additional information the

processor requires can be gained from existing controls such as water level switches and thermistors. However, other sensors not normally associated with dishwashers will be required to assist in the decision-making process. The most common of these sensors is the optical sensor. This type of sensor is used to detect the turbidity (cloudiness) of the water passing through the sensor.

Opposed mode optical sensing is the most popular system used for this purpose and is often referred to as direct scanning. In simple terms this means that a light source and light sensitive receiver are positioned opposite each other and the wash water is allowed to pass between them. The intensity of light reaching the receiver is dependent on how much soiling is in suspension in the water passing between the two points and how quickly it reached that level. This type of sensor can be used to provide information on the level and type of soiling. The way this can be done is as follows. The level of soiling on the wash load can be determined by how transparent (or not) the known volume of water within the load compartment becomes (a numerical value can be applied to this). What type of soiling is on the wash load can be ascertained by how long it takes to reach the transparency saturation value. Gravy and other water-soluble soiling will reach its maximum saturation level fairly quickly whereas grease and other less-soluble soiling will take longer. In this way a relatively simple

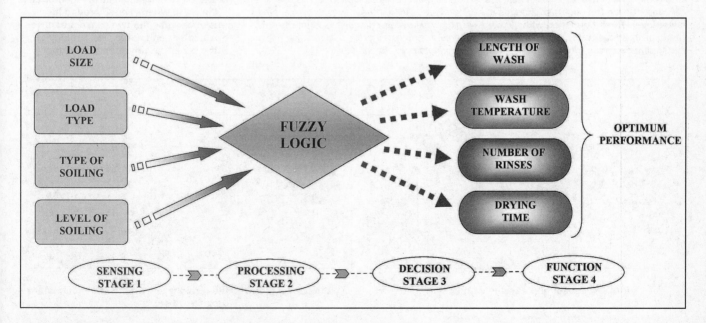

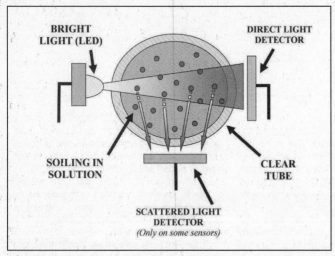

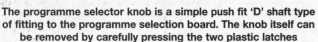

The programme selector knob is a simple push fit 'D' shaft type of fitting to the programme selection board. The knob itself can be removed by carefully pressing the two plastic latches

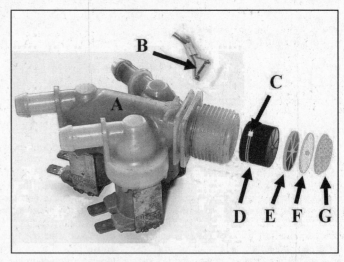

Triple water inlet valve with flow control sensor. Dishwashers are more likely to have single flow control inlet valves

optical sensor can tell the programme two important factors.

Note: *An important point to remember is* *that sensor inputs are not a one-off event, they are continuously monitored and if circumstances/sensor output changes, then so will the programme.*

The number of rinses can also be altered (increased or decreased) by optically sensing the rinse water.

The application of this type of technology can give rise to both financial and ecological savings. The time when you can simply put your crockery and utensils into your dishwasher and let it decide exactly how to wash, rinse and dry them is not too far away.

Note: *Fuzzy logic is not restricted to dishwashers in fact it has been around in industry for several years and applications range from industrial processes to anti-lock braking systems. Only recently has it emerged on the domestic appliance front and can now be found in clothes washing machine, microwave ovens, domestic vacuum cleaners, cameras and many other mass market items. This trend is set to continue.*

Electronic (analogue) water level sensors can detect even the slightest changes in water level. When combined with 'Fuzzy' logic programme routines and circuitry the appliance can in effect think for itself

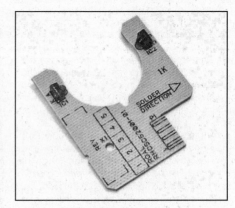

This close up of the turbidity sensor PCB shows clearly the light emitting source on the left and the light sensitive receptor on the right. When clipped around the translucent tube the two sensors oppose one another and detect the turbidity of the water passing though the tube

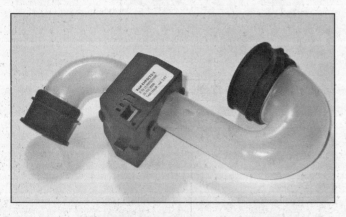

Turbidity sensor and translucent tube unit

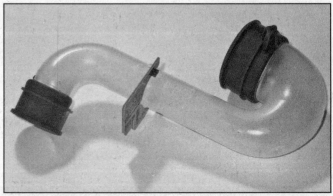

With the cover removed the turbidity sensor printed circuit board can be seen

Chapter 31
Fault and error codes

Many dishwashers now have the ability to detect problems that affect the correct functioning of the appliance. When a problem is detected the appliance will abort the selected programme and display an error code which relates to the specific problem detected. Depending on the make, model and style of the appliance there are two ways in which error code will be displayed:

• Numeric (1, 2, 3 etc.) or more commonly alpha numeric (E1, E2, E3 etc.) codes displayed by an LCD or LED panel on the front of the appliance.

• Where an LED or LCD display is not present on the front of the machine the error/fault code may be displayed by the flashing of a single light or a specific sequence of lights on the machine's facia.

The ability to assess and display a fault may appear to be an extremely complicated task to perform. However, as the appliance knows exactly where it is in the programme and exactly what is expected at that point (i.e. fill, wash, heat to a set temperature etc.) if the required action or function (i.e. operation of – pressure switch, thermostat/thermistor, spray arm sensor response) is not detected then a fault must have occurred.

This in-built automated fault detection system is in essence the same as that described in Chapter 8 *Functional testing* which can be used on appliances that can display error codes and those that cannot.

The ability to indicate what the problem may be could be seen as a benefit but for one major flaw – most if not all manufacturers of appliances choose not to disclose what the codes relate to other than the simple ones such are the taps turned on, is door closed etc.

Detailed error code information is generally restricted to their own service network or appointed agents leaving the independent repair sector in the dark as much as the customer when it comes to translating the fault code displayed.

This apparently somewhat restrictive practice does not mean that anyone other than a manufacturer's engineer can diagnose faults in the product but it does mean that you will need to treat the appliance as though it did not have the self-diagnosis feature. The information throughout this book has been produced to help those interested in appliance repair understand the practicality, function and technical depth to assist fault location and if deemed necessary repair of equipment whatever type is encountered.

Firstly the displaying of an error code is not a definitive fault-finding event and knowledge and understanding of the appliance, its correct installation and use will still be required to correctly identify the problem. Although helpful at times they are not essential.

Secondly the basic range of faults that are detected differs little between the whole range of makes and models. Unfortunately and for reasons known only to themselves each manufacturer chooses to use a different coding system which may even differ between models they produce!

Thirdly and most importantly the knowledge within this publication should help you diagnose faults without knowing exactly what a specific fault code means.

Although it is not possible to provide a definitive list of manufacturer's fault codes the following list has been produced to illustrate the diversity of systems whilst at the same time showing the similarity of what they relate to. Surely this is an area where an industry standard code would be useful.

As mentioned the following list should not be viewed as a definitive list of fault codes it merely serves as a general guide to what may be found.

If your particular make, model or code display is not shown then you can still use the information gained from other areas of the publication to assist you in your fault finding process. Alternatively you may find additional information relating to specific makes and models error codes using an internet search or by going to www.ukwhitegoods.co.uk which has an extremely detailed site for both users and independent service personnel.

UKWhitegoods also produce a very informative booklet relating to fault and configuration codes covering a wide range of makes and models which can be obtained directly from their website.

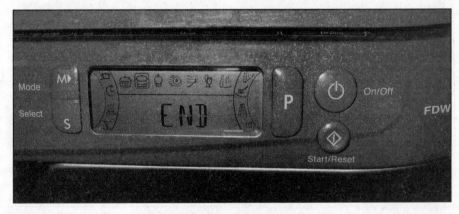

Typical LCD display panel

Typical user alarm code, details of which will be in the user hand book for the appliance

Typical error code – details of which are often restricted to the manufacturer's own service personnel

Typical error codes

Antonio Merloni dishwasher

The above may also apply to 'badged' versions such as Servis, Electra and other brand names

E1	LED 1 flashes	No fill cycle stops
E2	LED 2 flashes	Thermistor open or short circuit signalled when cycle completes
E3	LED 3 flashes	Temp too high/low (only during a test programme)
E4	Leak	Signalled when cycle completes
E5	Won't empty	Signalled when cycle completes

Baumatic dishwasher

E1	No fill
E2	No drain
E3	NTC thermistor/element fault
E4	Overfilling
E5	Cannot switch off automatically/programme not finishing (not for BDW 13, 14 or 15)
E6	Open circuit thermistor detected
E7	Short circuit thermistor detected

Candy & Hoover slimline dishwasher

E1	Filling time-out
E2	Drain time-out
E3	Heating fault
E4	Anti-flood protection
E6	Thermistor open circuit
E7	Thermistor closed circuit

Hoover Nextra dishwasher

E2	Filling time-out
E3	Drain time-out
E4	Anti-flood activated
E5	Thermistor fault
E7	Circulation, pump 'tachometric coil' open circuit
E8	Heating fault
E9	Turbidity sensor fault
Ee	Heating element safety switch open circuited
Eh	Heating element safety switch short circuit
Ei	Open circuit heater element

Hoover Late dishwasher

E1	No fill
E2	Temperature control fault (thermistor)
E3	Water not heating
E4	Not draining
E5	Flow meter not reading or pulsing correctly

Hotpoint BF72 dishwasher (made by SMEG)

Fault indication on this model is by facia LED sequence

E1	1st flashing with 5th lit	Flood protection system activated
E2	2nd flashing with 5th lit	Safety pressure switch activated
E3	1st 2nd flashing with 5th lit	Failed to heat in time allowed
E4	3rd flashing with 5th lit	Temperature sensor fault
E5	1st 3rd flashing with 5th lit	No fill
E6	2nd and 3rd flashing with 5th lit	Failed to drain in time allowed
E7	1st, 2nd and 3rd flashing	Flow meter detected when not fitted, reset required
E8	Same as E1	

Hotpoint, Indesit and Ariston dishwasher with 4 or 7 LEDs

These codes relate to models which have bit 100 PCBs indicated with serial number

LED 1	Overflow water in base
LED 2	Inlet valve
LED 3	Thermistor
LED 4	Time out filling
LEDs 1 and 2	Time out draining. **Note:** *1 and 2 can also relate to a software recognition error*
LEDs 2 and 3	Time out filling
LEDs 1 and 3	Filters blocked
LEDs 1 and 4	Software error
LEDs 2 and 4	Heater
LEDs 3 and 4	Timer hardware

Hotpoint, Creda, Ariston and Indesit dishwasher with LCD display

May also relate to other Merloni models

AL01	Anti-flood switch operated	
AL02	Valve or connections	
AL03	Time out	Drain
AL04	Thermistor (module)	
AL05	Circulation pump	
AL06	Time out	Filling
AL07	Not used	
AL08	Time out	Heat
AL09	Software recognition error	
AL10	Heating circuit	
AL99	Communications error	Connectors, cables etc.
H20	Time out	Filling (taps)

Indesit DE73 dishwasher

These codes are also used on several late model Hotpoint machines with digital display

A01	Aqua stop operated due to leak/overfill Machine drains until empty +1 min
A02	Heater relay, thermistor, safety stat or element fault Machine fills to level switch & wash pump runs
A03	Thermistor, machine drains until level switch resets + 1 min
A04	Unable to sense/reach temperature in 70 minutes Machine drains until level switch resets +1 min
A05	Level switch not resetting within 3 minutes 20 seconds of draining
A06	Not used see also H20
A07	Drain pump triac, check that drain pump is not disconnected/aqua stop operated
A08	Wash pump triac, check wash motor operation Machine drains until level switch resets + 30mins
A09	Main wash pump, check wash motor operation Machine drains until level switch resets + 30 mins
A10	Fill solenoid valve triac, check valve/operation Machine drains until level switch resets + 30 mins
A11	½ load valve triac or alternating w/motor action
A12	Relay open circuit check heater, replace module if this item is not separate
A13	Dispenser triac fault, wash cycle completes but with dispenser lid not functioning correctly
H20	Static fill time exceeds 6 minutes

LG dishwasher

EI	Leak error	Water level in tub drops during
	use	
FE	Overfill error	Excessive water in tub, drain
	pump activates	
HE	Heating error	No heat (time out) or
		temperature reaches 95°C
IE	Inlet error	10 minute time out on fill
OE	Drain error	5 minute time out drain time
		error
TE	Temperature error	Thermistor resistance incorrect

Loggixx dishwasher

A	Aqua sensor fault
B	Aqua sensor fault
C	No tacho pulses (i.e. motor runs at full speed 2,800 rpm)
D	Short circuit triac to circulation pump (pump keeps running)
E	Water points switching error between top & bottom basket
F	Filling error (time out 6 mins)
G	Water points error, triac fault on circuit board, short circuit
H	Heating error (time out) element, relay on module or pressure s/w
K	NTC error
O	Safety level switching error

Microtronic dishwasher

E10	Fill or empty time out
E11	Heater timed out. The heater has not reached the required level in a certain amount of time
E20	Temperature under range
E21	Temperature over range

Miele 'G' Series dishwasher

F0	No fault registered
F1	Thermistor or connections open circuit Should read 12kohms @ 20°C
F2	Thermistor or connections short circuit
F3	PCB/timer faulty
F4	Heating fault
F5	Heating fault or possible pressure switch
F6	No water intake detected (water supply or inlet valve)
F7	Fill fault (water level, overflow, flow meter, flow pressure)
F8	Heat level not reached (level switch, circulation pump)

Necht dishwasher

E1	Time out on fill
E2	Time out on drain
E3	Time out on heating
E4	Overfilling
E5	Programme jammed
E6	Open circuit thermistor
E7	Short circuit thermistor

Smeg dishwasher

For fully integrated dishwasher with display (not the latest type)

E2	Overfill detected
E3	Not heating
E4	Thermistor disconnected or open circuit
E5	No water intake
E6	Heating detected with no water present
E7	Not draining
E8	Read error Rest and try again
E9	Pause in test programme, not a fault code

Smeg 3 button dishwasher

With LCD Display

E1	Overfill detected
E2	Water level fault
E3	Not heating
E4	Temperature probe or the thermostat failure
E5	No fill
E7	No drain
E9	Same as E2

Chapter 32
Flood protection systems

Flood and leak protection systems of one type or another may be found on most dishwashers although there is no standard system or design and many variations and combinations can be found – some are extremely simple in both concept and design, whilst others are interestingly unique.

The following is a selection of some of the most common leak and flood protection systems currently in use.

Simple pressure switch version

This type of flood protection utilises conventional water level pressure switch principles and could be described as an overfill protection. In the event of the inlet valve or normal level switches failing the resulting overfill would be detected by the additional flood protection level switch. The switching action could be used to turn off the water inlet valve solenoid or start the drain pump to discharge the overfill. Unfortunately the overfill pressure switch is often connected to the same pressure vessel as the normal level switch and in some instances it may simply be an extra switch within the existing unit. A combined overfill configuration may itself fail to function when needed if blockages occur or pressure leaks from the common components. To avoid this problem separate pressure vessels and pressure switches would be the best design and many manufacturers use this option.

Sealed base and float switch

With this type of system the whole construction of the appliance is designed to channel any water leaks into the base of the machine. Even the inlet hose will be housed within a second plastic hose, should the inlet hose leak the water would be channelled to the base of the appliance. The base may simply be a shaped bottom plate added to a normally open bottomed machine and held in position with screws. Alternatively the base may be a large plastic moulding housing all the major components. Whichever type of base is used any leaks that develop, i.e. hoses, pumps, load compartment, etc. will be channelled into the base where they will collect in a specially formed recess. A float (normally expanded polystyrene) is positioned

within the recess. When enough water has accumulated within the recess the float will lift. This lifting action can be used to actuate a micro-switch to turn OFF the water inlet valve or mechanically close a valve within a special inlet valve unit to prevent further filling taking place. This type of mechanical float system is normally accompanied by other means of over fill protection, i.e. pressure switch. **Note:** *If you tilt the appliance or spill any water when working on appliances with this type of system, ensure that the base and recess are dry and free from water before functionally testing. Also ensure that the float and arm are not obstructed and are free to move.*

Water block inlet hose pressure activated

The water block hose is a mechanical protection system primarily to reduce the chance of flooding should a fill hose split or

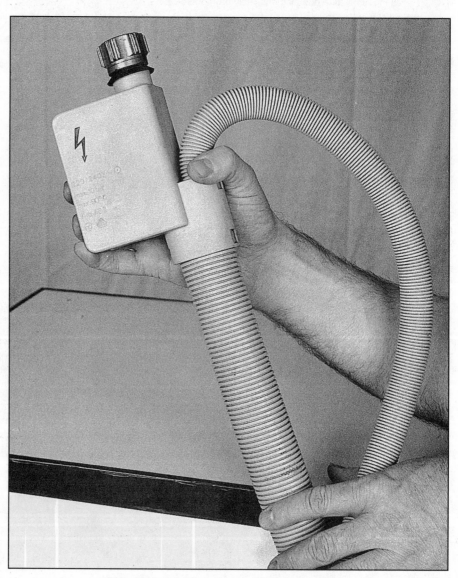

This dishwasher has a water block hose system

leak. The water block hose consists of several layers making a hose within a hose configuration. Only the inner hose carries the water from the inlet valve to the appliance. If the inner hose should perish or leak the pressure will be trapped within the next layer and used to close a mechanical valve situated at the inlet end of the hose. Most hoses have a means of indicating that the safety valve has been activated, for obvious reasons once tripped this device cannot be reset. If required this type of hose can be used to replace ordinary fill hoses to increase the level of protection.

Water block inlet hose electrical/mechanical

This system consists of a special one-piece inlet hose and inlet valve combination often referred to as an 'Aquastop' hose. It can be activated in two ways either electrically or mechanically via pressure (similar to the water

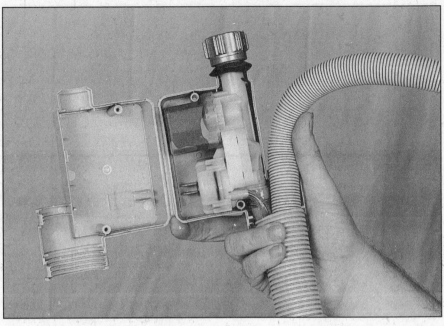

With the outer cover removed the inlet valve and wiring can be seen

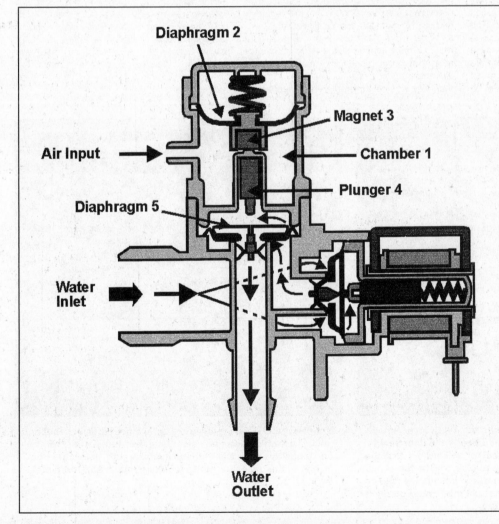

This flood protection valve consists of a standard solenoid operated valve combined with a second inlet diaphragm (5). Actuating plunger (4) is held away from diaphragm (5) by a magnet (3) which is attached to pressure diaphragm (2). Water can flow past the second inlet diaphragm (5) as long as plunger (2) is held at the top of the guide chamber. In an overfill situation air will enter chamber (1) and exert pressure on diaphragm (2). When the overfill is above a predetermined level the pressure within chamber (1) will lift the diaphragm and the attached magnet against its return spring and break the magnetic bond holding the plunger. The plunger drops and closes diaphragm (2) preventing any further water entering the machine (even if the solenoid is still energised). Releasing the air pressure from chamber (1) will allow the valve to reset as the magnet attracts the plunger to the top of the guide. **Note:** *It is possible for the plunger not to reset purely by magnetic attraction and may require tapping or inverting to ensure it resets correctly. Do not reset the system until the original overfill problem has been identified and corrected*

VALVE | INLET HOSE

PRESSURE TUBE

PIVOT

FLOAT | BASE & RECESS

This diagram depicts a sealed base float system. In this instance the water inlet can be shut off in three ways. Firstly a solenoid operated valve is used for normal water level control. Secondly if the base plate recess fills with water the circular float will lift and mechanically close the inlet valve. Thirdly the system incorporates a pressure chamber and diaphragm which can mechanically close the valve by air pressure from an overfill pressure vessel. As before do not reset the system until the original overfill problem has been identified and corrected

block hose). On some versions safety is further improved by the use of a water inlet valve with a two-solenoid configuration, i.e. two valves in series. The valve(s) and solenoid(s) are housed in a large protective container at the water entry point of the fill hose with the valve screwing directly on to the isolation tap connection. The power supply for the water valve solenoid(s) and the hose from the valve outlet to the appliance run through a bulky corrugated plastic cover. The reason for this configuration is to alleviate the constant pressure carried by

conventional flexible inlet hoses where the inlet valve is situated at the machine end. The fill hose consists of several layers with the inner hose carrying the water from the inlet valve to the appliance. Should the inner hose leak the pressure will be contained within the next layer and used to close a mechanical inlet valve, refer to *Water block hose* for details. For obvious reasons once tripped this device cannot be reset. **Note:** *In essence the 'AquaStop' system alleviates the potential for leakage problems that may not be covered by the appliance's*

internal flood protection system. However, the hose is bulky and the large end connection can be difficult to connect unless the correct plumbing requirements are in place. Additionally simple valve failure will result in a complete new 'AquaStop' hose being fitted which can be expensive. These points should be weighed against the incidence/failure rate of conventional inlet hoses, which are often and unwisely left under pressure (ideally the isolation tap(s) should be turned OFF after each wash cycle).

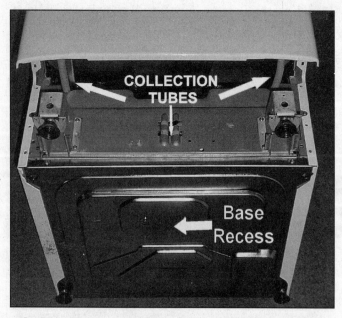

On this particular model the bottom of the load compartment has two grommet fitted plastic hoses fitted in the door seal to door recess. These are used to 'collect' and direct any leakage at this point down into the base of the appliance. The metal base of the appliance has a preformed recess to collect any leak or overfill. The two screws in the recess hold the flood protection device in place

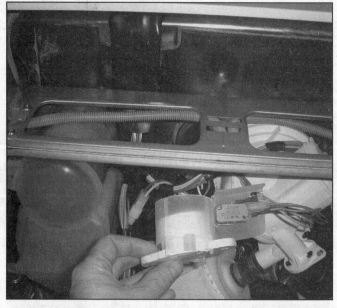

With the metal base removed the simple float (polystyrene) and micro-switch unit can be seen. When fixed to the base of the appliance the open top of the unit sits directly below the open ends of the collection tubes (centre of metal support plate)

Mechanical water block and flood protection hose

This is a rather interesting mechanical leak and flood protection water inlet hose system. A mechanical shut-off valve similar to the one described previously is situated at the supply end of the inlet hose. In this system the shut-off valve is actuated by a blast of air from the chamber fixed to the base of the appliance. The inlet hose, mechanical valve and a neoprene pressure tube connecting the chamber to the shut-off valve are housed in a plastic moulding and support tube. The base mounted chamber is a sizeable plastic unit containing a larger piston, return spring, latching mechanism and

trigger release. The chamber is primed by pushing a rod connected to the piston until the latch engages (quite some force is required for this process). A gap of around 12mm exists between the release mechanism (trigger) and the recessed base of the appliance. A small highly compressed piece of super dry sponge is then positioned within this gap. The unit operates as follows:

When water (even a relatively small amount) enters the recess the sponge quickly soaks it up and as a result expands. The expansion pushes against the latching trigger releasing the piston. The powerful return spring shoots the piston forward within the chamber, creating a powerful blast of air. The jet of air is transferred to the shut-off valve at the top of the inlet hose via the neoprene tubing and the

valve closes. Although it may appear to be relatively 'low tech' this particular system has many advantages. It is designed to alleviate the potential for most if not all leakage/flooding problems. It will work even when the appliance is not turned 'ON' or plugged in and it can be reset when the original problem has been corrected. Both the mechanical inlet valve and chamber can be reset and a new special trigger sponge fitted. **Note:** *The old sponge cannot be reused once it has expanded, do not attempt to reuse it and do not leave the system without one.*

Although the base chamber unit is large the inlet hose connection is only a little larger than normal, with the hose and shut-off valve configuration being less bulky than the previous two versions.

With metal base and front tube support removed the open ends of the ribbed collection tubes can be seen clearly

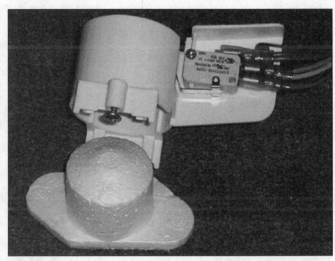

Close up of simple base mounted leak/flood protection unit

Float operated lead/flood protection unit (found on many Whirlpool, Ignis and Baucknect models)

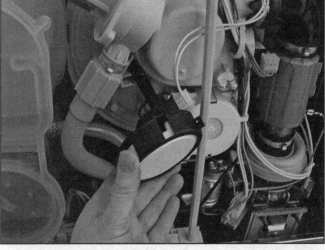

This type of leak/flood protection unit is held in position by plastic lugs on the support shaft locating in a recess in the sump moulding. Many of the components in this range of appliances are held in place by clips or bayonet type fittings

Chapter 33
Low insulation

What is low insulation?

Low insulation is best described as a slight leak to earth of electricity from the wiring of one or more of the components or wiring in an earthed appliance. If very slight, this will not harm the appliance but is an indication of faults to come and should be corrected immediately for safety reasons. The condition occurs during the progressive breakdown of the insulating properties of a normally electrically leakproof system.

How is it caused?

This can be caused by normal wear and tear over a long period, resulting in a breakdown of the insulating coating on wiring, motor windings, heater elements, etc. Such a breakdown of insulation may not result in a failure of the part at this stage and the appliance may still function as normal. This, however, is not an excuse to ignore low insulation; failure to trace and rectify low insulation is foolhardy because it compromises safety. Also extra expense is likely to be incurred in the long run. Faulty covers or misplaced seals will allow dust or damp to penetrate motor windings resulting in low insulation. If not corrected, this could lead to a complete failure of the motor, or worse. A simple renewal of the cover or seal and careful cleaning and drying of the Thermal Overload Cut-out (TOC) and windings may be all that is needed to save money and improve safety for all concerned.

How can it be detected?

When a service engineer tests for low insulation, he will use an instrument called a low insulation tester. The law requires repair engineers to test for low insulation, and there is a minimum allowable level as follows:

1 Between the earth pin on the plug and all earth connection points within the appliance, the maximum resistance should be 0.1 ohm, i.e. very little resistance – a perfect connection.
2 With the machine unplugged, select a wash programme and turn the machine on.

Leave one lead of the test meter connected to the earth pin of the plug and use the other lead to bond (join) the live and neutral pins on the plug. The minimum resistance should be 2 megohms, i.e. very high resistance – no connection at all.
3 Repeat the above test, after setting the machine to a rinse programme, (remember the machine's heater is normally only supplied with power when the correct level of water has been reached, it is wise, therefore, to test the heater separately). Electronic models with control relays/triacs will also have to have some components tested individually. **Note:** *Ensure that individually tested items are isolated from the PCB when testing items in this way.*
4 Testing of the heater can be carried out by removing both wiring connections to the heater. Connect one lead of the test meter to one of the free terminals and the other lead to the earth terminal, again the minimum resistance should be 2 megohms. Repeat the test using the other terminal.

These tests are carried out using a meter designed to test insulation by applying a high voltage (500V) at very low amperage (for safety). It is an unfortunate fact that many engineers do not possess such a device, and therefore do not check for low insulation. This does not mean that you should not! A meter to test for low insulation would cost upwards of £150 and therefore out of reach of most DIY repairers. An alternative is to utilise an in-line circuit breaker (see *Flowchart*). The appliance is plugged into the circuit breaker, which is then plugged into the socket. If an RCD already protects the circuit or socket then it can be used as the tester. As mentioned in *Basics – electrical,* the purpose of the device is to detect low insulation or leakage to earth and turn off the power to the appliance. Although this is not the ideal way of testing for low insulation, it will help in locating it and provide a degree of safety for the appliance and its user.

If any appliance trips an RCD (or similar) system, do not use the appliance until the fault has been rectified. If tripping occurs with no appliances or load on the system, then a fault in the house wiring is indicated and the trip switch should not be reset until the fault is found and corrected. Have your RCD tested regularly by an approved electrician to ensure that it functions correctly and safely at the correct speed of no more than 0.4 of a second. Such tests require an RCD test meter that calculates the trip time of the unit. On simple test the unit may trip but may be taking too long to do so for it to be classified as safe.

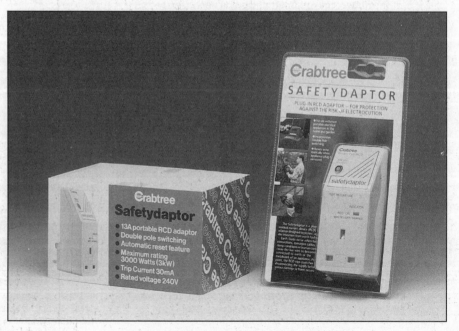

A quality double pole portable (adaptor type) RCD

Points to remember about low insulation

Ensure that any disconnection or removal of wires is safe, and not earthing via another wire or the shell of the machine, etc.

When disconnecting any wires during the testing of low insulation, it should be remembered that the machine must be isolated from the mains at all times, and the panels must be replaced before the machine is re-tested.

Before testing for low insulation with the use of a circuit breaker, all earth paths of the machine should be tested. This is done by connecting a test meter between the earth pin of the plug, and all other metal parts of the machine in turn. Maximum resistance should be 0.1 ohm. See *Electrical circuit testing.*

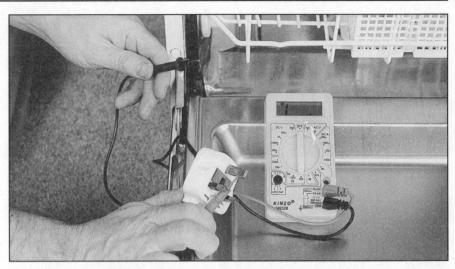

Getting ready to check for earth continuity from earth pin on the plug to the door hinge. As circuit is as yet incomplete, the reading on this digital meter reads open circuit

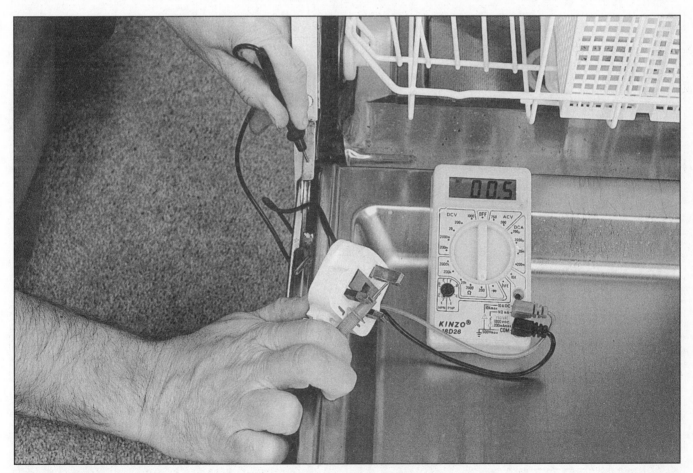

When the probe is connected to the metal of the door hinge, the reading indicates a complete or closed circuit. This confirms that the earth path is complete from the plug terminal to the metal hinge as it should be. Testing the earth path from the plug pin to the metal door hinge fixing gave reading of 0.5 ohms. Prior to testing the earth path test leads of the meter were touched together to find the resistance of the test leads which in this instance was 0.43 ohms. This figure was then deducted from the combined reading (leads and earth path) indicating the earth only reading to be 0.07 ohms and therefore within the required limits. If this test fails, investigate and cure the open circuit and do not use the machine until the fault is rectified. It is always advisable to check that all the items that have earth connections pass this earth continuity check, i.e. have a perfect (low resistance) earth path. Do not forget to check the supply also has a good earth (See *Plugs and sockets*)

LOW INSULATION FLOWCHART

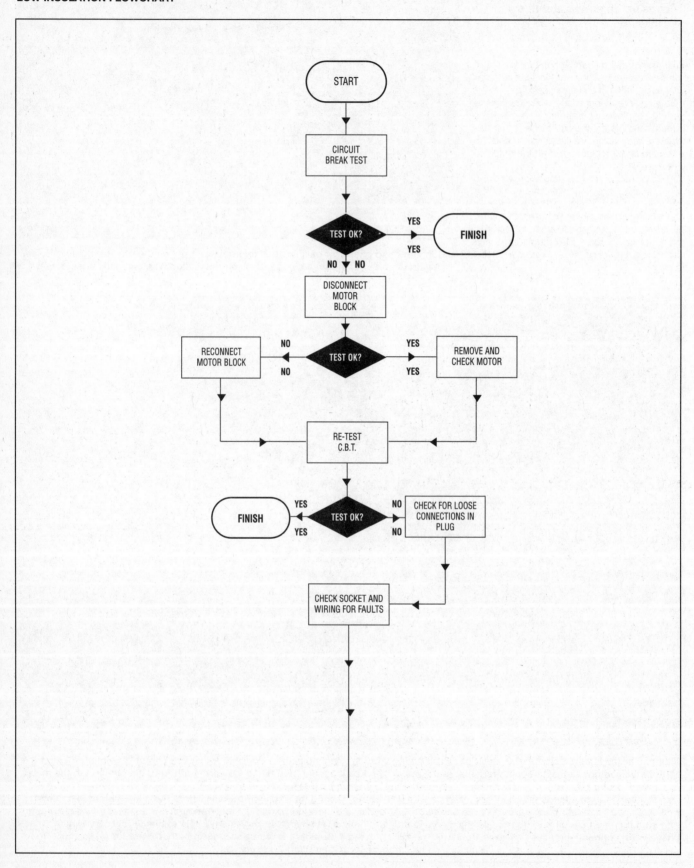

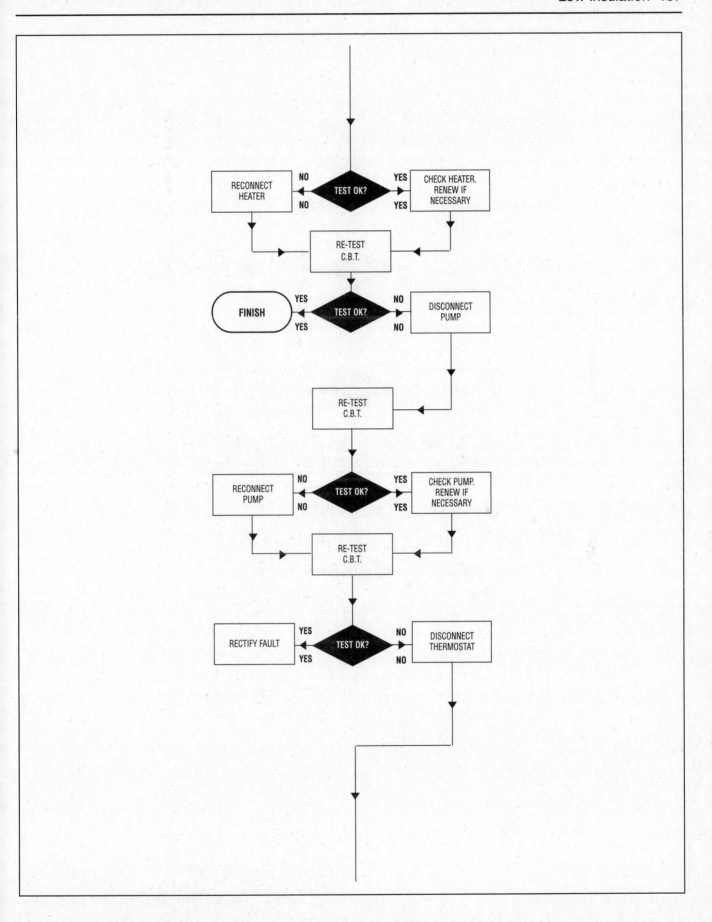

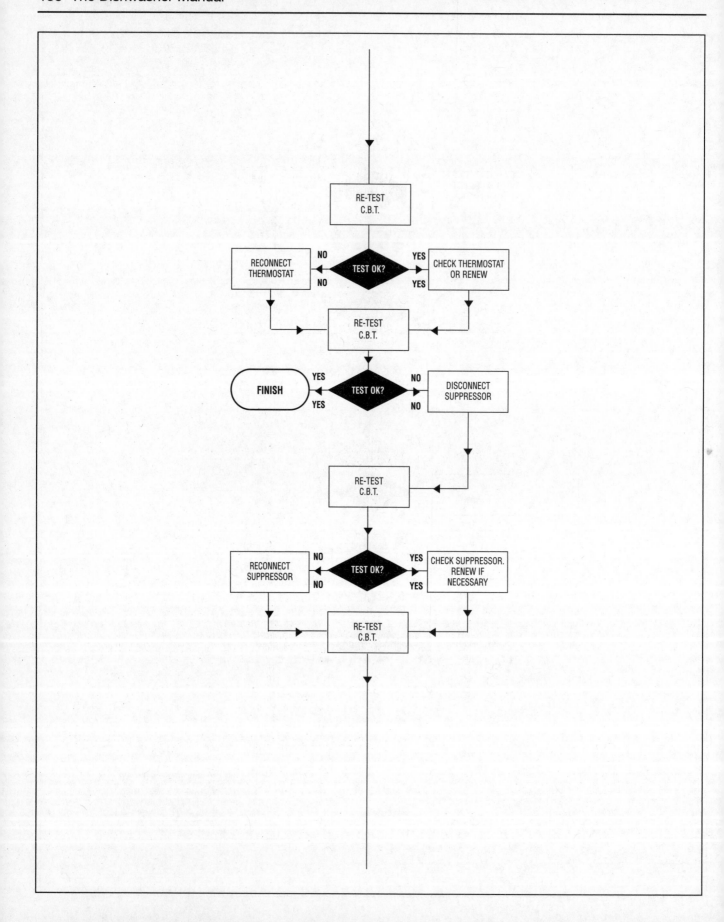

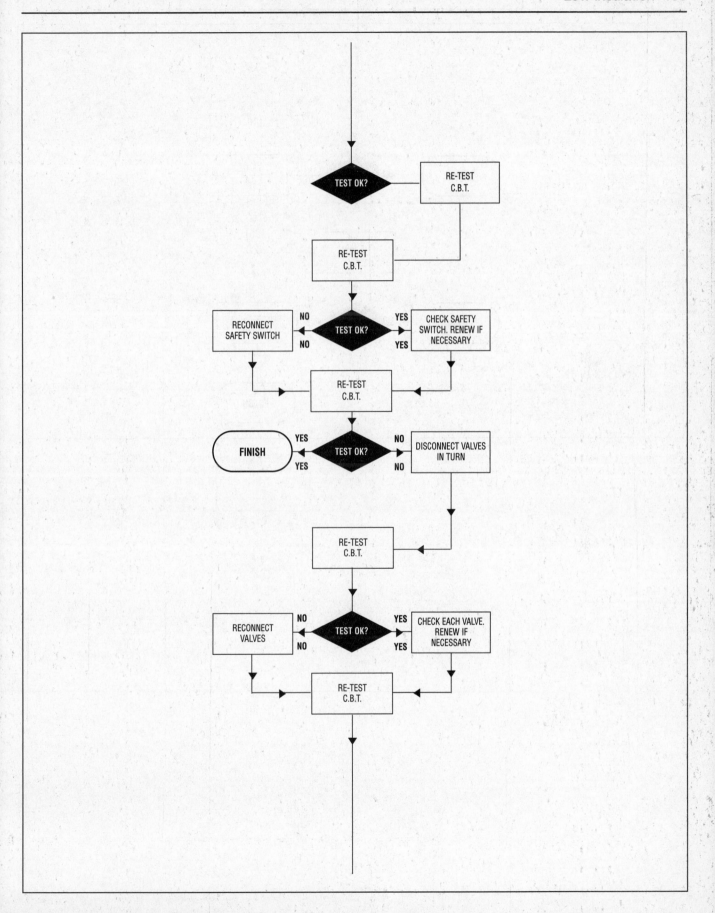

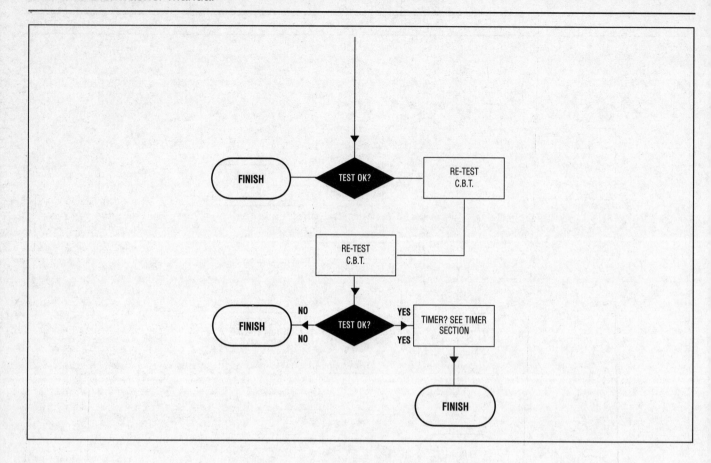

Chapter 34
The suppressor

What is a suppressor?

A suppressor is a device designed to eliminate the formation and transmission of spurious radio waves that may be produced by the operation of switches and motors within the appliance during its normal operation. When switching occurs within the machine and it is not suppressed, small sparks at the contact points may produce interference on radio and TV channels or audio equipment plugged into the same electrical supply circuit. The latter occurs due to transmission of the interference through the supply cables. Suppressors fitted to all domestic appliances are designed to eliminate both types of interference.

Why should all machines have them?

By law, all domestic appliances must be suppressed to conform to the regulations on radio interference, and it is an offence to use a machine not suppressed to these standards.

Where is it located?

Suppressors vary in style, shape, size and colour. Sometimes individual parts are suppressed, but more often the mains supply is suppressed at or just after the entry point (terminal block) into the machine and some suppressors are now an integral part of the mains lead. Those with four or more connections are called 'in-line' suppression as both the live and neutral supply goes through the suppressor (a 'series' connection) and on to supply the whole of the machine with power.

Do not confuse the suppressor with the capacitor(s) that may also be in the machine. They may look very similar but carry out distinctly different functions. (Refer to *The capacitor* in the *Pumps* chapter for further detail.)

An alternative to the in-line suppressor is the three wire suppressor which is generally a much smaller unit with leads that connect onto the live, neutral and earth connections of the appliance at or near the mains terminal block (in 'parallel' with the connections).

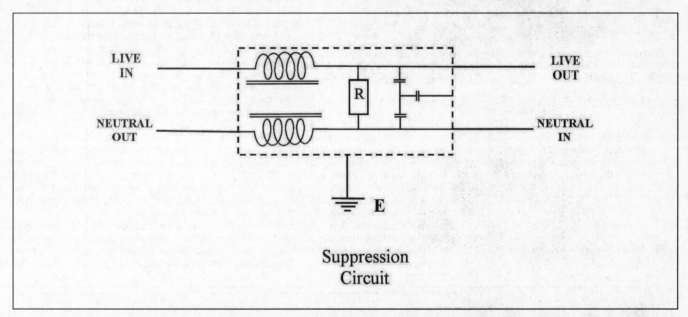

Suppression Circuit

A typical 'lead through' suppressor. With the appliance isolated from the mains supply and the suppressor removed from the appliance wiring the readings obtained using a simple multimeter should read as follows

Between Live and Neutral, very high resistance – you are effectively testing the resistor 'R' in the diagram and this usually has a resistance of around 47kΩ (470,000Ω)

Between Live In and Live Out – Very low resistance (continuity through the suppressor)

Between Neutral In and Neutral Out – Very low resistance (continuity through the suppressor)

Between Earth and Live – Infinitely high resistance (effectively no circuit detectable)

Between Earth and Neutral – Infinitely high resistance (effectively no circuit detectable)

Replace the filter unit if incorrect readings are obtained

Note: *Although the above diagram shows a circuit between Live and Earth and Neutral and Earth the circuit is through a series of small internal capacitors. When testing a suppressor with a battery powered multimeter (D.C. voltage) no circuit should be detected. However, the capacitance suppression circuit will conduct under A.C. (mains) supply. An Earth path in both appliance and supply is therefore essential not only for the safety of the product but for the correct functioning of this type of suppression unit*

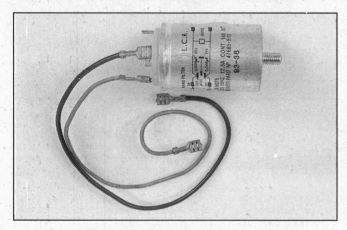

Large in-line suppressor unit with spade terminals

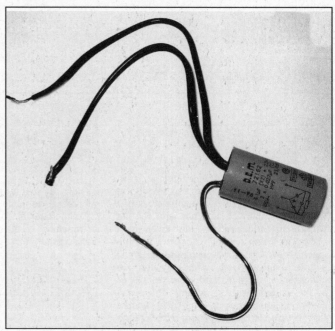

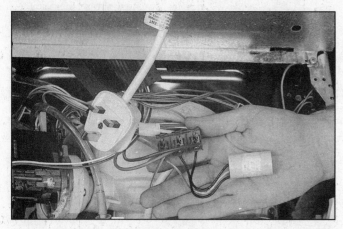

Small three lead suppression unit with plastic casing and earth lead connection

Typical small 'three lead' suppressor which in this instance has two black wires which need to be connected to the 'Live' and 'Neutral' connections of the mains connections and a clear plastic covered wire which is the 'Earth' wire and needs to be connected to the 'Earth' terminal. This type of small suppressor can be found on a wide range of appliances including dishwashers and due to the 'Earth lead' not being indicated by the normal colours of Yellow and Green care must be taken to ensure correct fitting. The two black wires can be connected to either the 'Live' or 'Neutral' terminals but the 'Earth' lead must only be connected to Earth terminal

Suppressors can also be called a mains filters because of their filtering effect in preventing interference escaping from the appliance.

Faults with suppressors (filters)

The main fault is one of short circuiting to earth usually resulting in the unit 'blowing' both the main fuse and itself. This is often accompanied by a pungent burnt smell. Renewal is a straighforward one-for-one replacement.

Open circuit problems can occur and the unit will fail to allow current to pass through as normal. See *Using a meter* section in the *Electrical circuit testing* chapter. When checking, inspect the top insulation closely and if cracked or at all suspect, renew complete unit.

In-line suppressors use the earth path as part of their filtering circuit, (although very little power passes through it). It is essential for ALL machines to have a good earth path. If a machine with an in-line suppressor/filter has a break in its earth path (due to cable, plug or socket fault) small electric shocks may be experienced when the user touches metal parts of the machine, especially if they are in touch with a good earth themselves (i.e. holding metal sink or work top when bending

down to machine etc.). It is essential that such faults are traced and corrected immediately. Always ensure that any electrical appliance has a correctly wired plug and that all sockets have a good earth path. See *Basics – electrical*.

Suppressors should not be bypassed or omitted, as to have an unsuppressed machine is an offence because of the interference that it may cause to others.

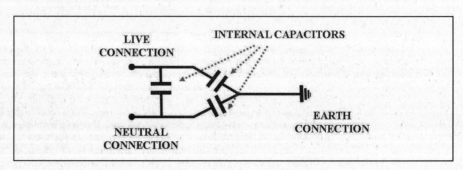

A typical 'three lead' suppressor

Three lead suppressors (arrowed) are generally much smaller than the lead through types and are often left unsecured as in this instance

Typical lead through suppressor secured to rear panel of the appliance

Square suppressor which is a simple 'clip fit' to the rear panel of the appliance

Unlike this separate suppressor some may be an integral part of the mains lead and can only be renewed as a complete item

Suppressor with overheated terminal connection – ensure all electrical connections are in good condition and a tight fit

Chapter 35
Electrical circuit testing

Using a meter

Throughout this book, references have been made to meters and their use in continuity testing of individual parts of appliances and their connecting wires. All such testing and checking for 'open' (i.e. not allowing for current flow), or 'closed' circuit (i.e. allowing current to flow), must be carried out using a battery powered multi-meter or test meter. Under no circumstances should inspection or testing be carried out on 'live' items, i.e. appliances connected to the mains supply. **Remember:** *Completely isolate the appliances from the mains supply before starting any inspection, repair work or testing.*

Although some meters and testers have the facility to check mains voltages, I do not agree with their use in repairs to domestic appliances. Faults can be easily traced by simple low voltage (battery power) continuity testing, proving that the simplest of meters or even a home-made one like the one described later are perfectly adequate for some faults. Remember that safety is paramount and under no circumstances should it be compromised. Always double check that the appliance is unplugged; a good tip is to keep the plug in view so that no-

one else can inadvertently plug it in. The simple home-made continuity tester described later will help trace faults only in the wiring of the appliance. A multi-meter similar to the ones shown will be required for individual component testing.

If you decide to buy a test meter, you could find yourself faced with quite a variety to choose from. Do not be tempted to get an over-complicated one as it could end up confusing and misleading you when in use. Before using your new meter, read the manufacturer's instructions thoroughly and make sure that you fully understand them. A 'Rapitest' meter is very simple to use when continuity testing and has a scale that reads 'open' circuit or closed' circuit. It can be purchased from most local DIY store and is reasonably priced. The meter will also help locate faults with car electrics, but as previously stated, using on live mains circuits should not be entertained.

Some multi-meters are able to show the resistance value of the item being tested as well as indicating simple continuity. This can be extremely useful if the correct value of the item being tested is known, i.e. correct resistance of an inlet valve, heating element, etc., although this is by no means essential. Detailed use of the multi-meter for this function will be found in its accompanying instruction leaflet.

Electrical fault finding

A simple continuity tester for checking wiring can be used to trace wiring faults in most appliances and is very easy to make. It uses the lack of continuity ('open' circuit) to its full advantage. To make this tester, you will need a standard battery, bulb and three wires 1 x 130mm (5in) and 2 x 250mm (10in). Connect the short wire to the positive terminal of the battery and the other end of that wire to the centre terminal of a small torch bulb. Attach one of the longer wires to the negative terminal of the battery and leave the other end free. The other wire should be attached to the body of the bulb again, leave the end free.

The two loose ends now act as the test wires. Press the two ends of the wires together, and the bulb will light. If not, check that the battery and the bulb and all connections are OK. When 'open circuit', the light will stay off, and when 'closed circuit', the light will be on. **Note:** *Low voltage bulb type testers of 1.5 volts or 3 volts are unsuitable for testing the continuity of components within the machines. Purpose made test meter like the ones shown will be required to test high resistance items such as pumps, timer coils, valves, etc. Ensure that the machine is isolated from the main supply before attempting to use a meter.*

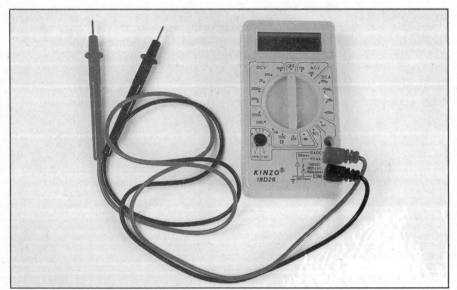

A typical digital multi-meter of the type to be bought in most DIY stores. Try to obtain a meter with a good information booklet. The meter shown was purchased for under £15 and proved to be useful for many other jobs around the house and car

A typical analogue multi-meter

How to test for continuity using a test meter

To test for an open circuit, note and remove the original wiring to the component to be tested. (If this is not done, false readings may be given from other items that may be in circuit.) The ends of the two wires of the meter should be attached to the terminals of the component that is to be tested and select the lowest ohms range scale (this is often a scale of 0 to 200 ohms). For example, to test a heater for continuity select the lowest ohms range on your test meter and place the metal probes of the test meter onto the terminals on the heater and watch the meter. If you are using an analogue test meter (one with a moving needle) the needle should move and indicate the resistance on an arced scale. However, if you are using a digital test meter then a digital figure should appear in the display. To check for the correct resistance of components that normally have higher resistance values (refer to component guide) then you will need to select the relevant ohms range scale on your meter. You will need to refer to the instruction booklet for your particular meter for how to change the scale setting (unless you have an auto-ranging digital meter).

If as in this instance the heater is 'open circuit', i.e., no movement or no figure displayed on the test meter, the heater can then be suspected and tested further by selecting a higher range scale on your test meter. If a closed circuit is indicated or a resistance reading is obtained which is in line with what was expected (refer to component guide) the heater continuity is OK.

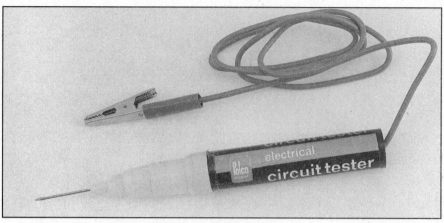

This simple continuity tester was purchased from a local automart for a very reasonable sum

Often the most effective way to trace a fault is to use a very simple, but logical approach to them. One such approach is called the leap-frog method and can be used to find the failed/open circuit part or parts. In this instance, let us assume that the appliance does not work at all when functionally tested, therefore you cannot deduce where the problem lies purely from the symptoms. A quick check of the supply socket by plugging in another appliance known to be OK will verify (or not) that there is power up to that point. This confirms that the fault lies somewhere in the appliance, its supply cable or plug. We know that during normal conditions, power flows in through the live pin on the plug, through the appliance (when switched on) and returns via the neutral pin on the plug. The fact that the appliance will not work at all even when plugged in and switched on indicates

that an open circuit exists somewhere along this normal live to neutral circuit.

Leap-frog testing – using a meter

First, test that the meter is working correctly, i.e. touch test probes together and the meter should indicate continuity (shows the resistance of the leads themselves). With the machine unplugged (isolated) connect one probe to the live pin of the appliance's plug and the other on the live conductor connecting point in the plug. Continuity should be found which confirms that the pin, fuse and their connections are OK, but faulty if open circuit occurs. If this check proves to be satisfactory, move the probe from the live conductor point in the plug to the live

Component	Typical Resistance	Special Notes
Plug fuse	None (very low – 'closed' circuit)	Check correct rating and condition of plug, fuse and socket, Change if found to be defective in any way
Inlet valves	3500 to 5000 ohms	If the circuit is OK, possible manual fault inside valve
Heater	22 ohms	Check also for low insulation
Pressure switch	Only open or closed circuit	See *Water level control* chapter
Thermostat	–	See *Thermostats and thermistors* chapter
Outlet pump (shaded pole type)	45 ohms	If the circuit is OK, possible manual fault inside pump
Outlet pump (permanent magnet type)	180 ohms	If the circuit is OK, possible manual fault inside pump
Main motor	Start winding Run winding	Refer to *Pumps* chapter for help
Harness wiring	None (very low resistance – 'closed' circuit)	Test each wire separately to suspect component, pulling connections and along its length to find possible internal open circuit. Outer insulation may however appear complete
Rinse aid solenoid (coil type)	3500 to 5000 ohms	Check also for manual fault and blockages
Detergent solenoid (coil type)	3500 to 5000 ohms	Check also for manual fault and blockages

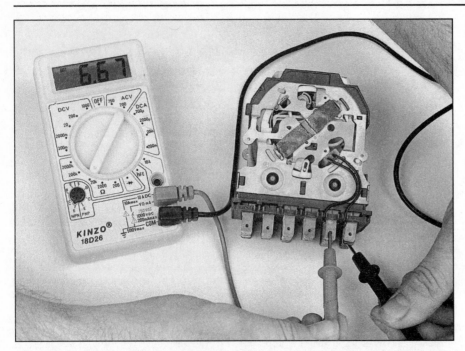

A simple continuity test (i.e. for 'closed' circuit) on this timer motor coil. The test could have been easily made with the timer in situ, but is shown here removed from the machine for clarity. The reading shown is 6.67kohms which is 6,670 ohms. All timer motor coils will have high resistance values in the kohms range if this circuit is ok. Note: *Most manufacturers would supply a complete timer unit for such a fault though it is sometimes possible to obtain the motor coils from pattern spares stockists*

The test on this pump stator proved to be ok, (i.e. closed circuit continuity). This meant that the supply or neutral to and from the pump required checking to discover the reason why the pump failed to work at any point in the programme

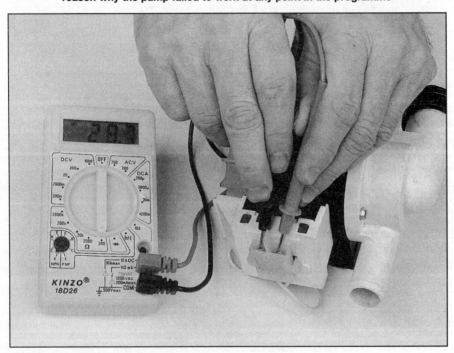

The ohms reading will differ from item to item. Test for open or closed circuits only. Any reference to an ohm (Ω) reading is a guide only as resistances differ from machine to machine. The objective is to test for either continuity or the lack of continuity of the item being tested

conductor connection in the terminal block within the appliance. Again, continuity should be found, if not, a fault between plug and terminal block is indicated. **Note:** *On cable continuity testing, it's best to move the cable along its length during the test to ascertain if an intermittent fault may exist.*

If this test is OK, move the probe to the next convenient point along the live conductor, in this instance, the supply side of the on/off switch, which may be part of the main programme switch on some machines (usually the front terminals).

Again, continuity is required. An open circuit indicates a fault between the terminal block and switch connection. The next step is to move the probe to the opposite terminal of the switch. Operate the switch to verify correct action (i.e. 'on' continuity, 'off' open circuit). If OK proceed to the next point along the wire, in this instance the door latch safety switch connection. Again continuity is required. If OK, move probe to the other terminal of the door safety switch – when the door latch is in the closed (locked) position continuity is required, operate the latch switch to verify correct action of the safety switch (i.e. latch closed switch 'closed' continuity, unlatched switch 'open' no circuit).

At this point we will assume that an 'open' circuit has been indicated both when the latch is latched and unlatched, so go back to the last test point and verify continuity up to that point. If as before this test proves to be OK then a fault has been traced to the door safety switch which requires renewal.

This simple, methodical approach is all that is required to find such problems. With more complex circuits it is best to break them down into individual sections, i.e. lead, switch, heater etc., and test continuity of each section from live through the timer and the individual parts and back to neutral. This may involve moving the live probe that would normally remain on the plug live pin to a more convenient supply point within the appliance to avoid misleading continuity readings from other items within the appliance circuit. With practice, faults can be found even in complex wiring in this way.

Note: *DO NOT consider tracing faults by looking for mains voltages. There is no need to consider or use such dangerous techniques. All testing can and should be carried out with the appliance completely isolated, i.e. switch off, plug out, using only a battery powered meter or tester to indicate continuity or open circuit.*

The ohms reading will differ from item to item and as a result may require that you select the appropriate scale on your test meter for high resistance items. Failure to select an appropriate scale on your meter can give rise to false 'open' circuit readings being obtained. Test for 'open' or 'closed' circuits only. Any reference to an ohm (Ω) reading is a guide only as resistances differ from machine to machine. The objective is to test for either continuity or the lack of continuity of the item being tested.

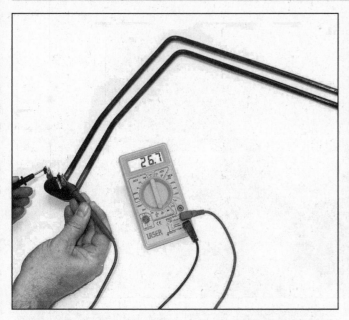

Testing this heater for continuity on the 0 to 200 ohms range of the test meter provided a reading of 26.7Ω which is within the range expected for a 2000 watt element. Although the exact reading obtained is of interest in reality you are checking for continuity (closed circuit – heater OK) or lack of continuity (open circuit heater failure)

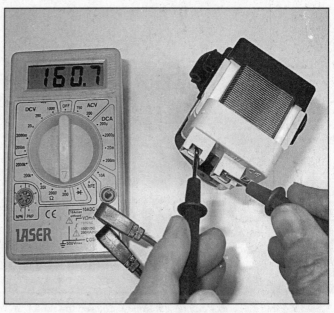

Checking this permanent magnet drain pump coil for continuity provided a reading of 160.7Ω which again could be detected using the 0 to 200 ohms range on the meter. Once again although the exact reading obtained is of interest in reality you are checking for continuity (closed circuit – coil OK) or lack of continuity (coil open circuit – failure)

Checking this water valve coil for continuity required the meter to be set to read kohms (thousands of ohms) in this instance the 0 to 20 kohms range as the coils of this type have high resistances and would appear open circuit if the wrong range was selected. The digital reading obtained is 3.75kΩ which equates to 3,750 ohms which is within the expected range. Yet again although the exact reading obtained is of interest in reality you are checking for continuity (closed circuit – valve coil OK) or lack of continuity (open circuit – valve coil failure)

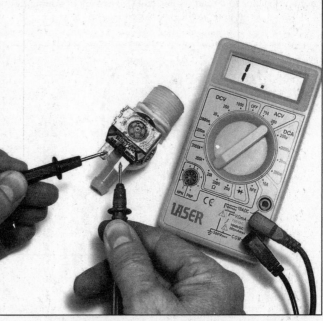

Checking this water valve coil for continuity on the kohms (thousands of ohms) range did not produce the expected continuity reading of between 3 to 4 thousand ohms as shown in the previous photograph. This indicates that the valve coil is open circuit resulting in the valve failing to operate when required to do so. When an open circuit reading such as this is obtained always check the leads of the meter by touching them together to check their continuity. If this simple test proves to be OK then check that a range scale suitable for the item being tested is selected

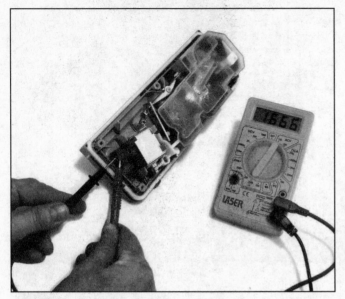

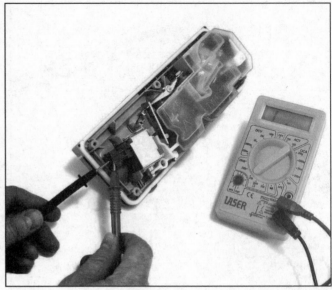

Checking this dispenser coil for continuity required the meter to be set to read kohms (thousands of ohms) in this instance the 0 to 2kohms range as the coils of this type have a resistance of 1 to 2kohms and would appear open circuit if the wrong range was selected. On this range the digital reading is shown in full as 1,666 ohms which would equate to 1.66kohms if a higher range had been selected but would have shown a false open circuit if too low a scale had been selected. Yet again although the exact reading obtained is of interest in reality you are checking for continuity (closed circuit – valve coil OK) or lack of continuity (open circuit – valve coil failure)

Checking this dispenser valve for continuity on the kohms (thousands of ohms) range did not produce the expected continuity reading of between 1 to 2 thousand ohms as shown in the previous photograph. This indicates that the coil is open circuit resulting in the coil failing to operate to open the dispenser flap for the wash process and dispense rinse aid when required. When an open circuit reading such as this is obtained always check the leads of the meter by touching them together to check their continuity. If this simple test proves to be OK then check that a range scale suitable for the item being tested is selected

This commercial meter can be used for low ohms readings as the scale can only provide readings up to 99.9Ω and would therefore be unable to test items with resistances above that level. Items such as the pump, valve coil and timer coil shown previously would appear open circuit on this meter. Before using a meter ensure that it is capable of reading the expected resistance and that it is set to the correct scale. Although this meter has limitations for simple resistance checking of components it does have the ability to check insulation which the simpler (and cheaper) meters do not

Before using your meter to check for low resistances – such as continuity testing a ribbon cable connection select the lowest ohms range on your meter and touch the test leads firmly together and note the reading obtained i.e. the reading of just the test leads (in this instance 0.4Ω). Deducting this reading from the reading obtained when checking for continuity will give the resistance of the item being tested

Chapter 36
Wiring harness faults

What is a wiring harness?

The term harness is used for all of the wires that connect the various components within the machine. They are usually bound or fastened together in bunches to keep the wiring in the machine neat and safely anchored.

What does it do?

At first sight, the harness may look like a jumble of wires thrown together. This is not the case. If you take the time to inspect the harness, you will find that each wire is colour coded or numbered (either on the wire itself, or on the connector at either end). This allows you to follow the wire through the machine easily. With practice, any wiring codings can be followed.

As most of the wires in the machine either finish or start at the timer unit (mechanical or electronic), it may be helpful to think of the timer (mechanical or electronic) as the base of a tree, with the main wiring harness as the trunk. As the trunk is followed, branches appear (i.e. wires to the valve, pressure switches, etc.). As the trunk continues upwards, it slowly gets thinner and branching takes place to the motor, pump, etc.

Each item is therefore separate, but linked to the timer (mechanical or electronic) by a central bond of wire. This can be likened to a central command post, communicating with field outposts.

The connecting wires to and/or from a component are vital to that component and possibly others that rely on that item's correct functioning. Luckily, wiring faults are not too common. However, when faults do occur, they usually seem to result in big problems, when in truth only a small fault has occurred, i.e. one poor connection can cause a motor not to function at all, and render the machine unusable. Do not fall into the trap of always suspecting the worst. Many people, including engineers, blindly fit parts such as a motor or a valve for a similar fault to that mentioned, only to find it did not cure the problem. Unfortunately the timer (mechanical or electronic) is usually blamed and subsequently changed. This does not cure the problem and is an expensive mistake. Stop, think and check all wires and connections that relate to your particular fault. Always inspect all connections and ensure that the wire and connector are tightly joined. Loose or poor connections can overheat and cause a lot of trouble, especially on items such as the heater.

Poor connections to items such as the rinse aid, detergent dispenser and door micro-switch will be aggravated by the movement of the door as it is opened and closed and may not be so apparent when the test is carried out.

One of the most difficult faults to find is where the metal core of the wire has broken and the outer insulation has not. This wire will appear perfect from the outside but will pass no electrical current. To test for this, see Chapter 35. This type of fault usually occurs on dishwashers at the base of the door's inner cavity where the wiring enters to supply items mounted within the door, such as rinse aid and detergent dispensers, etc. If the timer unit is situated in the door, all the wires must therefore at some point pass a fixed point to a movable one in the door. Although the manufacturers normally fit some form of protection at this point, it has to allow for the flexing of the cable during normal opening and closing of the door. It is this flexing that inevitably leads to a break in either the inner core or outer insulation of one or more of the wires present. Check and inspect thoroughly all points at which wiring enters or leaves the door base. Renew any suspect faulty covers or supports, etc. If a break or crack in the insulation is found at this point, renew the whole of the wire in question whenever possible. DO NOT simply tape or join the damaged wire at that point. As with any repair, ensure that the machine is completely isolated before this or any repair or inspection is carried out.

It must be remembered that such faults may be intermittent. That is to say that one reading may be correct and the same test later may prove incorrect. This is due to the movement of the outer insulation of the wire first making, then breaking the electrical connection.

When testing for such intermittent faults, it is wise to pull or stretch each wire as it is tested, as an unbroken wire will not stretch. A wire that is broken internally will stretch at the break point and rectification is a simple matter of renewal. Take time to do a few simple checks – it saves time, patience and money. **Note:** *Ensure that the harness is secured adequately to the shell of the machine, but allow a little slack to such items as the motor, heater, etc. Take care that any metal fastening clips do not chafe the plastic insulation around the wires. Also make sure that the wires are not in contact with sharp metal edges, self-tapping screws, etc.*

Warning: *Before attempting to remove or repair the wiring harness or any other component in the machine, isolate the machine from the mains electrical supply by removing the plug from the wall socket.*

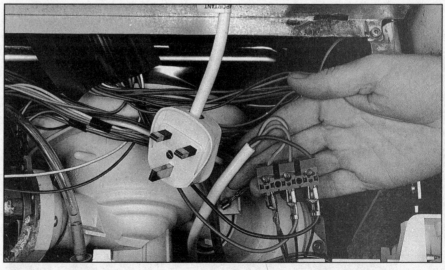

The terminal block is the first distribution point of the power into the machine. Ensure all connections are sound as heat will be generated if not

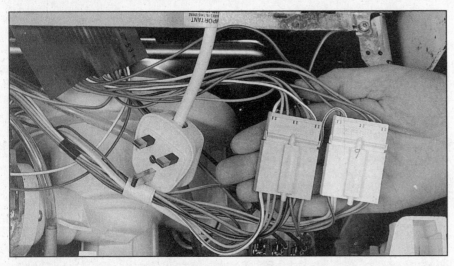

Harness connector block and support. Again, any loose connectors will overheat and cause problems. Ensure a secure fit

This close-up of the entry/exit point of the harness highlights the point of failure due to the constant flexing of the wiring when the door is opened and closed during use. Check this area thoroughly for any defects or poorly fitting cable protectors such as this

Door shown with outer cover removed. The entry and exit point of the wiring harness (arrowed) on a machine with door-mounted timers and switches is prone to break faults due to the constant flexing of the wiring. Check carefully all wiring at this point and renew completely if suspect. Also ensure that all protective guards and insulators are sound and refitted correctly.
The entry point and protective covering differ from make to make. It is essential for both safety and correct running of the machine that all wiring and insulation at this point are as original

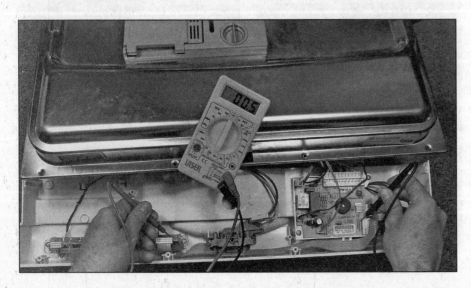

This type of ribbon cable between the programme board and the display LEDs can be tested by placing the test probes of the meter on the open connections at the relevant points on each connector block. In this instance a reading of 0.5Ω is shown but the original reading of the leads on their own (0.4Ω) must be deducted from this figure to obtain the true reading of the cable itself (0.1Ω in this instance). When testing the continuity of electrical connections such as this as low a reading as possible is required but the quality/accuracy of your test meter will have a bearing on this. An open circuit is an obvious problem however, high resistances in cables and connections are a problem especially on low voltage connections within electronically controlled machines

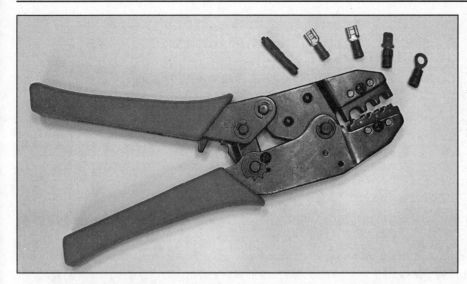

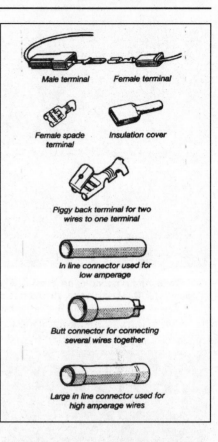

A ratchet crimping tool will correctly fit the connectors shown. The one shown in the photograph has changeable jaw ends (anvils) to suit the type of crimp required. The tool in the photograph has the colour coded jaws fitted that are used for correctly fitting the insulated terminals and connectors (those on the right-hand side diagram)

The terminal block is the first distribution point of the power into the machine. Ensure all connections are sound, as heat will be generated if not.
Note: *This appliance combines the terminal block with the mains suppressor unit i.e. the mains supply lead connects directly to the suppressor*

All of the above are 'crimp' fitted to inner and outer of the wires. When used make sure that they fit securely and will not easily part

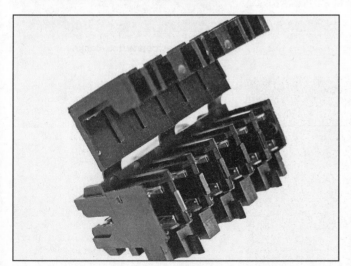

IDC connection block prior to closing cover showing that wiring is inserted without removing the outer insulation

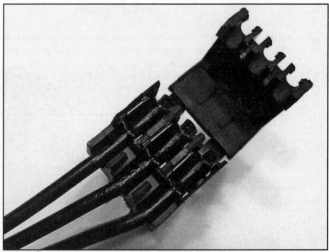

IDC connection block prior to closing cover showing that wiring is inserted without removing the outer insulation. It can be seen that the outer insulation has been breached by the internal 'V' shaped terminals

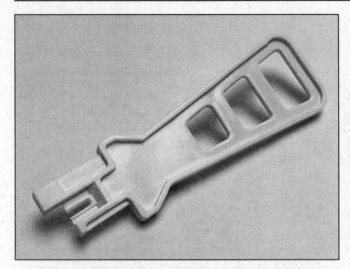

To ensure a sound connection within IDC connectors a dedicated IDC insertion tool should be used. The one shown is a low cost alternative to the larger ratchet version used commercially

The wiring harness of this dishwasher has a moulded flexible plastic sheath with the internal wiring separated into three sections creating a smooth curve to the wiring rather than a kink

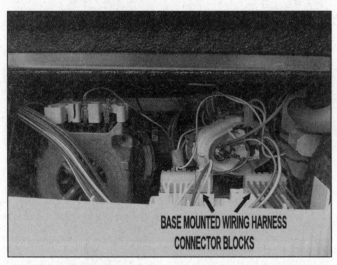

This particular dishwasher has a moulded plastic base. To gain access to the components mounted within the base requires the load compartment to be detached and lifted free. Block connectors easily disconnect the various components from the wiring harness. Water connections are simple male female fitments with internal 'O' ring seals

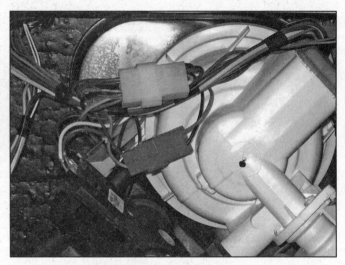

Typical wiring harness connector blocks

Chapter 37
Useful tips and information

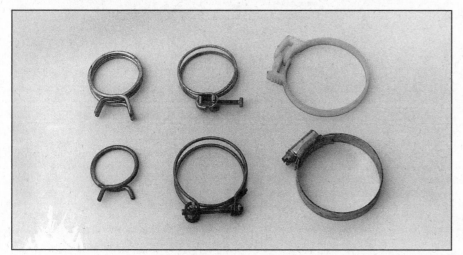

Shown above are the various types of clips in common use in today's machines. In the centre are the screw type wire clips. Top right is the new type toothed clip. This new clip is much easier and quicker to fit as grips or pliers are used to tighten jaws together. Left are two types of corbin spring clips. Care should be taken in removing this type of clip as they have a tendency to 'spring' even under tension. For removal, corbin pliers are best, but ordinary grips can be used with care. Lower right is a worm drive or Jubilee clip. This again is a simple but effective clip. Some machines may come with crimp type clips which are factory fitted and not reusable. Prise them loose carefully and renew them with worm drive type clips.

Check all hoses thoroughly for perishing and/or cracking. As with this pressure hose supplying the top spray arm, stretch the hose to enable a thorough check. (It is wise to check any new hoses before fitting.)

A suitable sealant should be used when fitting thermostat grommets, new hoses and door seals.

Odours or unsightly marks to the load cabinet caused by incorrect use can be alleviated by using a quality dishwasher cleaner. Read the instructions carefully before use.

To avoid problems with cleaning, use a good quality detergent and rinse aid.

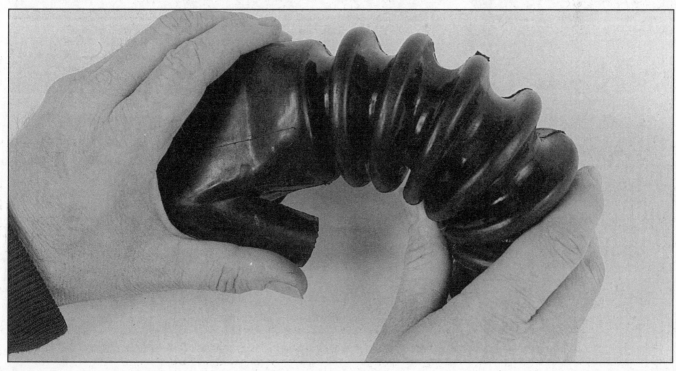

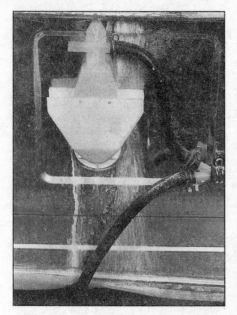

Some machines secure the basket rails with screws or bolts. Check these have not worked loose as when the cabinet is sprayed with water during the wash they can be the cause of a very difficult leak to locate. This machine requires the removal of the side panel to gain access to the nut on the fixing bolts. It had leaked for some time and several engineers had failed to locate the true fault blaming door seals, etc

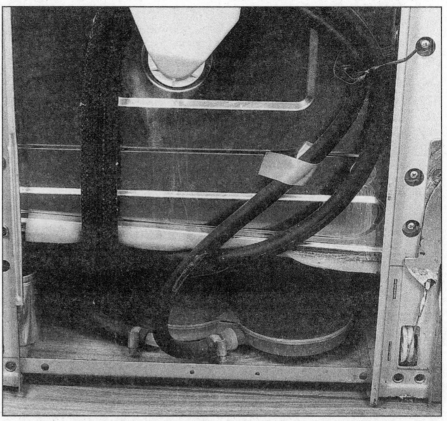

How it should look on a similar machine without rail bolt leak!

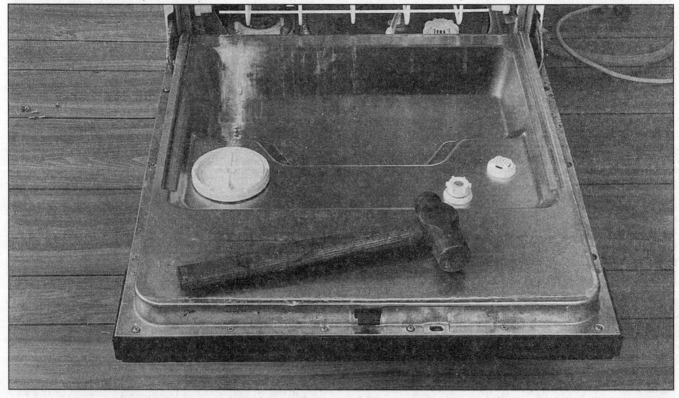

When removing door panels for servicing, it is wise to counterbalance the door. If not, when the panel is removed, the doors own spring counterbalance will slam the door shut

If a machine is looked after correctly and only the correct detergent, salt and rinse aid are used, the machine will look as good as new for years. The machine shown above is six and a half years old and is in constant use for a family of four. Note no scaling or deposits on the interior

Look carefully at all connections no matter what the original fault. This was not the reason for the failure in this instance, but if left it could be dangerous and will certainly fail in the near future. Prevention is always better than cure

Some dishwashers use this type of crimp fitted hose clip which cannot be reused

Many machines now have sealed bases like this one

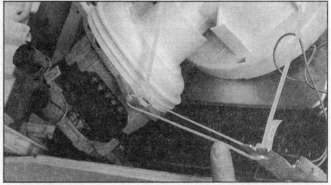

A tip on this type of system is to support the heavier items as you lower the base. Note: *Remember to remove the additional supports as you reassemble the machine*

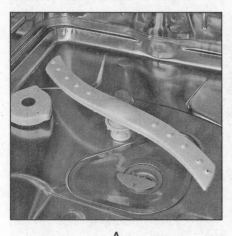

A   B   C

Many top and bottom spray arms are secured by a locking ring with a bayonet type of fitting. Such fittings require a slight turn clockwise or anti-clockwise to remove the arm for cleaning. However, this can be difficult when the components are wet and you are reaching awkwardly into the appliance. A tip is to hold the securing ring firmly with a cloth

Built-in appliances will have screws securing them to the cupboards or work surface. In this instance brackets were used to secure the appliance to the cupboards at either side

When the retaining screws/brackets are removed the appliance can be eased out of its position and the side panels removed (if fitted)

To work on built-in appliances like this one you will need to carefully remove the plinth cover. These are usually held in place by plastic clips attached to the board which clip onto the cabinet support legs. However, this may not always be the case and you will need to inspect the plinth closely to work out just how it was originally secured by the kitchen fitter

Note: *Prior to removing or touching the appliance ensure it is fully isolated from the mains supply. If only an above worktop isolation switch is used for this purpose double check that it is for the appliance you are to work on. Just because it is in line with the appliance it does not guarantee that it isolates that appliance. If in doubt isolate the whole circuit at the consumer unit prior to removing the appliance. Refer to chapter* Plugs and sockets

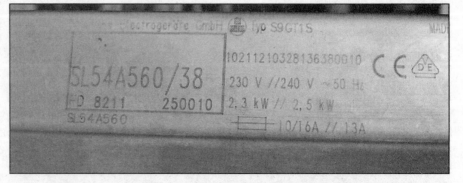

The location of an appliances model and serial number differs greatly between manufacturers and even models from the same manufacturer. The most popular locations on dishwashers are the outer edge of the stainless steel door panel (top or sides) and rear of the appliance. The dishwasher in the picture has the model and serial number etched into the top edge of the door inner. Although this cannot be lost or damaged it is rather faint and can be difficult to see in poor light conditions. Remember to obtain correct spare parts for your dishwasher you will need both the model and serial numbers

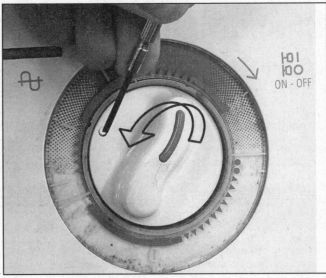

The knob of this model is used for both programme selection and to turn the appliance on and off and therefore needs to be secured to the timer shaft yet free to move. Closely inspecting the plastic moulding revealed that the knob is a cover which is latched to a second inner plastic moulding held in place by the small pip arrowed

Carefully pressing in the plastic pip (but not too far) and turning the knob slightly anti-clockwise unlatches it. The knob cover can then be removed to expose the inner fixing which in this case is a recessed nut

Close up of knob inner with plastic latch

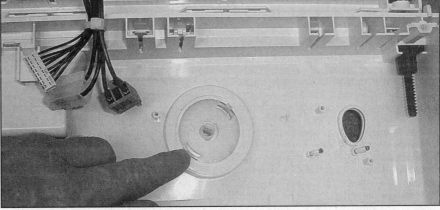

In common with many 'jog dial' selector knobs this one is held in place by securing lugs which need to be depressed from behind the facia. The plastic latches are only accessible with the facia removed

Note: *Take care not to damage or break this type of plastic latch as cosmetic parts can be difficult to obtain and more costly than you may expect*

Chapter 38
Buying spare parts

The aim of this manual has been to assist in the DIY repair of your dishwasher. I hope that now you will not only have a greater knowledge of how these machines work, but also the knowledge to prevent faults.

Above all, I hope that, armed with this information, you will feel confident enough to tackle most (if not all) of the faults that may arise with your machine from time to time.

However, all this knowledge and newfound confidence could be wasted if you are unable to locate the spare parts needed to carry out the repair. In the past this would have been a problem, but in recent years the availability of spares has increased for several reasons:

1 The reluctance of people to pay high call out and labour charges for jobs that they feel they can do themselves.

2 The general interest in household DIY coupled with the saving from call out and labour charges, gives a feeling of satisfaction when the job is successfully completed.

3 The growth in size and number of DIY stores in recent years.

4 The improvement in the availability of pre-packed spares.

Many independent domestic appliance companies have been reluctant to supply parts for the DIY market in the past, but the current trend is to expand the amount of pre-packed spares. This has been confirmed by the three biggest independent spares suppliers of genuine and non-genuine (patterned) spares. The range of 'off the shelf' spare parts in both retail outlets and mail order companies is most welcome, and many machine manufacturers who do not have local dealerships will supply parts by post if requested.

One way of obtaining the parts you require is to find a local 'spares and repairs' dealer through the *Yellow Pages* or local press. This is best done before your machine develops a fault, as you will then not waste time when a fault arises. In many instances you may possess more knowledge of your machine than the assistant in the shop, so it is essential to take the make, model and serial number of your machine with you to help them locate or order the correct spare part for your requirements.

You may also find it quite helpful to take the faulty part(s) with you if possible, to confirm visually that it is the correct replacement. For instance, most pumps will look the same from memory, although quite substantial differences may be seen if the faulty item is compared with the newly offered item. The casing or mounting plate, etc., may be different. It is most annoying to get home only to find that two extra bolts are required.

Patterned parts

Certain parts that are widely available are marked 'suitable for' or 'to fit'. These are generally called patterned or patent parts. Such terms refer to items or parts that are not supplied by the manufacturer of your machine, but are designed to fit it.

Some are copies of genuine parts and others are supplied by the original parts manufacturer to an independent distributor, which are then supplied to the retailer and sold to the customer. This avoids the original manufacturer's mark-up as it is not an official or genuine spare part. This saving is then passed onto the customer.

Many of the appliance manufacturers disliked this procedure in the past, as the parts were of an inferior quality, but this is not the case today as the supply of parts is very big business and quality has improved dramatically. Although great savings can be made, care must be taken not to save money by buying inferior spare parts. Check the quality of the item first wherever possible. A reputable dealer should supply only good quality patterned or genuine parts.

Many of the original machine manufacturers are now discounting their genuine authorised spares to combat the growth in patterned spares. This is very good as it can only benefit you, the customer.

Genuine parts

Parts supplied by the manufacturer of your machine or by their authorised local agent, are classed as 'genuine' and will in many cases carry the company's trade mark or colours, etc., on the packaging. Many of the parts in today's machines are in fact not produced by the manufacturer of the finished machine, but a sub-contractor who may also supply a distributor of patterned spares with identical items.

Patterned spares producers will only take on items that have volume sales and leave the slow moving items to the original manufacturer of the machine. Generally it is a long procedure to obtain spares 'direct' from the manufacturer as many are unwilling to supply small orders direct to the public. Another system used to deter small orders is to use a 'pro-forma' invoicing sheet that will delay the receipt of parts until your cheque has cleared.

With the increase in DIY, manufacturers are slowly changing their view regarding spares supply. This is simply to fend off the patterned spares, by making the original parts more available and competitively priced. Again this will in turn benefit the consumer.

Parts by post

Through the company below you can readily access almost every domestic appliance spare part available in the UK, the range of spares covering all major manufacturers and brands. Simply write or e-mail your requirements (**Note:** *This information was correct at the time of publication, but may change with the course of time*).

UK Whitegoods

Parts orders and inquiries can be sent by post, telephone or e-mail. All are supplied at competitive prices and payment can be made by cheque, credit or debit card, Paypal and NOCHEX.

Ensure you quote the make, model and serial number of the relevant machine(s).

19–21 Nursery Street, Kilmarnock
KA1 1RQ
Tel: 0845 226 3258
Website: spares@ukwhitegoods.co.uk
E-Mail: spares@ukwhitegoods.co.uk

EMW Electronics

The Barn, Millfield, OXTON, Notts NG25 0TD
Tel: 0115 9652118
Website: www.emwelec.co.uk
E-mail: sales@emwelec.co.uk

QER

This company specialises in the fixed price test and repair of all types of electronic and electro-mechanical controls used in home appliances (washing machines, dishwashers, tumbledriers, cookers, microwaves etc.) They

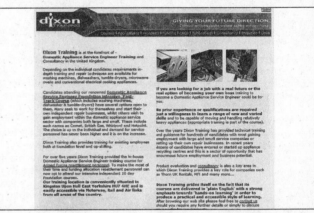

offer a mail-order timer and module repair service in the UK and Europe, whereby items can be sent to them for test & repair and are quickly returned. Popular items are usually available from stock, in advance of returning the exchange unit to them.

QER Ltd.
Quality House, Reedlands Rd
WORKINGTON, Cumbria, CA14 3YF, UK
Tel: 01900 606788
Website: www.qualityelectronicrepairs.co.uk
E-mail: contact@qer.biz

In conclusion

Finally, the decision between genuine and patterned spares is yours, cost and speed of availability may have to be taken into consideration, but do not forsake quality for a small financial saving.

As a guide we have compiled a list of manufacturers' names and telephone numbers where parts may be obtained. It may also be helpful to check your local *Yellow Pages*.

Further information

For those wish to consider a career in domestic appliance repair a detailed technical and practical training course is available – for further details contact www.dixontraining.co.uk

Contact details

Note: *This information was correct at the time of publication, but may change with the course of time.*

AEG	www.serviceforce.co.uk	08705 929 929
Ariston	www.theservicecentre.co.uk	08709 066 066
Bosch	www.bshappliances.co.uk	08705 678 910
Candy	www.gias.co.uk	0870 411 6600
Creda	www.theservicecentre.co.uk	08709 066 066
Electrolux	www.serviceforce.co.uk	08705 929 929
Gaggenau	www.bshappliances.co.uk	08705 678 910
Hoover	www.gias.co.uk	0870 411 6600
Indesit	www.theservicecentre.co.uk	08709 066 066
Miele	www.miele.co.uk	08707 554466
Neff	www.bshappliances.co.uk	08705 678 910
Servis	www.servisuk.co.uk	0121 568 8333
Siemens	www.bshappliances.co.uk	08705 678 910
Smeg	www.smeg-service.co.uk	0870 444 7083
Tricity Bendix	www.serviceforce.co.uk	08705 929 929
Whirlpool	www.whirlpool.co.uk	0870 600 8989
Zanussi	www.serviceforce.co.uk	08705 929 929

For out of warranty repairs you may also wish to try the repairs@ section of www.ukwhitegoods.co.uk

Chapter 39
Common causes of poor washing results

Poor washing can be due to the incorrect operation of the machine by the user, or by a mechanical or electrical fault of the machine. The most common user faults are listed below.

Misuse of the controls

a) To achieve good consistent results from your dishwasher, you must have a good understanding of your machine and its controls. Always remember YOU tell the machine what to do. If in doubt, read the manufacturer's manual.
b) Does the selected programme have the right water temperature and wash time for the load?

Incorrect dosage of detergent

The amount of detergent that you should use is usually displayed on the pack. Please remember that this is only a guide, and the amounts have to be adjusted to load size, type and degree of soiling, and the 'hardness' of the water supply.

The detergent is formulated to do several tasks

a) Break the surface tension of the water.
b) Remove the soiling from the load.
c) Hold the soiling in suspension.

Incorrect loading

a) Overloading the dishwasher will result in poor spray pattern within the load compartment, resulting in inadequate soil removal.
b) Some programmes are for reduced loads. If one of these programmes is used, reduce the load. If you are not sure, read the manufacturer's manual.

Other factors

a) How old is the machine? Like any purchase, a dishwasher has a restricted life span. In the case of an automatic dishwasher, the average life span is approximately eight years.
b) When was the machine last serviced?
c) Failure to check or refill salt container often enough.
d) Failure to check or refill the rinse aid dispenser at regular intervals, or adjust dosage control (if fitted).

Here in detail are some of the common and not so common causes of poor wash results. It should be remembered however, that most problems arise after a long period of time and possibly for a variety of reasons most of which are described in the following text.

Although the detection and cure of most of the faults listed will be relatively quick and easy, do not expect immediate results. In some instances, it takes several washes before an improvement is noticeable on crockery, etc. depending on the length of time the problem has been allowed to build up, e.g. incorrect washing programme or incorrect detergent dosage, etc. A way in which you can assess change is to remove one of the affected items and do not use it or wash it. After a period of washes have taken place you can compare the original problem with the current condition of the wash load. This simple comparison test can often be quite surprising. **Note:** *Ensure you allow at least six washes before making the comparison and try to select an item that you have at least two or more of.*

General poor wash results can often be seen as a thin layer of food left on the surface of plates etc., or by a film of a starch-like substance. This can be felt as a rough coating if you pass a finger over the surface and will show up clearly if a cloth dipped in iodine is wiped over the surface. Such build-ups and coatings are caused by:

a) The failure to remove surplus food prior to loading the machine. Items that have burnt on food etc., should be pre-soaked. If items are to be left for sometime in the machine prior to a full wash cycle, it is recommended that a pre-wash is used prior to the main wash.

b) If wash quality is poor and steps in a) are normally carried out, the spray arms should be checked for blockages of the jets and if necessary, cleaned. Also check for free rotation of the spray arms. It is possible that they could split along the joints or seams, therefore the pressure is lost resulting in poor washing. Check thoroughly and renew if suspect.
c) Poor loading of the machine can result in water not being able to reach all surfaces, resulting in a poor wash. Always load the machine with care, paying particular attention not to cause any obstruction to the spray arms and to allow good water circulation within the machine. (Never overload your machine.)
d) Check that all filters are cleaned regularly and that food deposits are not allowed to build up on them. Ensure also, that the filters are correctly positioned, otherwise food particles will be recirculated during the wash cycle. A kinked or restricted outlet hose will give similar results owing to failure to discharge soiled water from the machine.
e) If a 'sand-like' deposit is detected on items such as glasses or on cups that have been washed on the upper basket, the probable reason for this could be the top spray arm not rotating correctly.

Check
1 That large items stacked on the lower basket are not obstructing the upper spray arm.
2 That the upper spray arm is not blocked or split.
3 That your dishwasher is the type that feeds the upper spray arm by an open jet from the centre of the lower arm, ensure that any large items on the lower basket do not obstruct or cover the two openings.
4 The filter. If the filter in the sump is blocked, it will reduce the circulation pump supply and in turn reduce top spray arm power.
5 That adequate detergent was used for that particular wash. **Note:** *Under dosing can cause over foaming which greatly reduces circulation pressure. If in doubt, add more – too little detergent causes over foaming.*

f) If you are satisfied that steps have been carried out correctly, ask yourself whether the correct wash cycle was selected to combat the amount of soiling on the dishes. A wash that is either too cool in temperature or too short a cycle, can result in a poor wash. If you feel the wash programme you selected was the correct one and that all the previous points are satisfactory, then the next step is to check the thermostat as described in the thermostat and thermistors chapter.

g) If insufficient detergent is used for a wash programme, the particles of food and soiling from the dishes will be unable to remain in suspension in the water long enough to be pumped away. The result would be a uniform soiling of the wash load and over a period of washes, a marked deterioration will be seen. Remember too much detergent will do no harm, whereas too little does. Extra soiled dishes require extra detergent.

h) Faulty drying of the wash load may be caused by any of the following:

1 Insufficient rinse aid being dispensed at the end of the wash. This will result in lines or streaks on the clean dishes. See chapter on *Detergent and rinse aid dispensers.*

2 No rinse aid being dispensed will result in poor drying of wash load and is often accompanied by spotting on clean items. Check that the rinse aid tank is full and if it is full but not dispensing the rinse aid, refer to chapter on *Detergent and rinse aid dispensers.*

3 Too much rinse aid dispensed at the end of a wash cycle will leave smear marks and a greasy feeling to the dishes. For faults 1 to 3 check the rinse aid setting dial (if fitted) and adjust accordingly. The best results are obtained by setting the adjuster below the mid point on its scale and increasing slightly if required. Check by holding a washed plate in a horizontal position, in a way that it will catch the light, at eye level. The plate should have an overall even shine and should not be greasy or sticky to the touch. Adjust the setting as required.

4 Drying of the wash load will be adversely affected if the door is opened too soon after the end of the programme. When the machine switches off at the end of the programme, time should be allowed for the warm air inside the machine to dry the dishes before opening the door. Once the door has been opened, the residual heat escapes thus impairing the drying.

Quick trouble-shooting guide

Please read the rest of this chapter as well as this section

Too much foam in the wash solution

The detergent dosage must be increased – dishwasher detergent suppresses foam.

White spots, streaks or film on dishware

Use correct dosages of a good quality dishwasher detergent and rinse aid.

Poor results

Check filters.
Check spray arms.
Check detergent dosage.
Check water softener (if fitted).
Check water temperature.

Poor drying

Check rinse aid dispenser.
Check air vent in machine is free.
Check water is fully drained.
Check stacking of items.

Noise

Can be a problem with some machines – ensure correct placement and level of machine. Check to see if anything is impeding rotation of the spray arms.

Tarnishing/rusting of stainless steel

Do not leave items covered with salt or acid foodstuffs, use rinse and hold cycle. Do not leave in a damp dishwasher for long periods – drying by hand is best for these items. Only use a good quality dishwasher detergent.

Tarnishing of silverware

Do not leave items covered with salt or acid foodstuffs, use rinse and hold cycles. Do not allow undissolved product to come in contact with silver, otherwise black spots occur. Keep silver separate from other metals. Wash with a good quality product containing tarnish inhibitor. Use correct grade of salt in softener.

Tarnishing of aluminium

Usually caused by hot water – manufacturers advise that the tarnish is not injurious in any way, only unsightly. Remove article before hot final rinse to avoid tarnishing developing.

Crystal glass

Susceptible to damage with hot water – do not wash in a dishwasher.

On glaze decorations

Some on glaze decorations are not safe in a dishwasher. Wash a sample piece of suspect ware for a few weeks to check suitability, short washing cycles and lower temperatures will help keep decorations brighter.

wash in contact with silver or pitting may occur – use separate cutlery baskets.

Handles

Some glued on handles will not be safe at high temperatures. Bone, wood or plastic can be susceptible to damage by hot water. Test wash one piece for a few weeks.

Coloured aluminium

Colour can be removed – do not wash in a dishwasher.

Plastics

Thermosetting plastics can dull or crack in hot water. Thermoplastics can melt – special care may be needed. Do not force into positions on racks. This will cause distortion of item.

Glass

Stack carefully to avoid rubbing and jamming. Excessively softened water can attack glass. Do not use machine softener if water is already soft, i.e. do not fill salt reservoir.

Handles

Pieces of cutlery produced from two types of metal are susceptible to electrolytic corrosion. Knives produced with stainless steel blades and silver handles can corrode if left in the dishwasher.

Discoloration problems

There are several reasons why discoloration may occur in your dishwasher. Some are a direct result of chemical actions; others are often caused by misuse. Often things are not dishwasher-proof such as items with patterns on top of a protective glaze (check by close inspection of item), or the mixing of cutlery of different metals in the same basket, may have been loaded in the machine.

What follows is a guide to the more common and not so common problems, their causes and, where possible the remedies.

Problem 1

Crockery washed in the machine is acquiring a white coating and the inside of the machine is also acquiring the same white coating (even on stainless steel lined machines).

The normal detergent and wash action of the machine break down the food particles on the wash load. These combine with any calcium salts present in the water to form a water-soluble compound that is held in suspension in the water, ready to be discharged by the outlet pump. Insufficient detergent will result in the water no longer being able to hold such compounds in suspension. Such unstable compounds of calcium will then coat the wash load and interior of the machine. This may be a gradual process, as some of the compounds will be discharged depending on the lack of detergent.

Similar problems can occur if the water softener unit fails or is not replenished with salt often enough. See chapter *Internal water softeners*. If your machine does not have a built in water softener, ensure adequate use of detergent, but if the problem persists, it may be wise to fit a softener kit to your machine.

Calcium build-up may be removed or at least reduced depending on how long the problem has been allowed to continue. Your local pharmacist should be able to supply you with citric acid crystals for this purpose. Load the machine with the crockery to be treated and use 100g (3.05oz) of citric acid crystals in place of the usual detergent. If the dispenser will not take the full amount, the surplus can be put in an egg cup on the top basket. Select a normal wash cycle and allow the machine to operate normally. It would be wise to stop the machine mid-cycle to make sure the crystals have been fully dispensed. The action of the acid wash should remove the calcium (alkaline) build-up, although in severe cases, more than one wash may be required.

As with all chemicals, detergents and the citric acid crystals, care should be taken when used, and should always be kept out of the way of children.

Problem 2

A similar white deposit or coating on the wash load may be found which gives the crockery, and especially glassware, a salty taste. As this taste implies, the fault lies in a build up of salt, and is not a calcium problem as previously described.

The causes of these salt coatings are usually the result of a poorly fitting salt cap or seal, or a small hairline type crack in the cap especially if the cap combines a level indicator. Inspect closely and renew if in doubt. Always ensure that the salt container top is correctly and securely fitted and that the seal is in good condition.

If the fault persists when the cap and seal have been checked, the regeneration system or valve could prove to be faulty although this is very unusual. The deposit will clear slowly on normal washes once the source of the problem is rectified.

Problem 3

White crockery turning pink. This can happen for a variety of reasons, the main one being crockery itself not being dishwasher-proof. The pink colour is formed by a chemical reaction by the powder used in the dishwasher on the unprotected surface of the crockery. This discoloration is irreversible.

If the 'pinkish tinge' is appearing on crockery that IS dishwasher-proof, the most likely cause is under dosing (using too little detergent). Under dosing allows a silicate film to form on the items which in turn absorbs iron and manganese particles from the water resulting in a brown discoloration or a pink tinge or bloom.

Iron and manganese are present in most water supplies and their presence is quite normal until under dosing occurs which enables them to adhere to the surface of crockery. A return to correct dosage of powder will, over a period of washes, greatly improve the appearance of such stained items.

Problem 4

China items with unusual black marks or streaks. This problem is normally the result of a china item coming into direct contact with metal cutlery. The marks may be removed by soaking the item in a mild bleach solution. Heavier marking may require careful removal with metal polish, refer to problem 6. Ensure the items are washed thoroughly after cleaning.

Problem 5

Tarnishing of metal ware and cutlery. There are a great variety of metals used for cutlery and cooking utensils from silver and silver plate (EPNS) through to aluminium and bronze, and not all metals or the utensils made from them are dishwasher-proof.

Check when purchasing such items whenever possible. If you are unsure, here are a few points to watch for:

a) When loading your machine, do not mix cutlery of different metals as electro-chemical reactions may occur between them, which could result in discoloration and/or pitting of the surface.

b) Make sure the correct amount of rinse aid is dispensed. Even stainless steel is susceptible to slight tarnishing if water is allowed to remain on it until it evaporates. It is perhaps wise to remove stainless steel items from the machine as soon as possible after the drying cycle as the humid atmosphere can impair the stainless properties. **Note:** *Stainless steel requires the healing effect of oxygen from the atmosphere for its protective coating.*

Foods containing acids, e.g. vinegar or fruit juices, table salt etc. can also penetrate the protective coating of stainless steel if allowed to remain for too long on its surface. All these problems are more pronounced on inferior grades of stainless steel, a more prominent feature of which is pitting and rust marks or circles appearing on the surface. These are caused by iron particles within the item rusting. Pitting can also occur if the stainless steel item was poorly finished on production. The surface effect of stainless steel is achieved by high polishing, but poor finishing obviously results in poor stainless steel.

Bronze or bronze-plated items should not be washed in a dishwasher, as it is prone to rapid tarnishing. Any such items should be washed by hand and dried immediately.

Nickel silver, sometimes called 'German Silver' is an alloy and prone to acquiring a yellow tinge if washed in a dishwasher. This type of silver requires frequent polishing to keep in peak condition and washing by hand is recommended.

Solid silver and electro-plated nickel silver (EPNS) tarnish easily, even under normal conditions and require regular cleaning to keep them attractive. Items made of this silver can be washed in a dishwasher, and some manufacturers supply as an extra, a special basket for silver or EPNS items. This basket will remove the tarnishing on the items whilst the machine cleans off the normal soiling. This process is an electrolytic process between the basket and the cutlery. A special point to note is that if the plating on any EPNS item has worn through to expose the base metal, do not put it in the special silver basket, but wash it separately.

Problem 6

Discoloration or tarnishing of polished aluminium pots and pans can occur due to the high temperature and alkalinity of the wash water and certain minerals that it may contain. If such items are removed prior to the last heated rinse, further discoloration will be avoided.

Painted or coloured aluminium articles sometimes discolour for the same reason, so if you want to keep their bright appearance, wash them by hand.

Problem 7

The inside of the cabinet appears to be going rusty in places. Rust marks appear for several reasons. Some early machines had a plastic coating over the ordinary steel shell, but once the coating had chipped or flaked, the exposed metal rusted quickly because of the harsh environment within the cabinet. A coating of an epoxy resin over the rusted areas should help, but remember to clean the area thoroughly first and follow the resin manufacturer's instructions for mixing and drying times, etc.

Rust marks may also appear on stainless steel linings, but as the stainless steel used in manufacture is generally of the finest grade it is therefore suited to the job. Most rust marks will be the result of external nuts or clamps (made of ordinary mild steel) used for securing thermostats or heaters, etc. These marks may then migrate along the surface of the stainless steel at or around such points.

Check and cure the leak, renewing any badly corroded items to prevent further markings. The rust stains can easily be removed by using a cleaner, e.g. 3 in 1 Chrome Cleaner or Autoglym metal polish or any similar product.

If the plastic coating is chipped or flaked from the load baskets, rust marks will appear.

Again, this could be remedied by using an epoxy resin, but in severe cases, it may be as well to renew the baskets. Although the baskets are relatively tough, do take care when loading them with sharp items.

Problem 8

Blooming or rainbow effect developing on stainless steel cutlery and the surface of a stainless steel load compartment. This effect is the result of consistent detergent under dosing. The problem appears to be more evident when liquid detergents are used. Always ensure that the amount of detergent being used is sufficient for the level of soiling and size of load.

Problem 9

Damaged crockery and glasses. Modern dishwashers will rarely cause breakages or chipping. The more usual cause of damage is due to items being knocked during normal use forming small unseen cracks. The subsequent heating and cooling first expands and then contracts the item resulting in a larger, more obvious crack or chip. Overloading can also contribute to this problem as not enough room is allowed for the items to expand during the heating process.

Similar problems occur with glass, but the cause is generally 'ring structures' formed in the glass during manufacture due to stress within the glass. This allows particles within the glass to be etched away by the hot water

used during the wash and last rinse. Washing by hand would eventually give the same result, although it would take much longer because of the lower water temperature and the less aggressive detergent action.

Houses with domestic water softeners may encounter similar problems such as etching or cloudiness forming on the glass surface. Water that is softened 100% could have this effect on glass. It may be beneficial to contact the softener suppliers and arrange a bypass to be fitted to allow 5° of hardness through to the house supply. If the dishwasher is connected to artificially softened water then salt should not be added to the dishwashers internal water softening unit (if fitted).

Problem 10

Plastic components (i.e. dispenser unit, cutlery basket, etc.) within the load compartment turning pink or orange. This particular problem is normally the result of higher than normal levels of tomato ketchup, tomato based sauces and curry, i.e. bolognese sauces, fruit juices and curry being washed. Other causes may be the result of precipitation of high levels of iron from the water supply or the washing of dark red (possibly unglazed) earthenware. All problems within this category are aggravated by insufficient detergent or rinse aid dosage. Unfortunately once this type of staining occurs it cannot be removed but may fade with time.

Chapter 40
Jargon

Armature	Wire wound centre of brush motor.
Bimetal	Two different metals which have been joined together. When heated the strip bends in a known direction.
Burn-out	Overheated part of item.
Carbon face (seal)	Watertight flat surface seal.
Ceramic seal	Watertight flat surface seal.
Closed circuit	A normal circuit that allows power to pass through.
Contact	Point at which switch makes contact.
Continuity	Electrical path with no break.
Component	Individual parts of the machine, i.e. pump, valves, motor, etc. are all components.
Corbin	Type of spring hose clip.
Cycle	Programme or operation time.
Dispenser	Compartment that takes washing powder/liquid.
Drift	Soft metal rod used for bearing removal.
Door seal	Watertight seal for door.
DPC	Dynamic Performance Control
Early	Machine not currently on the market.
Earth loop test	Means of determining resistance of earth path.
Energise (Energize)	To supply power to.
Energised (Energized)	Having power supplied to.
ELCB	Earth leakage circuit breaker – see RCCB
Flowchart	Method of following complicated steps in a logical fashion.
Functional test	To test machine on a set programme.
Grommet fitting	Method of fitting hoses etc. whilst requiring no clips.
Harness	Electrical wiring within a machine.
Hertz	Periodic cycle of one second, i.e. cycles per second.
HF	Hardness factor.
'Hunting'	Oscillating.
IEE	Institute of Electrical Engineers.
Impeller	The blades of the pump that pumps the water.

Insulation	Material used to insulate a device or a region.
Isolate	To disconnect from the electricity supply and water supply, etc.
Laminations	Joined metal parts of stator.
Late	Current machine on market.
Make	1 Manufacturer's name. 2 When a switch makes contact it is said to 'make'.
Open-circuit	Circuit that is broken, i.e. will not let any power through.
Porous	Item that allows water to pass through.
Programmer	See Timers (programmers).
PSI	Measurement of water pressure, pounds per square inch, i.e. 138psi.
RCCB	Residual current circuit breaker (also know as RCD).
Regeneration	Restoration of resin granules with salt.
Rotor	Central part of an induction motor.
Schematic diagram	Theoretical diagram.
Seal	Piece of pre-shaped rubber that usually fits into a purpose-built groove, therefore creating a watertight seal.
Sealant	Rubber substance used for ensuring watertight joints.
Shell	Outer of machine.
Spades	Connections on wires or components that can be pulled off gently.
Stat	Thermostat.
Stator	Electrical winding on motor.
Suspension	A dispersion of solid or liquid particles in fluid.
Syphon	A way of emptying the machine via gravity.
Terminal block	A method of connecting wires together safely.
Timer	Programme switch.
TOC	Thermal overload cut-out. At a pre-set temperature, the TOC will break electrical circuit to whatever it is attached, i.e. prevents motors, etc. overheating.

Index